Liquid Natural Gas in the United States

A History

JOHN HRASTAR

McFarland & Company, Inc., Publishers
Jefferson, North Carolina

LIBRARY OF CONGRESS CATALOGUING-IN-PUBLICATION DATA

Hrastar, J.
Liquid natural gas in the United States : a history / John Hrastar.
    p.   cm.
Includes bibliographical references and index.

ISBN 978-0-7864-7859-0 (softcover : acid free paper) ∞
ISBN 978-1-4766-1509-7 (ebook)

1. Liquefied natural gas—United States—History.
2. Gas as fuel—United States—History. I. Title.
TP761.L5H73 2014   665.7'73—dc23   2014019903

BRITISH LIBRARY CATALOGUING DATA ARE AVAILABLE

© 2014 John Hrastar. All rights reserved

*No part of this book may be reproduced or transmitted in any form
or by any means, electronic or mechanical, including photocopying
or recording, or by any information storage and retrieval system,
without permission in writing from the publisher.*

On the cover: Texas natural gas well, LNG gas tanker,
natural gas flame (iStockphoto/Thinkstock)

Printed in the United States of America

*McFarland & Company, Inc., Publishers
Box 611, Jefferson, North Carolina 28640
www.mcfarlandpub.com*

For Fran, Mary, John,
Peggy and Kathy

Acknowledgments

The book took a while to research and put together, tasks which I did with relish. I am neither a historian nor a writer by trade, though, but an engineer. Although I was always interested in technology and made it a career, early in life I also developed an avid interest in history, which I now consider an avocation. Also, as I mention in the preface, this story caught my attention early, and it involves the history of technology, which made it doubly compelling. As anyone would recognize, these two facts do not, of themselves, guarantee an interesting book. I had to find the right balance between the historical and technical aspects. This took practice and help from others.

This process required the help and patience of many others who contributed in various ways. First, of course, I thank my wife Fran for her support, including her review of some sections. She also put up with the time this took away from other projects. My brother Tim and daughter Kathy, both writers, provided a great deal of support and writing suggestions, even though technology was not in their background. Technology was in the background of two others who helped out, colleagues from my first career at the Goddard Space Flight Center/NASA. Dolly Perkins and Jim Greaves, although their backgrounds did not include liquid natural gas, were willing and able to provide both technical advice and writing advice as reviewers. These reviews were very important in making the book more readable. Thanks also go to Stan and Leona Streiner, whose copies of the newspaper articles on the fire gave me a head start on the book, and who introduced me to some fire survivors that I interviewed.

Going from the history and technology research to a readable book took the help of all these family members, friends, and colleagues.

Table of Contents

Acknowledgments vi
Preface 1
Introduction 3

1—Inferno 9
2—Discovery and Growth 25
3—Growth to Shortage 48
4—Discovery of Gas Liquefaction 78
5—Liquid Storage 105
6—Setback 140
7—Recovery 178
8—Breakout: Moving the Energy 216

Chapter Notes 249
Selected Bibliography 263
Index 271

Preface

I remember the fire well. It was in October 1944, in Cleveland, and there was a red glow on the bottom of the clouds. We heard sirens wailing all afternoon and evening. I was seven years old and lived about six miles from the scene. Our family had friends and relatives in the area, although fortunately none were directly affected. When my mother was young she had lived in that neighborhood. I remember overhearing something from my father that day and passing along to a friend that "a gas station was on fire." I found out later that the neighborhood was an ethnic neighborhood, mostly composed of families of Slovene descent—my heritage. I also found out later that there was a more personal connection. I was related to the businessman credited with restoring the neighborhood after the fire, Anton Grdina; my mother was a Grdina, and Anton was her uncle. The mayor of Cleveland, and soon to be governor of Ohio, Frank Lausche, was a family friend. My father took me down to the scene sometime after the incident. We walked around one of the houses that had been flattened by an explosion, although not burned. It was quite a sight for an impressionable seven-year-old. I don't know if my father knew the people who owned the house or not; I didn't ask.

Several years later I learned some interesting facts about the fire that really piqued my interest. I learned that the fire was caused by the rupture of a tank of liquid natural gas (LNG). More than that, the plant that held the tanks of LNG was the first one in the world. The East Ohio Gas Company had built a plant to liquefy, store, and then regasify natural gas. Natural gas was in high demand, especially because of the war, but it couldn't be moved quickly enough through the existing pipelines to cover peak loads during cold snaps. At these times industrial customers had to be shut down to preserve gas for home heating; not something you want during wartime. Because of its volume natural gas is hard to store as a gas. If it is liquefied it can be stored in much smaller volumes—1/600 the volume of a gas—but the liquid is very cold, −260°F. East Ohio built the plant so they could collect gas at off-peak hours, liquefy it, and use it to shave peak loads during cold snaps. It worked well for three years. The plant failed spectacularly when one tank ruptured, spilling tons of liquid natural gas over the plant and neighborhood. Some gas ignited quickly and burned homes almost instantaneously. Some gas seeped into the sewer system and into homes, causing them to explode without burning. There were 130 fatalities.

Here was a major story, a major new technology in my own city; the start of a potential new industry. I didn't realize it at the time but the LNG industry essentially came to a halt for 15 years after the fire. The story of the cause of the fire and the changes made that allowed the industry to recover, though, had the makings of both a good history of technology and a technological detective story. The story started with the discovery, use, and growth of natural gas in this country, especially in Appalachia. It includes the story of two sister companies, East Ohio Gas and Hope Natural Gas, who grew together with the industry. They were both founded by John D. Rockefeller in the same week in 1898. Together they developed the Cleveland LNG plant. After the fire, one can trace the technological changes that eventually solved the design problems that had led to the fire, including materials and tank designs. These changes led to the rebirth of the LNG industry, a major energy industry.

Those aspects held my interest for the many decades I spent in my career in the aerospace science and engineering field. During that time I also cultivated an intense interest in history. After retiring (a second time) I went back to see if there was more I could learn about the incident. Surprisingly, there was little more I could learn from the material available on the history of liquid natural gas. There were many books on the evolution of natural gas as an energy source, and even some on the present LNG industry. However, there were none that covered the transition—the development of LNG itself. This was the historical gap that I intended to fill with this book. It was more interesting to me because of my personal connection with the fire, the city, and the neighborhood. Three professors from the Cleveland Case School of Applied Science, soon to become Case Institute of Technology, and then Case Western Reserve University, did the technical investigation of the fire. I started at Case ten years after the investigation was complete.

The story has new importance now that natural gas is a major topic of discussion, because of the discovery of vast amounts of natural gas not available before. The LNG industry, revived around 1960, is contributing to the distribution of this energy.

The research for the story was fascinating. The records for the original pilot plant in West Virginia had been lost, so the research went through many libraries, including the Library of Congress, archives at universities and historical societies, and the World Wide Web. Research on the Web is an education in itself. Doing research on the Web is a little like working in the Wild West; a lot of territory but not much law and order. At one point I was led on a tangent because some misinformation had made it to the Web and was propagated by many sites using that misinformation. Eventually, though, the story came together, and the history of liquid natural gas can now be traced to the present.

The liquid natural gas industry, which started in Cleveland in 1941 and survived a catastrophic fire in 1944, is now a thriving international energy industry. This book is the story of how this came to be.

Introduction

In October 1944, a fire erupted in Cleveland, Ohio, claiming 130 lives. It was a catastrophe for those involved and for the city. There have been many other city fires, both in war but also in peacetime. The Triangle shirtwaist factory fire in Greenwich Village in New York in 1911 resulted in 146 fatalities. The garment factory fire trapped many people—mostly young women—who were working in poor and unsafe conditions behind locked doors. The Triangle fire had a major impact nationally, which resulted in labor, political, and safety reforms for many years after. The Cleveland fire, known as the East Ohio Gas Company fire, also had an impact on an industry, although that impact was not obvious at first.

The East Ohio Gas Company fire was almost the death of an industry that had been born there just four years earlier. It took 20 years after the disaster for the rebirth, when the industry would finally recover and start to thrive. The industry is the liquid natural gas or LNG industry. The LNG industry is one that is not as familiar to the general public as the oil, gas, steel, and automotive industries are, but it serves an important function in the total U.S. and global energy industry.

The history of LNG is a typical American story; it grew from the oil and natural gas industry in order to fill a need. That need was to be able to store natural gas in a convenient manner, somewhat analogous to the way oil is stored in tanks so it can be used when needed.

Dramatic growth in the U.S. economy and industrial capacity in the late nineteenth and early twentieth centuries required an abundant source of energy in coal, oil, and gas. The two largest industries at the time, steel and railroads, depended on these energy sources. Coal, which fueled the industrial revolution, had been used for a couple of hundred years in England and elsewhere. For over a thousand years oil and gas had been known throughout the world. However, these energy sources had never been exploited on a large scale until after 1860, when the first oil rig was constructed in western Pennsylvania, by Edwin Drake and others. At the time oil was used to produce kerosene for lighting. An oil boom ensued, and oil barons, such as John D. Rockefeller, started producing and marketing oil and controlling the process from the top down.

Natural gas and oil had been discovered bubbling from the ground in various places around the world for millennia; Native Americans in Appalachia had discovered these bubbling oil and gas fields prior to European immigration. Early in the nineteenth century, gas had been collected and piped to villages to be used for lighting and cooking. In the early days, though, it couldn't compete with manufactured gas, made from coal, which could be produced where it was needed. Finding natural gas and keeping the flow going was hit and miss, and these readily available sources were soon depleted.

When entrepreneurs drilled for brine or oil, which had become a major fuel for lighting, they would often find both oil and gas, or just gas. They cursed the discovery of gas, because it was useless to them, and often dangerous, causing many explosions. Faced with this they would flare off, burn the gas; waste it. Sometimes these wells would burn for years. It took an astute colleague of Rockefeller, Daniel O'Day, to recognize the energy value of natural gas. It didn't take businessman Rockefeller long to exploit this energy. Rockefeller's businesses were centered in Cleveland. In 1898 he founded two sister companies, one in West Virginia, Hope Natural Gas Company, to produce the gas, and one in Cleveland, East Ohio Gas Company, to distribute and market it.

Once people became serious about using natural gas, a number of companies were formed, and they set about drilling specifically for it. These companies laid pipelines from the producing areas to the consuming areas, from West Virginia to Ohio, for example. The natural gas industry grew rapidly in the late nineteenth and early twentieth centuries. Natural gas was cleaner than coal and cheaper than manufactured gas. However, it consistently suffered from one disadvantage compared to coal and oil: you couldn't store it where you needed it. The bottleneck was in the pipelines. You could only push so much gas through a pipeline, and if you wanted more at the consumer end you had to build more pipelines or operate at dangerously high pressures in the lines. There is an upper limit to this. It is not economical to build pipelines for all peak loads, because then they would go unused for most of the year. Very large containers to store gas at the consuming end were not practical. This situation came to a head in Cleveland in the late 1930s when cold winters and gas shortages caused some industrial operations to be shut down to preserve gas for residential heating during cold snaps. Because Cleveland had a lot of heavy industry it was an early adopter of natural gas; and compared to other cities it felt the pressure to store gas earlier than most cities.

In the meantime, totally independent of this rapid exploitation of energy in the Industrial Revolution, the Scientific Revolution, starting in the Renaissance, was piquing the curiosity of many different scientists about the nature of gases. Robert Boyle was one of those scientists who started experimenting with gases in the seventeenth century. He discovered the basic relationships between gas pressure and volume. These experiments progressed over 200 years and led to experiments with liquefying various gases. These experimenters knew that water can exist in either the liquid or gaseous state (steam), and so they tried to liquefy other gases. By the end of the nineteenth century all gases, except helium but including methane, had been liquefied. Helium was liquefied early in the twentieth century. These two apparently unrelated threads, the natural gas storage crunch and the scientific interest in liquefying gases, came together in the minds of some innovators in 1937.

Liquid natural gas, mostly methane, takes up less than $1/600$ the volume that it does in the gaseous state; so if you could liquefy it you could store it in reasonable-size containers near the consumer. It could then be regasified and put into the gas mains when it was needed. Moreover, the liquefied gas could be stored at low pressure, less than atmospheric, and therefore not require thick steel containers to keep it under high pressure.

The science had been completed, and now two engineering problems had to be solved.

The first was to perfect a process to liquefy the gas on an industrial scale. The basic process had been developed by scientists about 50 years earlier; the engineers now scaled that up to the level needed. A similar process had been used in 1918 by the government, in Texas, to extract helium from natural gas to use for dirigibles. However, that gas was never stored but was put back into the gas mains. The second problem to solve was to build storage tanks to hold the liquid natural gas. This was the difficult job, because in order to store the liquid at low pressure it had to be kept at the very low temperature of −260°F. This was a challenging problem, because no one had ever tried to store large volumes of a cryogenic fluid, as LNG is, in a large container that was economical to build. Stainless steel had been used before to store these very cold liquids. However, stainless steel was not only expensive but was difficult to weld, and therefore impractical to use. Ordinary steel becomes brittle at these low temperatures and can shatter like glass under even minor impacts.

The engineers at the Hope Natural Gas Company in West Virginia experimented with different steel alloys and concluded that a tank built of 3½ percent nickel-steel would satisfactorily hold the LNG. In 1939 and into 1940 Hope built a pilot plant in West Virginia that liquefied natural gas, and a tank, insulated with cork, to store it. After a short, and apparently successful, trial run the Hope sister company, East Ohio Gas in Cleveland, immediately decided to build a full-scale commercial plant. The motivation seemed clear. East Ohio had been suffering from shortages during the previous cold winters, and they saw LNG as a way around temporary shortages. They decided that building an LNG plant, conveniently located in the city, was cheaper than laying another pipeline from West Virginia. It would liquefy natural gas on off-peak use days and store it in large spherical tanks; and when a cold snap came that gas would be regasified and put into the city gas mains to shave the peak gas load. In 1940 East Ohio built the Liquefaction, Storage, and Regasification (L. S. and R.) plant in the city. It consisted of the liquefaction facility and three spheres, about 60 feet in diameter, to store the liquid gas. Each sphere held the equivalent of about 50 million cubic feet of gas. The gas in these three spheres could heat about 1,600 average homes for about one year. This was the first commercial LNG plant in the world.

Thus the birth of the LNG industry can be dated first to 1939, and then to 1940, when East Ohio built a plant to solve a peak supply problem. Their intention was only to solve this problem, not start an industry. However, anyone cognizant of this operation could see that this had far-reaching implications for many others in the business. No other plants were built elsewhere at the time. The country was now about to enter a war, and there was a focus on war production. The ability to continue war production manufacturing, and simultaneously keep residential heating going by using this plant to shave peak loads, was a major step forward in managing energy demands. What was not realized at first, but became very obvious much later, was that the liquid gas could be not only stored but also transported. This attribute would make it much more competitive with oil in the future.

The death of the LNG industry, or at least the interruption of its growth, came at the same plant about four years later. The plant was operating so successfully, and the war production was so intense, that in 1942 East Ohio decided to add another tank with double the capacity of one of the spherical tanks. They built this tank, a rather novel design for a cylindrical tank, and put it into service in 1943. On October 20, 1944, as they were preparing for another winter of use, this tank ruptured, spilling its entire contents—

tons of LNG—onto the East Ohio plant and into the adjoining residential neighborhood, causing the disastrous fire. The city and the company were devastated, but with the help of a local businessman and the mayor, they recovered and rebuilt. Cleveland was finished with liquid natural gas. So, it seemed, was everybody else.

Nevertheless, the LNG industry was reborn; its advantages were too good for that not to happen. It took a long time—a full 20 years—before another LNG plant was built in this country. The investigations of the accident, and some ensuing lawsuits, revealed some deficiencies in materials—such as inferior steel and inadequate insulation—as well as siting problems. The investigations also uncovered the lack of appropriate regulations and inappropriate application of existing ones. However, perhaps the most important conclusion was that the concept of liquefying natural gas and storing it was not seen as inherently unsafe. The conclusion was that, if it is done correctly and safely, liquefying and storing natural gas is a perfectly acceptable industrial process.

Although some limited research was done by the plant developers for their design, serious peer-reviewed research on low temperature metals, independent of the plant, started while the plant was being built in 1940. This independent research continued for many years, even after the failure, because it was necessary to identify materials that could store cryogenic fluids for many reasons, including for rocket fuel. This research ultimately resulted in economical alloys that were acceptable for many cryogenic fluids including LNG. Research in insulation materials had similar results. The mistake of siting a plant with potentially hazardous fluids in the city was quickly realized after the accident and was not repeated. Eventually new codes were developed to cover the handling of LNG. All the issues that had contributed to the accident had been addressed and solved. The industry was set to come back.

The comeback was initiated by an innovator in Chicago who recognized that LNG could be moved from place to place—an attribute not previously appreciated. Although his original idea of moving LNG by barge up the Mississippi from Louisiana to Chicago didn't work out, the British were quick to pick up on the idea and follow through on it. In 1959 the energy-poor U.K. imported the first shipload of LNG from Louisiana on the *Methane Pioneer*, a converted World War II Liberty ship, and thus started the rebirth of the LNG industry. The rebirth started a domino effect, and quickly LNG was being produced in Algeria and shipped to northern Europe.

The U.S. industry restarted in earnest in 1965 with the first of many new LNG peakshaving plants that would be built over the next few years. Soon satellite plants sprung up. Satellite plants could not support their own LNG facilities, for various reasons including lack of a gas source, but could store and use LNG shipped to them from other plants. The industry grew into a global LNG market in which liquefaction and export facilities were built around the world to supply LNG to importing countries. The U.S. built several import terminals but today remains a small part of the global LNG industry that originally started in this country in 1940. The changes made to materials and design, as a result of the East Ohio Gas Company fire, have contributed to the successful operation of a global and safe LNG industry.

There are many books about the discovery and development of natural gas and a few books about the LNG market. This story focuses on the history and development of liquid natural gas, how it was possible, why it was attractive, the disaster that almost stopped it, and the ultimate recovery into a thriving industry.

Chapter 1 describes the inferno of October 1944 as seen by eyewitnesses. The flames were estimated to have soared hundreds of feet into the air at temperatures of 2,000°F to 3,000°F. Chapters 2 and 3 look at natural gas and its growth as an industry from the early nineteenth century through the establishment of Hope and East Ohio by Rockefeller in 1898. These chapters cover the reasons for the growth that eventually led to shortages in supply by the late 1930s. By that time everyone wanted natural gas, but the early Appalachian wells were running dry. Chapter 4 steps back 400 years to look at the work by scientists such as Robert Boyle and Michael Faraday in examining the physical laws of gas and the curious phenomenon of gas liquefaction. The liquefaction of natural gas provides the physical basis for the LNG industry. Chapter 5 explores the challenges faced in developing a suitable LNG process and storage facility, specifically the development of the first commercial LNG plant in Cleveland in 1940. The developers were faced with challenges in using metals at low temperatures that no one had faced before; specifically how to build a facility at reasonable cost to operate at −260°F. The setback caused by the fire is examined in Chapter 6. Why did it happen? What were the mistakes, if any, that could have been avoided? We will see that answers to these questions, and changes because of them, would allow the industry to eventually recover. The recovery itself is reviewed in Chapter 7. In this chapter the sequence of events that provided the basis for the rebirth of the industry is detailed. These events include the development of new materials and designs. Finally, Chapter 8 explores the breakout of the industry, its accelerated growth, and its integration into the global energy industry. This chapter also includes speculation that natural gas could be the ideal fuel that transitions the human family from fossil fuels into a future of totally renewable energy. A transition is necessary if the human family is to survive for another millennium or two.

1
Inferno

On Friday, October 20, 1944, World War II was in full force on two sides of the globe. In Europe the U.S. First Army was about to conclude the multi-week battle for Aachen, Germany. Aachen was within the Siegfried Line, roughly on the border of Germany with France; it was the first German city taken by U.S. forces. The battle had lasted since October 2 and was to conclude on October 21 with a U.S. victory. The Battle of the Bulge was only a few weeks away in December.

In the Pacific, MacArthur's forces had just landed on Leyte in the Philippine Islands and were consolidating their beachheads. A few hours after the troops landed, MacArthur waded ashore to fulfill the promise he had made in 1942 to return to the Philippines. Later that day he made his famous "I have returned" speech to the Philippine people. The war was still far from over, however. This day also saw the first of the Japanese kamikaze attacks on the U.S. fleet near the Leyte landing.

In Cleveland, Ohio, most of that day was quite calm, but by the end of the day one of its ethnic neighborhoods would resemble these two war zones. It started as a typical fall day in Cleveland, cloudy with a temperature in the 40s. It was very busy this Friday because the city had a major role in war production manufacturing. Most people were either at work or at school. Since this was during the war, the workforce also included many women. The residential neighborhoods were quiet, with many of the wives and mothers still at home doing household chores or shopping in the neighborhood. This demographic distribution would cost many lives but also spare many others by the end of the day.

The afternoon started quietly and peacefully in the St. Clair–Norwood area of Cleveland. At about two o'clock, John Roy Feightner, the assistant chief engineer of the liquefaction plant, and his team had just topped off the plant's tank 1 with liquid natural gas (LNG). They were shutting the liquefaction process down by removing the refrigerants from their circuits. Everything in the plant that day had been in good order. With the tanks topped off they would probably not have to top off the tanks again for another few months. They were about halfway through the shutting-down when he and two colleagues stopped to chat near the north-center door of the compressor building. By 2:30 p.m. things had changed. He testified later,

> We heard a rumble, like distant thunder, and we stepped out of the door, center door, on the north side of the compressor building, and looked to the east, where the noise had appar-

ently come from, and seen that vapor rolling there ten or twelve feet above the ground. We immediately suspicioned that there was a large liquid leak in that vicinity and there was only one thing to do, and that was to try to get out ... as we seen the vapor, and before our eyes could leave the vapor, it caught fire.[1]

Others had seen it also:

Feightner, still in the yard, noticed that "a heavy white vapor rolled from" the cylindrical tank "to the ground and spread toward East 61st Street." Within ten minutes a thin fog hugged the gutters throughout the neighborhood. An employee of the American Gas Association glanced out a window and saw "blankets" of gas shoot out from the sides of tank four before he turned and ran from his office. A loud whoosh and intense heat signaled the tank's explosion into fragments of flying metal, insulation, and flame, calculated by a surveyor working near the site to have shot twenty-eight hundred feet into the air. "Then the whole sky ignited, and men working in the open yard crisped and died like moths."[2]

In 1944 the city of Cleveland was still growing. The 1940 census showed it as the country's sixth largest city at just over 876,000, right behind Los Angeles. It peaked in the 1950 census at almost 915,000. Along with Detroit and Chicago it was one of the most vibrant Midwest manufacturing cities. It was an immigrant city. Its population swelled in the late nineteenth century and early twentieth century with the mass immigration through Ellis Island, mostly from eastern and southern Europe. It included Poles, Czechs, Slovaks, Slovenes, Serbs, Croats, Italians, and many others. Once in the U.S., they tended to have large families, which contributed to large urban population growth. As in other cities that experienced immigration, these families tended to congregate in certain neighborhoods where they could help one another settle in.

Cleveland was a particular destination for many from Slovenia, a small country of about two million people, the northernmost part of what was once Yugoslavia. One of the Slovene neighborhoods was around the St. Clair–Norwood–East 61st street area, centered on St. Vitus Parish. It was a predominantly Catholic, Democratic, working-class neighborhood. In fact, the mayor of Cleveland was from that neighborhood and was running for governor of Ohio in 1944. He was elected just weeks after the fire. The houses were well-kept, but small and wooden-framed, on small 30-foot lots; they were close together. The yards were also neatly kept. The industriousness of the people was typical of any immigrant population that wanted "to make it" in their new country. There was a small Slovenian newspaper, the *Ameriska Domovina* (American Home), published just around the corner on St. Clair. The Norwood Theater marquee on St. Clair was showing *Going My Way*.

Also typical for ethic neighborhoods in Cleveland was the proximity of industrial operations, such as manufacturing plants. This was true of the St. Clair neighborhood. The East Ohio Gas Company had many workers at their Number 2 Plant at East 55th Street. The plant stretched between East 55th Street and East 63rd Street just south of the New York Central Railroad tracks. These tracks were only a few hundred yards south of Lake Erie. The area between East 55th Street on the west, St. Clair on the South, East 63rd Street on the east, and the railroad tracks on the north was shared between these residents and the East Ohio Gas Company, with only a fence between them. Figure 1-1 shows the plant and the accompanying residential area. The dotted line on the map shows the extent of the fire damage.

The plant was one of the oldest industrial sites in the city. In 1846 the Cleveland City Gas Light and Coke Company was formed to manufacture artificial gas and distribute

1. Inferno

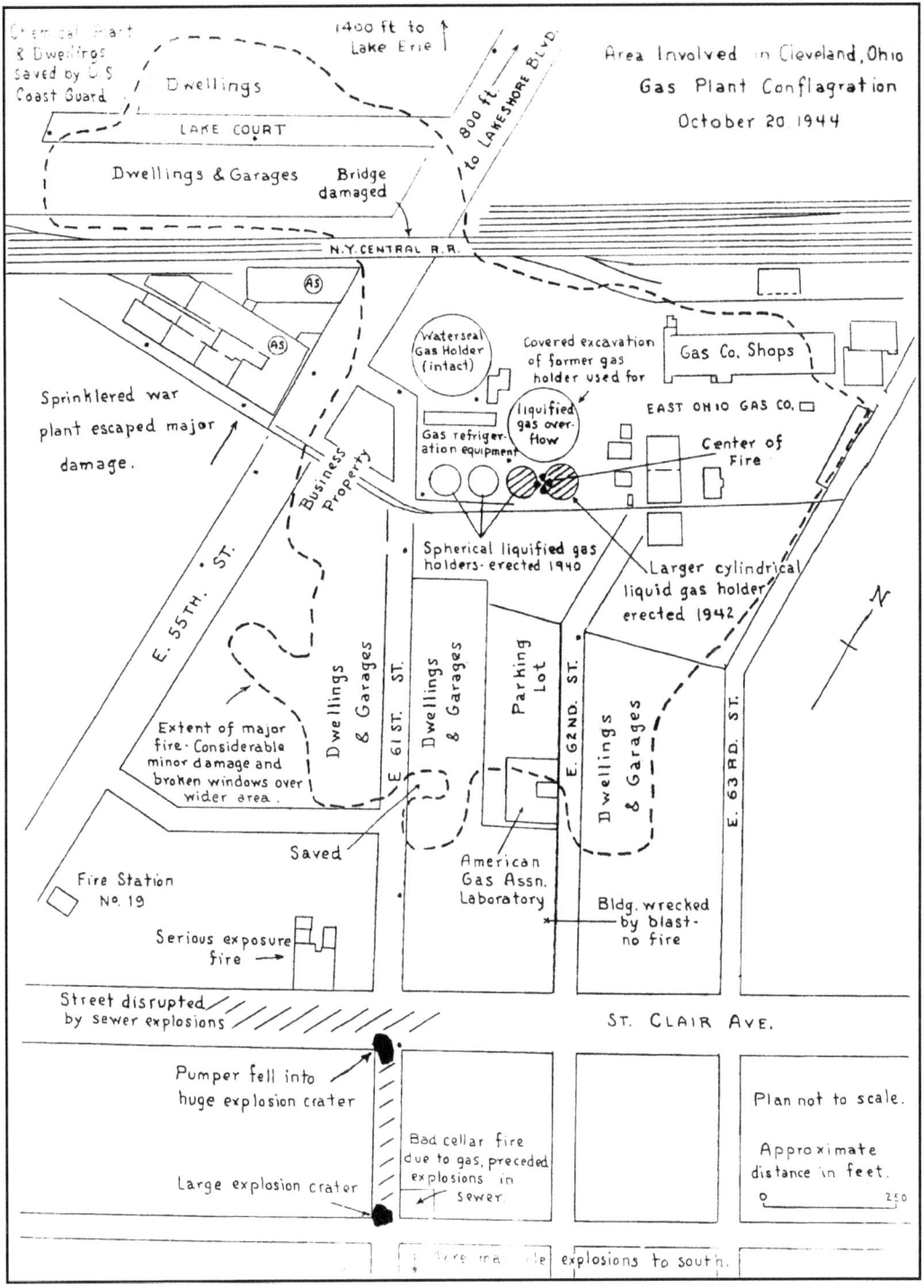

Figure 1–1. Map of the area (Cleveland Public Library Digital Gallery).

it in a network from the St. Clair site. East Ohio had owned this industrial land ever since the company's founding in the late nineteenth century. In 1902 the East Ohio Gas Company brought natural gas to the city and used the same distribution system.[3] The American Gas Association also had a laboratory on East 62nd Street. St. Vitus Parish is just south of St. Clair near East 61st Street (not shown in figure 1-1). The East Ohio plant area was about 10 acres south of the railroad tracks. It included many operations that had been there for years, such as a meter repair shop. Within the Number 2 Plant was the Liquefaction, Storage, and Regasification (L. S. and R.) Plant. It was surrounded by a high fence, and access was limited for safety reasons. Many of the other plants in the area were doing war production work. The Cleveland area had the country's fifth largest concentration of war-related business.[4]

East Ohio had chosen this site to erect the world's first commercial liquid natural gas (LNG) liquefaction, storage, and regasification plant. The purpose of the plant was to store natural gas as a liquid, which can be done at low pressure (three to five pounds per square inch) and which takes only $\frac{1}{600}$ the volume of the gaseous form. At this ratio of gas volume to liquid volume it was feasible to store large amounts of natural gas in a relatively compact location. The low pressure meant the complexity of very high pressure storage tanks could also be avoided. This liquid gas would then be regasified and used to supply natural gas to industry and consumers for peak periods, such as cold snaps, when the normal supply could not meet demands. When stored as a liquid though, natural gas is at a temperature of −260°F.

The plant was constructed in late 1940 and was in operation by early 1941. It had been a particularly bad winter the year before and gas supplies were again going to be hard to get, so a plant that could be used for peak periods would help ease shortages during those times. East Ohio decided to build this plant based on the good results of an earlier pilot plant. Three large spherical tanks were built for storing the liquefied natural gas. Figure 1-2 is an aerial view of the original construction. One can see the third spherical tank being constructed. Each tank was approximately 60 feet in diameter and would hold approximately 600,000 gallons (more than 80,000 cubic feet) of liquid natural gas. This is equivalent to approximately 50 million cubic feet of natural gas in the gaseous state.[5] Thus the three tanks held about 1,800,000 gallons of liquid natural gas at −260°F. The Lake Erie shoreline is shown at the top of the picture. Later, in 1942, they decided to add a fourth tank, of a different design (cylindrical), to almost double the capacity of the gas in storage. Figure 1-3 shows all four tanks prior to the fire.

What John Roy Feightner and the American Gas Association employee saw that Friday afternoon was the vapor from the liquid natural gas as it poured out from a rupture in one of the storage tanks, tank 4. This changed not only the rest of their day but the lives of many in the neighborhood. Feightner and a supervisor in a nearby plant identified first hearing a "concussion" or "distant thunder," or a "tremendous roar." This was most likely the initial rupture of tank 4. Feightner was only about 100 feet from the tank. He and a colleague managed to survive by jumping into a nearby water tank. A flame soon accompanied the rupture.

Opposite, top: Figure 1-2. Construction of the original tanks (Cleveland State University Library, Cleveland Press Collection). *Bottom:* Figure 1-3. Four LNG tanks prior to the fire (Cleveland Public Library Digital Gallery).

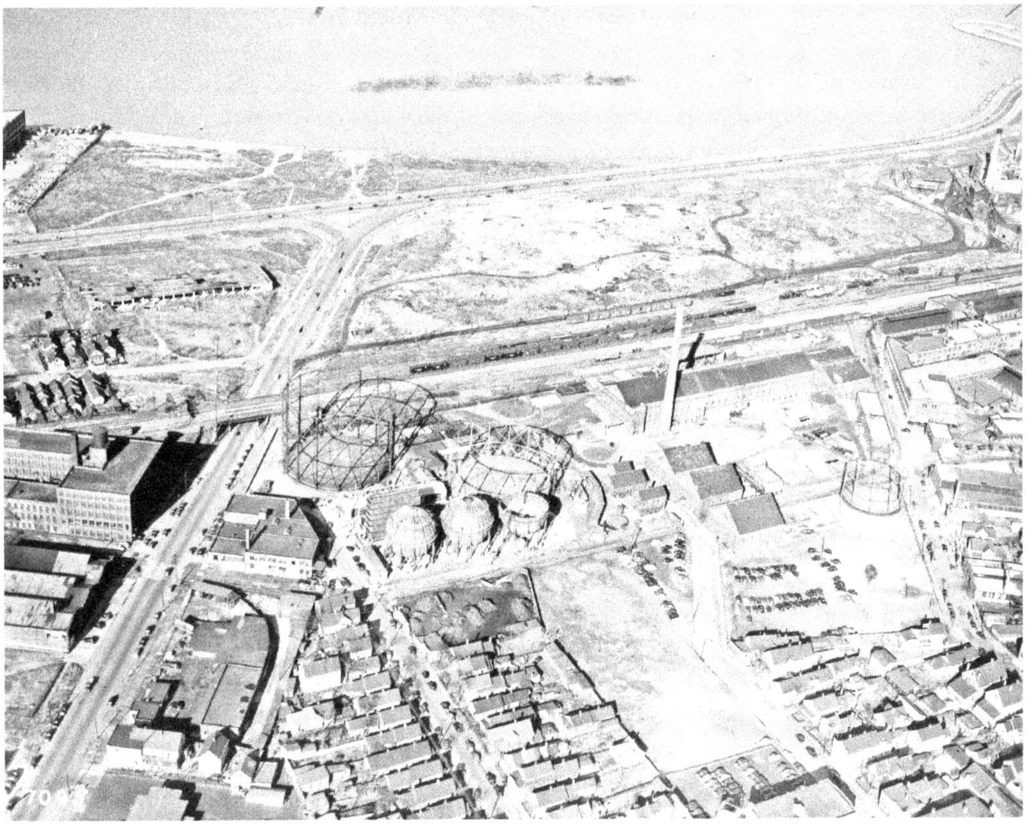

Although a flame may have started at that time, all the liquid gas pouring out of the ruptured tank did not immediately catch fire. Liquid natural gas itself is not flammable. Its boiling point at one atmospheric pressure is −164°C (−264°F), so although an open container would boil vigorously at room temperature it would still take a while to boil away. There was too much liquid to vaporize instantaneously. Although some flame may have started right after the initial rupture, much of the gas would have poured out as a liquid. There is ample evidence that this is exactly what happened. It poured down the gutters in the streets, into the basements of homes, and into the sewer system. As the liquid quickly flowed out, it was just as quickly boiling off into mixtures that would become flammable and/or explosive. The explosive mixture ranges from 5 percent to 15 percent by volume of gas. This was quickly realized as the liquid boiled off. The gas itself is colorless, so the white vapor that soon covered the area was the result of the cold gas interacting with the water vapor in the air.

The inferno spread very quickly after that. Within minutes, probably only several seconds, flames engulfed all the gas company buildings on the property. The clock in the compressor house stopped at 2:40:48. Those able to escape the area ran for the fences around the plant. Most gates were closed to limit access to the sensitive area around the tanks, so they tried to scale the fences; many didn't make it. Charred bodies and body parts were found draped over the fences. "All that was left were his shoes," said Bernard Leimbach about one of the victims he saw.[6] It is likely that most of the fatalities occurred within the first several minutes of the initial fires. Apparently very early a blast of flame shot to the northwest, engulfing the Lake Court neighborhood, as seen in figure 1-1.

Ann Cimperman worked at Lamson and Sessions on East 63rd across the street from the East Ohio plant. She worked there with many Slovenes from the area. The plant made fasteners, so they were said to be working at "Boltsona." Her office overlooked the gas storage spheres across the road. She remembers that day:

> At about 2:30 that afternoon, I stood up from my desk to return a set of files to another room, and as I often did, glanced out the windows in the direction of the tanks. Suddenly there was a tremendous rumble, and a blast of fire shooting out from one tank, looking as though it were spewing hot lava into the sky. It now shone bright with the most shade of orange, tinged with gray, which no doubt, were pieces of flying steel through the air. I stood there blinded for a second, and unable to move, but feeling the floor beneath me swaying, and desks and file cabinets rolling from one side of the room to another. Glass was flying everywhere, as the heat of the explosion shattered all the windows. This afternoon, so quiet and serene, was now a nightmare of horror.[7]

There was panic, screaming, shouting, praying. Someone shouted out that they may have been attacked by Germans. This was a common response by many in the area, because the war was still on. Ann and a friend ran outside, only to find that they were trapped within a chain link fence topped by barbed wire. The gate was locked. Ironically, this fence was intended to keep intruders out of the plant, which was doing defense work for the war effort. She was lucky to find some soft earth below the fence. Using her hands, she dug a hole under the fence so she could escape. She took her shoes off and ran over glass and stones, at times being chased by fireballs three feet in diameter. She finally escaped to St. Clair, crossing the street by jumping from hood to hood on cars caught in the traffic jam. Others were not so lucky.

John Penca also worked at Lamson and Sessions. He only worked there part time, though, because he still attended East Tech High School. He worked in the manufacturing area distributing wooden kegs. These kegs would be filled with the nuts and bolts that were produced there. At 2:40 that afternoon, he was on a break which he spent outside on East 63rd Street. He happened to be looking west toward the East Ohio plant when he heard a large hiss, like air escaping. This was quickly followed by a large fireball above the parking lots south of the tanks. He describes the fireball as being like that of an atomic bomb; it seemed to cover everything. He knew one of the tanks had failed, but he couldn't tell which one because there was a two-story building blocking his direct view. The noise he heard was a dull thud, not a sharp crack like a firecracker or bomb. As soon as the fireball appeared the heat hit him in the face, and he knew he had to get out of there. He started running east along the New York Central Railroad tracks and could feel the heat on his back. He ran as far as East 67th before he stopped. About three p.m. he returned to East 63rd Street, where saw many bodies, the houses on East 61st and East 62nd burning, cars and tires burning, and a lot of fire and police activity. He then went down to St. Clair, where he saw a lot of manhole covers flying 100 to 150 feet in the air propelled by exploding gas in the sewer system.[8]

The flames spread very quickly, trapping most who were in their houses at the time. A typical home in the area was a wooden structure on a 30-foot lot, as shown in figure 1-4.[9] A fire would have spread quickly amongst these closely spaced homes even without gas fireballs, which helped spread the flames that much more quickly. The fire at its height may be seen in figure 1-5.

One of the first homes to go was that of Anthony Kasic. His home at 1002 East 61st Street was only about 400 feet from the ruptured tank. Days later, his son-in-law Frank Zigman was watching as workmen dug through the rubble. He had recently just dug out his own home a few doors away at 1008. As he watched, the coroner pulled three charred bodies from wreckage. He was hoping that his wife and daughter had missed the fire and were staying away, but sadly that wasn't the case. "That's Mary and Pat and Josephine," he said when the charred remains were exposed. Mary was his wife, Pat his daughter, and Josephine his sister-in-law. His other daughter had been in school. He found out later that all three had been to the dentist earlier and had returned about 20 minutes before the fire. "I was getting along fine at my work. I even had a promotion. I begged Mary to move from this neighborhood over to the West Side. We were too close to those tanks. I was always afraid something like this would happen. But Mary wasn't. She always laughed."[10]

As the liquid gas quickly vaporized it turned into many fireballs that bounced around the neighborhood, causing other fires. The flames were estimated to be at least 2,000°F and maybe as high as 3,000°F. Fireballs danced above the nearby St. Vitus church and school, although these buildings were not severely damaged. As the liquid raced through the sewer system the pressure increase of the vaporizing gas and explosions from the gas caused a number of manhole covers to be ejected from the streets and fly several feet into the air. This manhole explosion phenomenon continued well south of St. Clair, beyond the most severely damaged area. Some of these covers arced over buildings in the area, and some injured passersby. It happened to homes and businesses in the area also. The gas would get into the basement, be ignited by some source such as a pilot light, and then explode without a fire. Figure 1-6 shows a home that was flattened by an internal explosion.[11] Although most of the homes were destroyed or damaged by fire, some were flattened this way. Cars were wrapped around telephone poles by these explosions. One such explo-

16 Liquid Natural Gas in the United States

Figure 1-4. Typical neighborhood home (Youngstown Historical Center Dominion East Ohio Gas Company Collection).

Opposite, top: Figure 1-5. Height of the fires (Cleveland State University Library, Cleveland Press Collection). *Bottom:* Figure 1-6. Home flattened by an internal gas explosion (Youngstown Historical Center Dominion East Ohio Gas Company Collection).

sion on St. Clair caused a crater below a fire truck that was pumping water for the fires. The truck fell into the crater. The firemen managed to escape, and the gravity-fed pumper kept up operation and continued to pour water onto the fires. When John Penca came back to St. Clair he saw the hole in St. Clair; when he went to look at the hole he saw the fire truck.

Father Baraga had been working at St. Vitus when the sky was filled with a reddish-orange color and he heard a loud explosion like a sonic boom. He immediately thought the tanks had exploded. He hurried to his sister's house on East 62nd Street, where he found his sister and his niece going into the basement to seek protection from what they thought was a bombing. The rear of the house was already on fire. He hurried them out, and minutes later burning timbers collapsed into the basement.[12]

There were numerous explosions. Some were gas balls exploding above the area like anti-aircraft shells. At least two explosions were large, one about 15 minutes after it all started and one about an hour later. There were numerous small gas tanks in the area that could explain these explosions. Subsequent investigations found large pieces of tank 4 scattered over the area, apparently carried away by the rush of the liquid that poured from the tank. The rock wool insulation from the tank was also spread all over, carried by the same liquid. The spherical tank, number 3, right next to tank 4, received the direct flame from tank 4. It is not known exactly when, but its steel supports melted, the tank fell over and ruptured, adding thousands more gallons of the LNG to the inferno. This also could have been a source of one of the explosions that were heard. It was determined later that tank 4, the one that failed, did not explode but ruptured.

Witnesses and newspapers reported seeing people fleeing the blaze clutching babies, chickens, strongboxes, dresser drawers, a beloved new mixer, and even a can of gas. The latter may have been because of the gas rationing that was in effect during the war.[13] Another reported someone running down the street holding a squawking chicken by the legs. The chicken may have come from the Lake Shore Poultry store on East 67th street, which had been doing brisk business earlier in the day, or it may have come from one of the coops in the neighborhood. Keeping chickens in the backyard in these neighborhoods was not uncommon.

One of the sad secondary effects of the fires, besides the loss of life and injuries, was the cash that was lost. Many of these people had lost everything when many banks failed only about a dozen years before this. Therefore they no longer trusted the banks and instead saved their cash at home. Afterwards, when they searched through the rubble, many found tin boxes with the outside burned off and ashes inside where the cash was. A representative from the Treasury Department came to help identify any cash that could be replaced. After the fire one man insisted on going back to his house with the agent. He borrowed a ladder and descended into the basement of the destroyed house. He went to the standing chimney and started counting bricks; he pulled one out. Behind it was a jar filled with a roll of cash. The outside ones were charred but the center ones were still green. He handed these over to the agent, who carefully packed them in a box. At that point the agent asked him why he didn't put the money in a bank. The man replied that if it had been burned it would have been no different than the time during the Depression when he put his money in a bank and got back 10 cents on the dollar.[14]

After the first alarm at about 2:43 p.m. the response was rapid. Within a short time many fire companies responded. Eventually there were 28 pumpers from the city department, a Coast Guard fire boat, and six auxiliary pumpers from the Civilian Defense unit. They would pump over seven million gallons of water before the main fire was under control by midnight. Fires in the area continued for days.[15]

Figure 1-7 shows a ground-level view of the devastation from the neighborhood near East 61st Street. Figure 1-8 shows the complete devastation of East 61st Street and East 62nd Street. The location of the failed cylindrical tank (no. 4) is shown at A. Location C is the spherical tank that was brought down by the fire. The surviving tanks are at D and E.

The death toll was reported at various numbers, but the one finally settled on was 130. Of these only 109 were identified, mostly gas company workers (73) but also two nearby workers, two roofers, and 32 residents.[16] Had the tragedy happened at a different hour the toll would have been different. If it had happened only one-half hour later, all the children would have been home from school. Had it happened at night most of the gas company workers would not have been there, so their toll would have been reduced; but the residents would have all been home, and that toll would have been worse. As mentioned previously, the wartime situation probably had some effect. Some women that might have been home in peacetime may have been away working, as many women did during the war. The 21 unidentified seems high for a close-knit neighborhood. However, it was not uncommon for residents of these ethnic neighborhoods to take in boarders, usually single men without nearby families, to make a little extra money. Other single men

Figure 1-7. Post-fire view of the plant and nearby homes (Cleveland State University Library, Cleveland Press Collection).

Figure 1-8. Aerial view of the destruction from the east (Cleveland State University Library, Cleveland Press Collection).

on the plant site could also add to this total. Hundreds were injured, almost 100 homes were destroyed, and hundreds of automobiles were destroyed. It was difficult to identify the victims; "All that identified many of these workers was a set of car keys, a corner of a ration stamp, or a metal compact that was carefully cataloged on the card clipped to the bag containing their bone fragments.... One female casualty was found in a Sixty-first Street basement with a tobacco can containing $765 wrapped in a charred cloth, believed to be an apron."[17] The horror and devastation of the incident is captured quite well by Don Robertson in his novel *The Greatest Thing Since Sliced Bread*. It is a coming-of-age novel about a young boy and his little sister. It culminates in the fire and describes the burning telephone poles, birds fried in flight, and exploding automobile tires.[18]

Aftermath

By all accounts the community, the city and the gas company all acted responsibly after the accident. East Ohio quickly sought out and reimbursed victims. Some suits, however, were filed against some of the companies involved in the construction of the plant. As Boyle reported,

[Mayor] Lausche, irritated by reports that lawyers were signing victims to contracts guaranteeing themselves as much as 30 percent of any damages recovered from East Ohio, asked the Cuyahoga County Bar Association to form a legal commission that would represent claimants free of charge. When East Ohio announced the opening of an office where claimants could file a statement of their losses, foregoing legal representation, the mayor encouraged the formation of a Slovene Relief Commission to help victims prepare their claims for submission to the company. East Ohio, though uninsured, announced it would pay from existing funds.[19]

Another local businessman, Anton Grdina, took the lead in rehabilitation. He organized the Norwood–St. Clair Rehabilitation Corporation and drove it to rebuild. The group collected money from local merchants to buy the land. The lots were divided into 45-foot segments (instead of the original 30 feet), and 16 single-family brick homes were constructed on East 61st and East 62nd streets. This is now one of the neatest neighborhoods in the area. Figure 1-9 shows one of these replacement homes. Figure 1-10 shows a grassy softball field where the tanks used to stand. A new cross street between East 61st and East 62nd streets, Grdina Avenue, and a local park were named in his honor.[20]

Miraculously, the other two spherical tanks survived the conflagration, still full of LNG. However, with fires still burning in the area, everyone was very nervous about their presence. East Ohio quickly acted to empty them. They had no facilities left standing to regasify the liquid, so they used the steam from a locomotive on the nearby railroad tracks

Figure 1-9. Replacement home.

Figure 1-10. Softball field where the tanks once stood.

to supply the heat for regasification. There were still mostly steam locomotives on the railroads at that time. Diesel and electric locomotives were not yet common. They successfully emptied the two tanks by completing the regasification without incident. This gas went where it was supposed to go eventually—into the city gas mains.

Within days East Ohio announced they would not rebuild the LNG facilities; they dismantled the remnants of the plant. Instead they built more conventional office and shop facilities on the land and used part of it for the park mentioned above. About the same time, they announced that they would be storing the natural gas they received in underground caverns and rock formations that are common in the northeast Ohio, Pennsylvania, and West Virginia region.

Everyone wanted to get this behind them and forget it. However, it wasn't that easy. Although they got through the war and the early years following, there were still the same problems of natural gas shortages that had caused them to build the L. S. and R. plant in the first place. In the winter of 1946-1947, industry did face curtailment of some activity so domestic consumers could use the gas to heat their homes. In 1947 the East Ohio president J. F. Robinson said, "We are positive we won't get into the difficulties in the domestic field we encountered last winter, unless people go wild in converting to gas burners.... The East Ohio alone is spending more than $5,000,000 this year for the sole purpose of *improving conditions for industrial and domestic consumers on peak days*" (emphasis added).[21] He went on to say they were laying more pipelines from their storage fields near Canton and that they had elected to improve their underground storage facilities. He need not have worried about "people going wild in converting to gas burners," because at about the same time the Ohio Public Utilities Commission prohibited new installations and conversion of coal and oil heating equipment to gas.[22] Most consumers at that time still used coal for heating, but conversions were becoming more popular.

So the accident had a major impact on Clevelanders, not only because of the tragic loss of life and property, but also because of the long-term gas shortages that went on for a few more years. Cleveland no longer had the large quantity of liquid gas in reserve for "peak shaving," the ability to store gas for a string of cold days. Recent gas pipelines to bring gas to the area from the new Texas gas fields eventually helped to ease shortages.

This was a catastrophe for the city, but it recovered. There have been other industrial accidents over human history that have impacted many people. Mining accidents, for example, go back hundreds if not thousands of years, but the community and the industry make changes and go on. The impacted function is too important to stop just because of a setback. For example, the Triangle shirtwaist factory fire in Greenwich Village in New York in 1911 cost about as many lives (146) as this fire. The clothing industry of course did not halt. However, in that case there followed significant changes in labor and safety laws, and there were political impacts.[23] In this case there were changes in codes, materials, and designs that allowed the LNG industry to eventually come back.

There are times, however, when an incident can have a more far-reaching impact. When the *Hindenburg* burned in New Jersey in 1937 it effectively ended the service of lighter-than-air ships, at least the ones using hydrogen. Aviation was rapidly changing, so that change went largely unnoticed. However, it seems there are signs that we are still living with that now. Hydrogen gas would make an attractive fuel for an internal combustion engine. It would produce zero carbon emissions, only water. Its use would be no more hazardous than the use of gasoline, which we have learned to handle. Yet whenever this is pursued, the rejoinder is often something like, "Look what happened to the Hindenburg."

The difference between this catastrophe and many others, such as mining accidents, is that this was the *first* commercial use of liquid natural gas. It was the possible birth of a new industry. When something new fails so spectacularly at the beginning, especially if it takes so many lives, there is a natural reaction to say, "Wait a minute, maybe this isn't such a good idea after all." There was no chance of turning back on the use of natural gas itself; it had been proven to be a very effective fuel ever since the early commercial uses about 50 to 60 years prior to this accident. However, liquefying the gas and storing it nearby had not yet been entirely proven, even though this plant had operated successfully for over three years. The characterization of the technical consultants who were on the failure review board, that "energy unleashed in the overnight fire was equivalent to the combined 25,000,000 horsepower [sic] in all hydroelectric plants west of the Mississippi River," didn't help to calm any fears either.[24]

This was a pivotal moment. East Ohio quickly washed their hands of it and wanted to move on. Near-term projects in other places were cancelled. There was almost nothing done with LNG on a large commercial scale for about 15 years, and it was over 20 years before the LNG industry really started to move. In retrospect it seems obvious that the recovery would be necessary; the world's appetite for energy was just starting to climb dramatically. The intervening years were used to look deeply at the causes of the problem, the reasons for the high casualty count, and what needed to be done to make this a safe industry.

How did this happen? How did we get to this point? The next two chapters will examine the growth of the industry and how it eventually led to the need for a plant to liquefy and store natural gas.

2
Discovery and Growth

Arc of Energy

    Energy is the ability to do work. What does that mean? Work means you can get something done. If you move an object across a table you do work on the object. You expend energy when you do that work. Energy exists in many forms in the universe such as thermal (heat), electromagnetic, kinetic, potential, electrical, chemical, nuclear, and gravitational. Energy can neither be created nor destroyed. It is constant, but it can be transformed from one kind to another; for example, from mechanical work to heat. Two common forms of mechanical energy are stored, or potential, energy, and motion, or kinetic energy. When you push the object across the table the work you do is the force you apply times the distance the object moves. You supply the energy to do that work from the potential energy in your body. For thousands of years, in order to accomplish any work humans had to supply all the energy from their own bodies. A man might lift a rock over his head, increasing its potential energy, and then drop it on a nut to be cracked. The potential energy of the rock changed to the kinetic energy of the falling rock, which was applied to split the nut. Through sunshine and food he would increase his chemical energy, which would allow him to continue to do more work in order to live.

    Eventually humans learned, accidently at first, that the materials around them contained stored chemical energy that, if released, could provide them benefit. They didn't think of it that way of course, but they did take advantage of these materials when they learned. Wood and coal started as fuels for warmth and cooking. Eventually it was realized that the energy in these fuels could be translated into mechanical energy that could then be used to supplement or replace the energy that people had to apply to every task. One of the first machines invented that changed the chemical energy contained in coal to mechanical energy was Thomas Newcomen's steam engine, which was used to lift water out of a coal mine ... so more coal could be mined. Although Newcomen's steam engine was one of the first to change the chemical energy of coal into mechanical energy, the human use of the energy in wood and coal had started many millennia before that.

    Ever since humans started using fire we have been on a continuous search for fuel for the next fire and for even more energy. Most likely an accidental fire started by some natural occurrence, such as lightening, demonstrated the power of fire and at the same time showed the objects that fire consumed, trees and grass for example. Early archeological evidence shows that wood fires have been used for tens of thousands of years, if not longer, probably for warmth, light, and food preparation. Early in that period humans had to learn the limits and properties of their fuel. For example, grass burned, but very quickly; so it was not a useful fuel. Wood fires were much better at providing sustained warmth, but the wood had to be dry. Thus collecting dry firewood became a major part of the human subsistence efforts for thousands of years. The wood could be gathered and brought to the cave or campsite. For most of human history this fuel sufficed to meet our needs.

Wood is carbonaceous; that is, as an organic material it contains carbon; about 45–50 percent of wood is carbon.[1] When it burns it releases energy as heat and light. This chemical process is called combustion or rapid oxidation; the carbon in the wood combines with oxygen in the air. When this happens, the energy released is called the heat of combustion. The heat of combustion of wood is low, making it a relatively inefficient fuel, but at least originally, a plentiful one. The results of wood combustion are gases such as carbon monoxide and carbon dioxide, which are released into the atmosphere.

However, a few thousand years ago, a relatively short time in human history, it was discovered that coal could also be used as a fuel for fires. Coal is almost all carbon. It is also a fossil fuel; it was formed millions of years ago by the decay of organic material under high pressure. It has a higher heat of combustion than wood. The heating value in joules per kilogram for anthracite coal is almost twice the value for wood, so one can get almost twice as much heat energy by burning coal as by burning wood.[2] (A joule is the unit of energy in the International System [SI] of units. It is equivalent to one newton-meter. The units used hereafter will not be consistently in one system but rather in the system used by those who developed the ideas and processes to be discussed. See table 4-3 on units.) Up to a point, wood is easier to gather and use than coal; coal must be mined from underground. However, there is a limited supply of wood that can be used for construction and fuel. Forests can be quickly denuded as population grows and more and more people cut down trees for fuel. England had its first fuel crises in the thirteenth century with a shortage of wood: "By 1230 England had cut down so many trees for construction and fuel that it was importing most of its timber from Scandinavia, and turned to what would have then been called an alternative energy source: coal."[3] Like wood, coal is a carbonaceous material that releases carbon monoxide and carbon dioxide into the air. It is also a dirty and smelly fuel. Nevertheless, because of its abundance and heating value it became the fuel that drove the Industrial Revolution. It has one of the same advantages as wood, in that it can be moved to the place where it is to be used. Thus it eventually made its way to steam locomotives and steam ships. It is still used as the primary fuel for powering plants around the world that generate electricity. Although it has a higher heating value than wood, it is heavy and bulky to move around. When the navy depended on coal to power its steamships in the early twentieth century, it required coaling stations around the world to assure the necessary supply. Negotiating the rights and hauling the coal to these stations was no small achievement.

Oil is still higher on the evolutionary development of energy. By the time it was discovered in this country in the latter half of the nineteenth century, the U.S. Industrial Revolution was in full swing using coal as its energy source. Nevertheless, it didn't take long for entrepreneurs to grasp the potential of oil and exploit it. The heating value of oil is at least 30 percent higher than that of coal and about three times that of wood.[4] More importantly it is easier to store and ship than coal and, although still giving off pollutants, burns cleaner than coal. There is no particulate matter, such as soot, when oil is burned.

Kerosene, refined from oil and used for lighting, was one of the first derivatives of oil. Use as a lubricant quickly followed, and of course eventual refinement into a heating fuel and then to gasoline for automobile transportation use. Crude oil, like coal, is a fossil fuel and also like coal, is mostly carbon (80–87 percent carbon and 10–15 percent hydrogen).[5] Oil is a mixture of several different hydrocarbons, long chain molecules composed of various combinations of hydrogen and carbon. The most common are alkanes, also known as paraffins, which are saturated hydrocarbon chains containing only straight or branched chains of carbon and hydrogen atoms. They have the general formula C_nH_{2n+2} and have five to 40 carbon atoms per molecules. The story of oil as an energy source and its importance in the world economy is well told in Daniel Yergin's book *The Prize*.[6] An advantage of oil over other fuels is that it is much easier to transport than coal. Therefore, it is the most common fuel in use today for transportation, that is, for automobiles, trains, and airplanes. Oil, as wood and coal or any hydrocarbon fuel, releases carbon monoxide and carbon dioxide into the atmosphere. Carbon dioxide is not toxic in itself but is a greenhouse gas that, in increasing concentrations, contributes to global climate change. This negative impact of hydrocarbons is causing a reevaluation of the use of hydrocarbon fuels for the future.

Other sources of energy such as solar, wind, and water have been used for millennia but so far have had practical limitations. The sun could be used for heat and drying when it was available. The energy though, could not be stored and used at night or on cloudy days. When it was finally harnessed, wind could be used to turn mills and grind grain. It, however, was unreliable because it could stop, leaving the windmill lifeless. Similarly, the power of falling water could be used as a continuous source for driving mills and even manufacturing operations. The disadvantage these all share is that they can only be used in place and when available. Although it wasn't appreciated for most of human history, these are "clean fuels"; they don't produce harmful emissions. Ironically, these "alternate fuels" of the present will now become more important as we deal with the environmental impact of hydrocarbons. Modern wind turbines are becoming a common sight in open areas. They are also being considered for offshore "wind farms" on various coasts. Likewise, solar cells to gather electricity directly from the sun are showing up on home roofs as well as commercial buildings. There are also "solar farms" in desert areas, where concentrated solar energy can be used to generate electricity and distribute it on the local grid.

Nuclear energy is the only "new fuel" available. It is clean with respect to the atmosphere; it produces no hydrocarbon emissions. However, there are cost, safety, and waste disposal issues that must be addressed when building nuclear plants. The 2011 Japanese earthquake and tsunami that destroyed a nuclear power plant have caused even more doubt about the long-term use of nuclear power. Nevertheless, nuclear power will continue to be an important source for generating electricity for a long time.

Electricity is an energy source that everyone is familiar with. It powers our factories, appliances, lights, and, increasingly, our automobiles. In itself it is a clean fuel; that is, it has no environmental impacts. However, it is a secondary fuel. Energy obtained from one of the other sources, usually a fossil fuel, must be used to generate the electricity. In the future it will most likely be a combination of the cleaner fuels such as solar, wind, and nuclear that will be used. This transition will undoubtedly happen at some point in the future not only because of environmental factors but because the fossil fuels are a finite resource that even now are becoming more expensive to extract. Although the transition is starting, for the present time we will still depend on fossil fuels, and we will have to do so for some time to come.

In the middle of this mix of energy sources is natural gas, another fossil fuel. Natural gas was discovered almost by accident and in significant quantities as men searched for oil. At first it was considered a nuisance and even dangerous. Now, though, it has become a very important fuel with new ways devised to extract it. It has advantages over coal and oil. Even though it is a fossil fuel and results in greenhouse gases, it has fewer other pollutants than oil or coal. It could provide a good transition in the switch to cleaner fuels in the future.

Natural Gas

Natural gas is a fossil fuel found underground, as are the other fossil fuels. As with other fossil fuels it is of organic origin, decayed organic material under pressure for a long time. Natural gas is often found with oil, especially in the shallower deposits, because they are formed in a similar process. In deeper deposits, because the temperature is higher, the formation of natural gas is more probable than oil. This process of formation is called *thermogenic* because the gas is formed by high temperatures and pressure underground. A *biogenic* process, caused by the activity of microorganisms, can also generate methane, the primary constituent of natural gas. If biogenic gas is found in the earth, it is usually near the surface and is often lost to the atmosphere. It is the process that takes place in animal intestines and landfills. For these reasons it is not a great contributor to the natural gas supplies we use. An *abiogenic* process, meaning *not* resulting from the activity of organisms, in which gases deep under the earth's crust, rich in hydrogen and carbon, rise toward the surface and combine to form methane, is another process by which natural gas is formed. This theory of the formation of natural gas by an abiogenic process is more problematic; that is, it is not accepted by all geologists as are the thermogenic and biogenic processes. As the natural gas rises from deep in the earth it will mostly be trapped either under impermeable rock domes, often along with oil deposits, or within porous, sponge-like sedimentary rock.[7]

Natural gas is a mixture of many gases. The largest constituent is always methane, but the mixture can vary considerably depending on the source. A typical composition includes methane (CH_4), which has four atoms of hydrogen to one atom of carbon, at 70–90 percent, followed by ethane (C_2H_6), propane (C_3H_8), and butane (C_4H_{10}), combining for 0–20 percent. About eight percent is carbon dioxide and other gases, including nitrogen and trace gases.[8] In a series of test wells in northeastern Ohio and Pennsylvania the U.S. Geological Survey found the methane percentages ranging from 76 to 94 percent and only trace amounts, if any, of carbon dioxide.[9] In Texas much higher levels of helium can be found in natural gas, which became important as will be discussed in a later chapter. Natural gas found at shallower depths, with oil for example, will tend to be "wetter," that is, have more of the accompanying hydrocarbons. "Dryer" gas, that is, containing less of the other hydrocarbons, will be almost pure methane. This is the case for gas found at greater depths.[10]

EARLY DISCOVERIES

Natural gas deposits leaking through the surface of the earth have been observed for thousands of years. Greeks, Persians, Romans, and Native Americans all observed instances of "burning springs." These were gases leaking from shallow deposits that would catch fire either by some natural means, for example, lightening, or from some man-made fire source. Often these would burn for long periods, sometimes years.

In Greece, about 1,000 BC, a goatherd noticed his charges acted peculiarly in a certain area. He and his neighbors experimented and found they got light-headed in the area. They surmised that Apollo was inspiring them, so a temple was built there, overseen by a priestess. Her duty was to inhale the gas (no flame was mentioned in this instance) and utter prophecies. Thus the Oracle of Delphi became famous.[11]

Over the centuries others observed this mysterious flame that seemed to burn forever:

> Plutarch (AD 60–140) mentioned a lamp which had remained alight for centuries. St. Augustine (AD 354–430) described a perpetual lamp in the Temple of Isis which neither wind nor water could extinguish.... In 1550, in a vault on the island Nesis, near Naples, there was found a still-burning lamp which had been there from the beginnings of the Christian era. And in the Middle Ages a perpetual lamp was found in the tomb of the father of Constantine the Great in Yorkshire, where it had been burning since the third century.[12]

These sources or burning springs often would be associated with some gods or perhaps some evil spirits. The remains of an old temple remain at a burning spring noted first around AD 967 on the Caspian Sea near Baku, Russia. The Chinese also became aware of these natural springs and started to use flames that could be produced from them to heat cooking pots. By 68 BC sources were well known in a couple of Chinese provinces. By AD 100 they were using bamboo pipes to carry the gas to places where they would use the flames to evaporate water to extract salt crystals.[13] According to Waples, "In Europe, the noted 'Fontaine Ardente' (burning fountain), near Grenoble, France, was said to be the source for natural gas lights in the first century AD. Also in ancient times, gas fires lighted the city of Genoa, Italy.... Gas wells were also known in Japan in AD 615."[14] Thomas Shirley submitted a paper to the Philosophical Society of London in 1667 in which he said that eight years earlier he had seen a spring "where water die burn like oyle" and "did boyle and heave like water in a pot."[15]

Most of these observations were accidental; that is, gas seeping from the ground was observed and even used, as by the Chinese, but not a result of purposeful drilling for gas. As plentiful as these observations and use were, there was never a concerted effort to take advantage of the gas, even though it had the desirable properties of a fuel.

There were many sightings during, and before, the early European settlement of North America. David Waples chronicles many of these in his book *The Natural Gas Industry in Appalachia*. These included sightings by Native Americans who obviously had known about these for many years and had shown the European explorers the phenomenon. Huron Indians had shown a French missionary (Joseph de la Roche) a "fontaine de bitumen" (oil and gas spring) in North America in 1627 near Cuba, New York. In 1669 the explorer de la Salle was shown a gas source by a Native American guide, which they torched and burned, in Ontario county, New York. These accounts are numerous, including even many observations by George Washington.[16]

A lot of the sightings were in Appalachia, for example in Ohio, Pennsylvania, and what is now West Virginia. Washington saw evidence of these burning springs in Pomeroy, Ohio, during the French and Indian War, and on the Kanawha River near present-day Charleston, West Virginia, in 1775. Another site discovered by a wilderness scout named Jesse Hughes was discovered on the Little Kanawha, just east of Parkersburg: "Thomas Jefferson recorded in his *Notes on the State of Virginia* in 1781 that thrusting a lighted candle at the site produced a flame. Oil and natural gas ignited at the location burned for months."[17]

One story had Tom Paine and George Washington, in 1783, at the Rocky Hill country estate in New Jersey discussing a nearby creek that sometimes caught fire. Washington theorized that it might be "bituminous matter," similar to oil slicks or coal dust. Paine argued that it might be "inflammable air," swamp gas (methane). They decided to do an experiment and went to the creek at night.

> "General Washington placed himself at one end of the scow, and I at the other," Paine recalled, "Each of us had a roll of cartridge paper, which we lighted and held over the water, about two or three inches from the surface. Washington's soldiers prodded the river mud with their poles, and when the mud at the bottom was disturbed by the poles, the air bubbles rose fast, and I saw the fire take from General Washington's light and descend from thence to the surface of the water, in a similar manner as when a lighted candle is held so as to touch the smoke of a candle just blown out, the smoke will take fire, and the fire will descend and light up the candle. This was demonstrative evidence that what was called setting the river on fire was ... the inflammable air that arose out of the mud."[18]

It turns out that after a few fits and starts the natural gas industry was born in and around Appalachia.

According to Castaneda, "During the nineteenth century, the 'burning springs' were little more than curiosities. People who had seen such springs knew that when lit, the springs produced both light and heat. There was no practical method of capturing the gas emanating from the springs and bottling it or redirecting its flow through pipes."[19] Early settlers kept finding natural gas in other ways, not always with good results. They would find it when drilling for brine. The salt derived from brine was used for food preservation, and tanning. Drilling for brine in that area would often result in a natural gas strike. In one strike on the Ohio River near Pittsburgh in 1820 the gas caught fire and destroyed all the nearby buildings.[20]

Around this time one person decided to take advantage of the desirable lighting properties of burning natural gas, that is, its cleanness and brightness. In 1821 William Aaron Hart (1797–1865) drilled a 17-foot-deep hole in the Canadaway creek in Fredonia, New York, one of the areas that experienced the bubbling gas. He succeeded in reaching gas using a one and one-half inch bore hole. He capped the hole with a gas holder to capture the gas, collecting 88 cubic feet of gas in 12 hours. Later in 1825, using three-quarter-inch lead pipe, he was able to supply gas for lighting and food cooking to some local stores and buildings in Fredonia.[21] This was the first practical use of natural gas in this country.

There was not a straight-line increase of natural gas after that. Despite its advantages for lighting and food preparation (space heating came much later), natural gas was not a reliable source of energy. Even if you found it relatively easily, as in this case, it was not known how long it would last, so building a distribution system was risky. Eventually the Fredonia source ran out. The distance that the gas could be moved depended on the natural pressure of the gas in the well, and that varied from well to well. If the pressure was low the gas could not be moved far because pressure losses in the pipe due to friction limited the distance it could be sent. Unregulated pressures also led to risks of explosions. In other words, natural gas, when found at all, could only be used near the source of the gas well.

Handle with Care

As mentioned above, the lack of control of any natural gas, found either accidently or because you were looking for it, could cause problems. Explosions occurred and fires were started. It is, after all, a fuel. In the incidents listed above there were certainly injuries and probably some fatalities. But by this time the search for gas and oil was becoming profitable, so these incidents did not cause the exploration to stop.

However, the early nineteenth century was right in the middle of the Industrial Revolution in the U.S. This revolution had started in England about 100 years earlier and demanded a lot of energy. The English had long since denuded their forests of wood for fuel and had turned to coal as the energy source. It was not only more plentiful than wood but had the advantage of higher heat content than wood. The use of coal meant going underground to mine it. This was dangerous not only in itself but also because of what was found with the coal.

On May 24, 1812, an explosion and fire in the Felling colliery near Sunderland, England, killed 92 miners. The fire raged for many days. A second explosion at the same colliery in 1813 killed an additional 22 miners. It was estimated that over 300 miners had been killed in similar incidents over the previous five years. The deeper mine shafts needed to gather more coal were bringing more tragedies. The reason was "fire-damp," a lethal, explosive gas found in the coal seams. At first it was thought to be hydrogen. After the second explosion in 1813, matters became urgent and help was sought from scientific quarters. A Safety Committee led by the Duke of Northumberland and the Bishop of Durham was formed to look for a solution. They went looking for Sir Humphrey Davy (1778–1725), head of the Royal Institution.[22] However, he had just left for an extended tour of Europe accompanied by his wife and lab assistant Michael Faraday (1791–1867). Ironically, in the autumn of 1814 near Florence, Italy, Davy and Faraday heard of gases leaking from nearby rock formations: "Davy forgot about everything when they discovered that the mysterious gas could be stirred up from mud with a stick, and could be ignited even in heavy rain, burning beautifully with a 'very pale' blue flame, like methylated spirits or 'the flame of spirits of wine.'"[23]

They bottled it, and analyzed it back in Florence, and found it to be methane; the same gas (known as "fire damp") that had been causing the problems in the coal mines. So the gas that had been bubbling up for centuries, the natural gas, was primarily methane. This is not surprising, because the minerals it has been found with, coal and oil, were themselves fossil fuels, as is natural gas or methane.

In 1815 Davy was on another trip but was interrupted by news of another accident, which killed 57 men. He came back to start working on a solution. He was successful. He devised a lamp covered with a fine-gauge iron mesh that could be used in the presence of methane and not cause an explosion. This lamp was a major success in reducing these mining tragedies. This was an example of what people expected of science at the time: the scientific method at the service of mankind. Here was the Scientific Revolution enabling the work of the Industrial Revolution. These early disasters with methane were even more destructive of human life than the later disaster in Cleveland in October 1944.

This whole story of "Davy and the Lamp" can be found in Holmes's *The Age of Wonder*.[24]

Manufactured Gas—The Predecessor and Competitor

Natural gas didn't take off right away, not only because of the reasons listed above, but also because by the time Hart had drilled into Canadaway creek manufactured gas was becoming more popular.

Manufactured gas is just that, a gas manufactured from another material. The most common manufactured gas is coal gas. Coal gas results from the destructive distillation of bituminous coal, a process called carbonization. The coal is heated in an oven or retort to high temperatures with a limited supply of oxygen. The result is coal gas, coke and various tar residues. The carbonaceous coke is used as a fuel and as a reducing agent for smelting iron ore. The coal gas byproduct was used for lighting and heating. The final coal gas, or town gas, contained more than 50 percent hydrogen, carbon monoxide and some other hydrocarbons.[25] It was one of the first gases discovered by the first person to work with gases, Flemish physician and chemist Jan Baptista van Helmont (1577–1644) (see Chapter 4).

Prior to the general use of coal gas in the nineteenth century, others after van Helmont experimented with it. Johann Becker (n.d.) of Munich produced it by heating coal around 1681, and the Reverend John Clayton (1657–1725) of Wigan, England, did it around 1684.[26] However, the pioneers of the manufactured gas industry were probably the Scottish mechanic and engineer William Murdock (1754–1839), and a German national, Friedrich Albrecht Winzer (1763–1830). Murdock used coal gas to light his home in 1792. Later he equipped a business with coal gas lighting, using old gun barrels as piping. He went on to build a coal gas works in Soho in 1802. Winzer, later known as Winsor after he moved to England, promoted coal gas for heating. He built the first public street lighting in Pall Mall in London in 1807, using sheet lead rolled into pipes. He eventually incorporated the London and Westminster Gas Light and Coke Company in 1812. By 1815 the company had 26 miles of main gas lines.[27] Thus by early in the nineteenth century the manufactured gas industry was established and had started growing, in and around London.

The U.S. was not far behind in the establishment of the industry. This was led by the portrait painter Charles Wilson Peale and his son Rembrandt Peale. The senior Peale helped develop a pine tar process to produce gas for lighting in 1813. It was set up to use in a museum to promote an exhibit, "Gas Lights Without Oil, Tallow, Wick or Smoke."[28] According to Peebles, "On June 17, 1816, Rembrandt Peale and four other prominent local men, formed the Gas light Company of Baltimore, the first manufactured-gas company in America. The company was formally incorporated on February 5, 1817, and the first street light was supplied with gas two days later."[29] They used pine tar as the feedstock for this manufactured gas at first, but by 1822 had switched to coal.

Although manufactured gas preceded the first commercial use of natural gas in Fredonia by just a few years, at this time it had greater staying power. One did not have to look for it, drill to unknown depths, or deal with varying pressures, as one did for natural gas. Most importantly, one could build a gas plant near a city where it could be distributed without the need for long-distance pipe lines. Thus although coal gas and coke, the byproducts of coal, were expensive to manufacture, they could be sold, so it became a long-lived industry. Eventually manufactured gas was replaced by natural gas, but not completely for over 160 years. The last conversion to natural gas from manufactured gas took place in Muirkirk, Scotland, on September 19, 1978.[30] Coincidentally, William Murdock, the manufactured gas pioneer, was from Muirkirk.

After the Baltimore system was established, manufactured gas companies started in other cities. The Boston Gas Light Company started in 1822 and the New York Gas Light Company in 1825.[31] Manufactured gas plants started to increase in numbers, not peaking until the 1920s. Pittsburgh got gaslight in 1837. In 1846 the Cleveland Gas Light and Coke Company was formed. By 1850, in Cleveland gaslight was introduced in public buildings including St. Paul's Church. This inspired a little ditty:

> The glory of the stars and moon
> And comets, too, may pass;
> Then let 'em go-however soon,
> For Cleveland's burning gas.[32]

The original lighting in Cleveland was in the downtown area. However, part of the operation was in a northeast industrial area that eventually became part of the East Ohio Gas Company Plant Number 2, the site of the disastrous fire in 1944. The company applied to spread gaslight to the west side in 1856. In 1866 a new company, the People's Gas Light Company, purchased some of the pipes and equipment of Cleveland Gas Light and served the west side of the city. The two firms both operated in the city until natural gas was introduced in 1903.[33]

By 1859 there were 297 companies across the country supplying a population of almost 4,900,000 people.[34] As manufactured gas was improved and more widely distributed it was used mainly for lighting in public places. It was still too costly for the average household. For the first half of the nineteenth century homes were still using whale oil and tallow candles for lighting.[35]

During its evolution, first as a lighting fuel, later as a fuel for cooking and heating, manufactured gas in the U.S. used basically only three processes or different ways to produce the gas: coal gas, carbureted water gas, and oil gas.

Coal gas was the first. As was discussed previously, it was the first one used early in the century. It was made by distilling bituminous coal in an airless furnace or retort to produce a combination of gases than could be burned, at first for just light. About 40 percent of the coal would result in the coal gas, which was composed of carbon monoxide, hydrogen, and nitrogen.[36] It also produced some undesirable byproducts such as coal tar and contaminated water. Many of the byproducts are toxic and/or carcinogenic, such as ammonia, cyanide, sulfur, and heavy metals such as arsenic. It is estimated there are 52,000 or more former manufactured gas plants in the U.S., so the toxic cleanup is significant.[37] Of course it also produced coke, which was a useful fuel in its own right. Coal gas has a heat yield of only 149 BTU per cubic foot, well less than that of natural gas.[38] (A BTU, or British Thermal Unit, is a unit of energy and represents the amount of energy needed to heat one pound of water one degree Fahrenheit.) Because coal became plentiful, coal gas was an attractive fuel for lighting.

In 1873 carbureted water gas was developed by Professor L. Lowe of Pennsylvania. Carbureted water gas is made first by making water gas (made by injecting steam into the hot coal in the refractory chamber) and then injecting oil into the heated container of water gas. Thus it is a mixture of the gaseous products of coal and petroleum. Carbureted water gas is composed of carbon monoxide, hydrogen, methane and small amounts of illuminating gases. The carbon monoxide component required great care so as not to cause asphyxiation of the users. It has a higher heat yield, 300–350 BTU per cubic foot. Once developed it became the dominant manufactured gas, because of its efficiency, starting in the 1870s.[39]

Oil gas was the third manufactured gas of the manufactured gas era. It was the only manufactured gas to not use coal. Instead the oil, like coal before it, was heated in an airless furnace, in essence "thermo-cracking oil in a steam environment to produce the raw gas rather than distilling coal."[40] This was also developed in the 1870s along with the carbureted water gas; both had to wait for the availability of oil before they were possible. Oil gas was first used in Saratoga, New York. Produced from naphtha and light oils, it was a better grade of gas for lighting; however, because it used oil it was expensive. It had about one-half the heating value of natural gas.[41]

The manufactured gas industry continued to grow for over 100 years. It had major advantages over other fuels, especially in lighting public areas. Later it came to be used for cooking and heating as well as lighting. It was dirty in its own way but still cleaner than coal and brighter than whale oil. The residual tars from all manufactured gas processes also polluted well beyond the time the plants were in operation. We are still cleaning up from all the manufactured gas plants that existed in this country at one time or another.[42]

However, it did have one major disadvantage compared to wood, coal, and later, oil. It could not be stored easily or moved easily to another place. It shared this disadvantage with natural gas. Manufactured gas could, though, be manufactured close to the place where it was needed. This resulted in a proliferation of plants, as stated above. At first there were many small plants, actual "kits," that were available to even very small communities. Eventually piped distribution systems were made available and central plants were more common.[43]

Nevertheless, there was always the need for some capture and storage for both natural gas and manufactured gas. Gasholders were developed for this purpose. A gasholder (sometimes referred to as a gasometer) was simply an inverted container, similar to a paper cup or collapsible drinking cup, to catch and contain the gas. The first one at Fredonia for the natural gas collected there was just an inverted copper container. These containers are needed in the manufacturing process to store gas at least temporarily to help maintain the pressure in the system and provide a buffer for the distribution. These evolved into usually large cylinders with movable tops, which stored the gas. A schematic of a gasholder is shown in figure 2–1. One can see the frames of three gasholders in figure 1–2. The largest one is in the center left. Their frames, and the shadows of the frames, stand out because all three are empty; the tops are near the ground level. Note how large they are compared to the spheres being constructed.

The gas was contained by the inverted "cap" at the top, which essentially floated in the water. A weight on top of the movable roof helped determine the pressure of the gas. The water at the bottom provided the seal. The pressure was not high, so although this was a convenient way to store gas temporarily, the container had to be very large to be effective. In later years some of these reached 200 feet in diameter. Thus it was not a good way to store large amounts of gas, either manufactured or natural; the size quickly became prohibitive (see Chapter 3).

Thus by 1860 when oil started to become available, manufactured gas was a large and growing industry. The oil boom changed everything—although not at once.

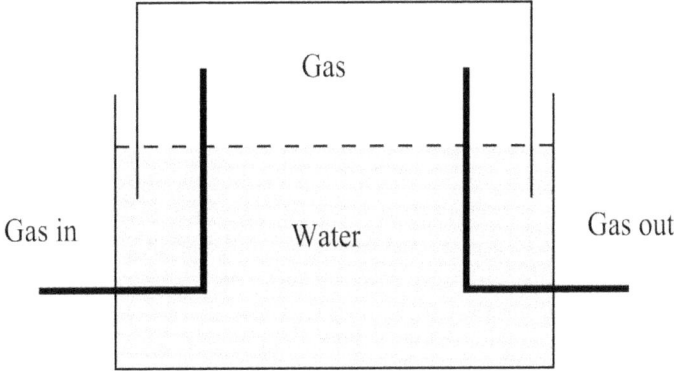

Figure 2-1. Variable volume gas container.

Start of the Oil and Gas Revolution

The Industrial Revolution in the U.S. was starting to hit its stride in the first half of the nineteenth century. It started in 1793, when Eli Whitney invented the cotton gin. Although manually powered, the gin gave new life to the cotton industry of the South. By 1807 Robert Fulton's steamboat, *Clermont*, made its maiden voyage from New York to Albany. It used wood to fuel the steam engines. In 1810 there were more than 80 cotton-spinning mills, mostly in New England. These used water power to supply the energy. The Erie Canal opened in New York in 1825, and in 1830 the Baltimore and Ohio Railroad began with 14 miles of track.[44]

Canals and railroads were being built because the country was growing at a rapid rate, especially in the Pennsylvania and Ohio regions. Between 1830 and 1840 the population of Pennsylvania increased 27.8 percent and that of Ohio increased 62.4 percent.[45] There were rapid changes in other parts of the country as well. In 1830 when Andrew Jackson was president, he started moving the Native Americans from east of the Mississippi to west of that river. This vast, forced migration culminated in the Cherokee "Trail of Tears" migration in 1838. The Texas Revolution and battle of the Alamo took place in 1836. Arkansas was admitted to the Union in 1836, followed by Michigan in 1837. This type of expansion meant the need for energy was increasing, which usually meant wood and coal. However, drilling also increased, mostly for water and brine, but then for gas when it became widely known that it could be used as a fuel.

From the time natural gas was first used commercially in Fredonia until the oil boom started around 1860, natural gas development was slow. It was not as easy to get to as manufactured gas. That was because manufactured gas was made out of the plentiful coal deposits in Appalachia, and coal was easier to handle than natural gas. A number of wells were drilled, mostly looking for brine or water, but they often resulted in the discovery of natural gas. Sometimes the gas was then used in the area. Other times it was just wasted into the atmosphere or burned off. Gas was found in Saw Mill Run near Pittsburgh around

1830 and in western Virginia at the Kanawha Salines in 1831, where it was used to boil the brine from the well to make salt.[46]

There were examples of this all around the area. For example, in Ohio natural gas was found near the Muskingum River in 1836 and was used there to boil brine.[47] In Centreville, Butler County, Pennsylvania, it was used for the same thing.[48] All these were hit and miss. In the latter half of the century there was a search for oil, which meant more drilling, and as a result more gas was found. Often gas and oil were found together, in which case the gas was unwanted and therefore wasted. In Erie, Pennsylvania, in 1854 a deep well (1,200 feet) was sunk looking for oil. Oil was not found, but brackish water and gas were found. The gas was used locally to provide light for a few homes in the area.[49]

Seepage of oil from the ground had been experienced as long as natural gas had. The Huron Indians, who had shown Joseph de la Roche the oil and gas spring near Cuba, New York, were using this "very good oil" for medicinal purposes. Later, in 1749, Peter Kalm (1716–1779), a Swedish naturalist, reported near the same area that the Seneca Indians were using the local oil to soothe many pains and ailments.[50]

By the middle of the nineteenth century entrepreneurs were searching for a substitute for whale oil. Whale oil was used frequently for illumination but had the disadvantages of becoming rancid after a while, smelling foul while burning, and being scarce and therefore expensive. In 1846 a Canadian geologist and medical doctor named Abraham Gesner (1797–1864) demonstrated a new lighting fluid, a clear fluid that gave off a pale yellow flame. It turned out to be a very good lighting fuel. He had distilled it from coal and, therefore, it was also known as coal oil. He named the fluid kerosene from the Greek *keroselaion*, meaning "wax oil." Gesner later went to New York, where in 1854 he helped found the North American Gas Light Company. Initially kerosene was also expensive. However, when it was discovered that kerosene could also be distilled from oil, the sales for illumination took off.[51]

Samuel Kier (1813–1874) was an owner of salt wells who saw the oil that seeped into the salt wells as a nuisance. He recognized the oil as similar to a medicine his wife was taking for an illness. When he had it analyzed, it turned out to be identical to his wife's medicine. In 1853 he started to market it as "Kiers Petroleum or Rock Oil."[52] He used the term *rock oil* to distinguish it from mineral oil or whale oil. He claimed to have sold 240,000 half-pint bottles by 1858 at one dollar per bottle.[53] Later, working with others, it was determined that petroleum could be distilled for use in lighting. It took some experimentation to get it to it to burn with less odor, but it was done. He built a still and began selling "carbon oil" for one dollar and fifty cents per gallon. Kier was also credited with developing the kerosene lamp, which made the use of kerosene practical.[54] So Samuel Kier was another entrepreneur, like Gesner, who helped to make kerosene the illuminant of choice.

The rush for oil was now on. Also, from then on the discovery of oil and gas would often occur together until gas was eventually sought for its own uses.

A New York lawyer, George Bissell (1821–1884), suspected that the coal oil (kerosene) that was being used then (the 1850s) for illumination was probably similar to rock oil. He and a partner found some investors to finance the purchase of some properties in Titusville, Pennsylvania. There had been oil seeping out of the ground there for years. They had some chemical analysis done and confirmed the oil could be used as an illuminant. They formed the Pennsylvania Rock Oil Company in September 1855 and leased 1,200 acres of land around Titusville. The company, later renamed the Seneca Oil Company, hired Edwin Drake, a former dry goods salesman, to search for the oil in the area. Drake decided to drill for oil instead of digging for it. He hired an old salt well digger to do the drilling. The operation was similar to many in the area that had been used to drill for either water or brine. They were successful; they struck oil after drilling only 69 feet, on August 28, 1859.[55] The story of oil after that is well known, or, as they say, the "rest is history."

From this point on natural gas, oil, and manufactured gas would grow together. Although manufactured gas was a competitor, and probably did delay the widespread introduction of natural gas, it was getting people accustomed to using gas for many functions, especially illumination. This spurred the development of a gas distribution system, for example, the laying of pipelines. Similarly, drilling for oil spurred drilling in general; sometimes gas was struck instead of oil, and often both would come together. The drillers eventually figured out that the gas pressure was often the mechanism that would cause the oil to gush from the ground when a well was drilled.

The 40 years at the end of the nineteenth century were years of exploration, development, and consolidation of the oil industry and, by extension, its stepchild, the natural gas industry. More and more people started drilling for oil and often came up with gas instead. Disappointed, they sometimes left it to blow off or flared it off. Sometimes when they did find gas, an enterprising entrepreneur would try to use it. Such was the case of "Buffalo Joe" Stilwell in 1867. He drilled a gas well near Oil City, Pennsylvania, and piped the product into a dozen houses. In 1865 drillers in West Bloomfield, New York, who sought oil hit gas at only 480 feet. They deserted the well because it wasn't oil. The well was later purchased by the Bloomfield and Rochester Natural Gas Light Company. They built a 25-mile pipeline to the city out of hollowed-out Canadian white pine logs. Although these logs did not last long, this was harbinger of another new industry, the pipeline industry.[56]

The exploration continued with gas finds in Ohio and Pennsylvania. One find in Pennsylvania about five miles north of Titusville, drilled in 1872, was estimated to have an open flow of four million cubic feet per day at a pressure of 75 pounds per square inch. A loud roar was associated with this well as gas gushed from the ground. They built a three-and-one-quarter-inch pipeline five-and-one-half miles into Titusville, which served approximately 250 domestic and industrial customers.[57] The growth continued, with gas being used increasingly for industrial purposes also. In 1874 it was used for iron making near Pittsburgh, and in 1876 it was used in a cutlery works in the same area. In 1885 a six-inch line was laid from wells east of Oil City to the communities of Oil City, Franklin, and Titusville.[58] Natural gas lines were now being laid in competition with existing lines used for manufactured gas. The industry expanded, despite the known problems of the time, such as the variable pressures from the various wells that made it somewhat hazardous to use, as well as new problems that came up. As natural gas became more available people found that their gas burners would not work at the same settings as they had for manufactured gas; they had to be adjusted to work satisfactorily.[59]

One reason for this expansion was cost. Natural gas was very inexpensive compared to manufactured gas. There were no meters early on. Waples quotes the *Oil City Derrick* newspaper as saying, "When it was at its height consumers were informed they could burn all [the natural gas] they wanted—there were no meters—for 50 cents a month."[60] Thus price competition was a major incentive for the new industry.

The Natural Gas Industry—A Product of Its Age

The last 40 years of the nineteenth century were indeed active for the natural gas industry. However, it was only a part of the very active time of growth known as the Gilded Age. The age might also have been described as dynamic, frenetic, and tumultuous. This was true for all facets of American life at the time including manufacturing, energy production, politics, society, and culture.[61]

The Civil War clearly was a major change agent, as was its fallout. The war itself caused the death of over 600,000 Americans; it is still the deadliest war in our history and in the Western Hemisphere. In the fallout from the war we went from the abolition of slavery (13th Amendment) to the period of Reconstruction, through the end of Reconstruction in the 1870s, to the institutionalization of segregation through Jim Crow laws; all this in a period of 35 years. It took another 65 years, into the 1960s, after that to catch our collective breath and correct many of the injustices of the Jim Crow era.

The war was a catalyst for many other changes. For example, the transcontinental railroad was started during the war and completed in 1869. Between 1860 and 1880 railroad mileage tripled.[62] This ushered in a dramatic expansion of the railroad industry with consequent cutthroat competition for dominance. This paralleled the growth in other industries, for example steel and oil. A great deal of this business was of dubious legality but was justified by the philosophy of social Darwinism; that is, only the fit would and should survive. This, as you would expect, put downward pressure on wages, hence the birth of labor unrest and unions. It also encouraged risk taking, whether in one's job where you might take a risk to keep your job, or in deciding to drill for gas, and risk fire and explosion.

The entrepreneurial spirit is demonstrated by the number of patents issued in a very short time. The total number of U.S. patents issued through 1860 was 41,030. By 1900 it was 674,357, so that 40-year period saw the number of patents increase by over 633,000.[63] These were the times of the inventions of Edison and Bell. Natural gas and electricity were both in their infancy but they started to compete with each other for use as illuminants.

The country grew at a rapid rate in this period from 31.7 million in 1860 to 75.7 million in 1900, 139 percent.[64] Although most of this was a homegrown growth, there were at least two waves of immigration, mostly from various parts of Europe. These immigrants were competing for jobs and therefore put more pressure on wages. They also stirred a backlash of nativism, which could sometimes turn violent. Most of the immigrants ended up in the cities, contributing to overcrowding in many of them. New York City grew from 805,658 in 1860 to 2,050,600 in 1900, an increase of over 150 percent.[65] Thus they, and the others in the city, became ripe for political organization; political bossism grew as the voters were organized.

These factors, unbridled capitalism, social Darwinism, wage pressures, potential social unrest, which put a strain on the social fabric, also contributed to a progressive response. Andrew Carnegie, who made his money in steel, started the concept of private philanthropy in this country when later he started to give away his vast fortune. Jane Addams started a settlement house in Chicago to help the poor, especially immigrants, to cope with the urban environment. The American Red Cross and the Salvation Army in this country were started in this period. The increase of alcohol drinking led to rise in drinking establishments after the war. This in turn led to a reaction, which was the rise of the temperance and prohibition movements. The Woman's Christian Temperance Union was formed in Cleveland in 1874. The drive for woman's suffrage started in this same active social period.

This period was also background for another revolution that was to take place in transportation in the twentieth century. In 1876 Nikolaus August Otto (1832–1891) developed the four-stroke internal combustion engine. It was based on an earlier two-stroke engine that ran on coal gas. Because these engines ran on coal gas they depended on the city gas supply and, therefore, were stationary engines.[66] Gottlieb Daimler (1834–1900) and Karl Benz (1844–1929) were determined to turn this development into something that could be used for transportation. They were competitors and made their first road tests very close to one another. Benz ran his three-wheeler powered by a two-cycle, one-cylinder engine early in 1885. In 1886 Daimler tested a one-cylinder engine, four-wheel carriage.[67] Henry Ford (1863–1947) came up with his first self-propelled vehicle, the Quadricycle, in 1896.[68] The world was on its way to the transportation era of the twentieth century, which for the most part depended on oil.

The industrial age was now in full swing, and nothing was more important than energy. Energy in this period meant coal. Coal and coke use went from 0.52 quadrillion BTU in 1860 to 6.84 in 1900, a 13-fold increase. Oil and natural gas were virtually zero in 1860, but went to 0.23 and 0.25 quadrillion BTU, respectively, in 1900. The latter two were still very small energy contributors compared to coal. Oil and gas each produced only about 3.5 percent of the energy produced by coal in 1900.[69] However, both were very strong growth industries. Gas, already being used for some industry, was originally a stepchild of oil but grew rapidly as an industry as oil grew as an industry.

When you talk about the growth of the oil and gas industries you have to talk about John D. Rockefeller.

Rockefeller and the Oil and Gas Industry

John D. Rockefeller (1839–1937) became rich in the oil industry, but he never drilled a single well; it was too risky. Instead he made his money in the refining industry. He was born in New York State, but his family moved to Cleveland when he was young. He spent most of his business life there. He was very good with numbers, especially ones that involved money. He quickly became a good businessman. He was a good leader who surrounded himself with knowledgeable men who respected his leadership. He started in the produce business when he was only sixteen, and in 1859 he went in the business to trade produce with a partner, Maurice Clark.[70] By this time there was a new railroad in Cleveland, access to east and west markets via the lake and Erie Canal, and growing refining businesses based on the recent oil discoveries. Rockefeller, Clark, two of Clark's brothers, and Samuel Andrews (a self-taught refiner) decided to get into the refining business in 1863. They manufactured kerosene at their Excelsior Works in Cleveland, which became the largest refinery in Cleveland, producing 505 barrels of kerosene a day.[71] Two years later, in 1865, Rockefeller bought out the Clarks and owned the business himself. Andrews apparently became an employee of Rockefeller. Cleveland by this time had numerous refineries located near railroad tracks that linked them with the oil fields of Pennsylvania. In the 1860s and 1870s Henry Flagler became a close friend and business partner of Rockefeller. Flagler was, like Rockefeller, unobtrusive and dignified but also ambitious, patient, and shrewd in business. They developed a lifelong friendship through their business partnership. In 1867 Henry Flagler teamed up with Rockefeller in the refining business. Rockefeller wanted to gain more control and consolidate the refining industry. He and Flagler wanted to bring in more capital to do that. On January 10, 1870, they and three others established the Standard Oil Company in order to bring more capital to the refining business.[72]

Standard's main product was kerosene. It was now becoming the standard source for lighting homes and other establishments. It was a good illumination source, replacing the more expensive candles and whale oil; it was also brighter than either, and cheaper than manufactured gas for illumination. The story of Standard Oil is well known for its various business practices, which were denounced even then as brutal. It was brutal, in the sense that they didn't just try to beat the competition, but destroy it; put it out of business. By controlling all aspects of the business, including the suppliers, they could set prices as they wished because they were then competing with no one. They tried for monopoly status through horizontal integration; they bought many other refineries. By 1872 Rockefeller had control of 21 of the 26 Cleveland refineries. A decade later the company controlled 90 percent of the nation's refineries.[73] They went in for vertical integration in trying to control everything from the sources through the transportation. For example, they had their own tracts of land to grow the timber to make their own barrels. They constantly worried about the oil fields of western Pennsylvania running out. Eventually oil was found elsewhere, and Standard expanded.

To break out of the hold of Standard, the producers in the oil region of Pennsylvania (northwest) built a pipeline from that region to a railroad connection of the Pennsylvania and Reading Railroad at Williamsport. This pipeline, called Tidewater, was a gamble. However, by 1879 oil was successfully flowing through it. Standard was surprised and realized its stranglehold on shipping oil was in jeopardy. They quickly responded by building four long-distance pipelines from the oil region to Cleveland, New York, Philadelphia, and Buffalo. Standard Oil was now in the pipeline business also.[74] In 1881 Standard formed the National Transit Company to consolidate its pipeline operations, mostly, at first, for oil.

As has been mentioned, the discovery of oil was often accompanied by the discovery of gas or vice versa. Once found, oil could be stored in barrels and moved by rail to where it could be refined or used. This was not the case with gas. It had to be used on site or locally with makeshift pipelines. Nevertheless, the value of natural gas as a fuel was starting to be appreciated.

Rockefeller was not one to waste anything. In the early 1880s he had at Standard an Irish native by the name of Daniel O'Day who kept him abreast of natural gas progress. O'Day was also convinced that gas could be made safe, useful, and profitable, and he convinced Rockefeller of that. So in the early 1880s Standard Oil got into the natural gas business. Led by O'Day, National Transit not only moved more aggressively into pipelines but got into the gas producing business as well. By 1884 it expanded further by acquiring United Pipelines, and by 1886 it had spent seven million dollars in the acquisition of nine natural gas companies operating in New York, eastern Ohio, and Pennsylvania. In 1886 Standard (National Transit) formed the National Gas Trust and transferred seven of its natural gas affiliates to it.[75] The dictionary defines a trust in the legal sense as a responsibility where one person (the trustee) holds title to a property (the trust) for the benefit of another (the beneficiary). In its most benign commercial definition a trust is "any large industrial or commercial corporation or combination having a monopolistic or semi-monopolistic control over the production of some commodity or service."[76] However, the more appropriate definition for this case, under the definition for commerce, is "an illegal combination of industrial or commercial companies in which the stock of the constituent companies is controlled by a central board of trustees, thus making it possible to manage the companies so as to minimize production costs, control prices, destroy competition."[77] The trust was the vehicle that Rockefeller and others used to gain both vertical and horizontal control of a commodity so as to limit or destroy competition. At this time it was not illegal. The Sherman Anti-Trust Act of 1890 is what eventually made this combination illegal.

Prior to the National Gas Trust of 1886, in 1882, Standard and its affiliated companies had formed the Standard Oil Trust. It was formed from the combination of 41 companies, 14 of which were wholly owned (including Standard Oil of Ohio) and the others partly owned. It was set up to buy, transport, store, refine, and market petroleum products.[78] Thus the trustees could purchase, dissolve, merge, or divide the companies they controlled. The stockholders of the companies became trustees of the new trust. The agreement was signed by nine trustees including Rockefeller on January 2, 1882. Standard Oil of New Jersey and Standard Oil of New York were organized under the trust in 1882.[79]

By the late 1880s some within the Standard Oil Trust were doubtful of the advisability of its connection to the gas business, especially through the National Gas Trust; they worried about public criticism. In 1888, concern by one of the trustees, Benjamin Brewster, that the public would see this gas trust as a monopoly on natural gas (correctly) caused him to recommend that the trust's certificates be transferred to the Standard Oil Trust. Why the Standard Oil Trust would be seen in a better light than the gas trust is not clear. His recommendation was accepted and the gas trust disappeared, but Standard's interest in natural gas development did not.[80] In 1892 the Ohio Supreme Court ordered the Standard Oil Trust to be dissolved, but it effectively continued to operate from its New York office.[81]

By this time there were numerous small gas companies that had been established in the oil region of northwest Pennsylvania. One was the Oil City Fuel Supply Company, created in 1881 to produce gas from Venango County and to serve Oil City and the borough of Siverlyville. In 1886 the United Natural Gas Company (UNG) formed to produce gas and distribute it to Venango, Forest, Butler, Armstrong, Clarion, Warren, Elk, and McKean counties. UNG constructed pipelines to Oil City, Meadville, Sharon, and Bradford in Pennsylvania, and, later, to Buffalo and Salamanca, New York.[82] Standard's National Transit was part of this mix. For example, in 1886 Pennsylvania Gas Company (PGC) contracted with National to lay an eight-inch line from Warren to the Erie County municipality of Corry. PGC had been formed a year earlier when the Warren Light and Heat Company bought some smaller firms and changed its name to PGC.[83] This is only a small sampling of the natural gas activity in Pennsylvania at the time.

Hope and East Ohio

This was an almost ideal time for the Standard Oil Trust to consolidate some of the companies it owned and to form other companies. By 1898 National Transit pipelines were delivering most of the natural gas being consumed in this country, so expanding production and distribution seemed like the next step.[84] In 1898 Standard Oil of New Jersey, through National Transit, established two new companies that would ultimately have a long association with one another, one that would eventually lead to the liquefaction, storage, and regasification (L.S. and R.) plant in Cleveland that would be the site of the 1944 fire described in Chapter 1. The purposes of the two companies were complementary. One was formed to supply the natural gas, and the other was formed to market and distribute it.

The Hope Natural Gas Company and the East Ohio Gas Company were established within weeks of one another in 1898, East Ohio on September 8 and Hope on September 17. The incorporation fee for Hope in West Virginia was 61 dollars and the issued stock was only 200,000 dollars.[85] The original certificate of incorporation stated the purpose of Hope:

> Producing, purchasing and acquiring natural gas and piping and transporting the same from the place or places where the same is produced, purchased or acquired to a point in a line between the States of West Virginia and Ohio on the Ohio River about four miles below Moundsville, and there to sell or supply said gas to any other person or company desiring to purchase the same, and with the right to lay and maintain all lines of pipe and to take, purchase, acquire and hold all such lands and leaseholds for oil and gas purposes, and such other real and personal property as may be necessary or convenient for the purpose of producing, transporting, selling and supplying natural gas.[86]

Interestingly, this does not include the right to sell gas in West Virginia; later this was changed to include West Virginia. Clearly Hope was set up for one reason only: to sell gas in Ohio. The founders were "hopeful" that natural gas would be the wave of the future, so the company was named Hope. This name seems a little bit like hyperbole, since natural gas was already a major source of energy and growing fast. The founders were all from Standard and therefore were backed by a company with the largest capitalization in the country, probably the world.

There was a lot of oil activity in Pennsylvania as discussed above, but there was always a fear of running out of gas supplies. For example, the original supply for the Fredonia, New York, enterprise ran out before more was found. However, there were indications that West Virginia would be a good source for natural gas. Signs of natural gas in West Virginia had come as early as the eighteenth century, as we have seen. So Hope was used to establish and consolidate Standard's gas interests in the state. They acquired wells from the South Penn Oil Company as well as operating and non-operating leases of the Carter Oil Company, Mountain State Gas Company, and the Reserve Gas Company. Hope also had 40,000 other acres under lease.[87] Hope would be in the business of producing gas for Ohio.

All of the Hope founders had worked at Standard, and most also had connections to Oil City in Pennsylvania and had worked in Ohio. Oil City became the headquarters of Hope. Elizur Strong of Oil City was the first president. He had worked for National Transit and had helped to lay pipelines in Ohio to supply gas service to many cities, such as Canton, Massillon, and Akron. C. N. Payne was from Titusville and was manager of Standard's pipelines before coming to Hope. Captain John Tonkin, also of Oil City, worked for Standard in Ohio for a while as a manger in the River Gas Company at Marietta, Ohio.

H. W. McSweeney from Oil City was a Standard Oil attorney who helped to put Hope together, as did Robert Hampton, a wealthy investor.[88]

East Ohio had five founders also, the ones who incorporated the company. Daniel O'Day headed the group that included R. L. Bates, T. A. McLaughlin, R. C. Warner, and H. C. Scheide.[89] Its principal office was in Lima, Ohio, simply because many of the men happened to live there, just as many of the Hope leadership came from Oil City. The industry was new, so it could come to you rather than you having to move to it. Daniel O'Day was the same one that gave advice to Rockefeller and urged him to get into the natural gas business. O'Day became an incorporator of many natural gas companies and also headed National Transit when it built the pipelines in Ohio. Standard had many men it considered talented and moved them around the trust to serve in many positions simultaneously. Another example of this was Elizur Strong, who was president of both Hope and East Ohio when they were incorporated. He is the one who directed the long-distance pipeline installation from West Virginia to Akron.[90]

East Ohio was started as a marketing company by Standard to bring gas to northeastern Ohio, to places like Akron, Massillon, Canton, and generally to the industrial Mahoning Valley in Ohio. It was planned eventually to go to Cleveland also. The link-up between Hope and East Ohio did not take long. East Ohio was incorporated on September 8, and the Akron franchise was granted on September 26, 1898. According to the Ohio Historical Society, "During the winter of 1898-99, the National Transit Company built a 10-inch wrought iron pipeline that stretched from the Pipe Creek on the Ohio River to Akron [93 miles], with branches to Canton, Massillon, Dover, New Philadelphia, Uhrichsville, and Dennison. The first gas from the pipeline burned in Akron on May 10, 1899."[91] Pipe Creek is across the Ohio River from Round Bottom, West Virginia, near Moundsville, where according to the Hope certificate of incorporation it (Hope) was to deliver the gas it produced. This was known as the "Akron 10-inch" line. At the other end, the line from Hope in Wetzel County, West Virginia, started as an eight-inch line. It became a 10-inch line as it went through Marshall County, West Virginia, up to Round Bottom, West Virginia, where it crossed the river to Pipe Creek; "the firm had thirty-two miles of pipeline and one customer—East Ohio."[92] Although not the first, it was one of the early interstate pipelines. Records show that the ditch diggers for the Akron 10-inch were paid $1.25 per day plus room and board. All of the digging, of course, was done by hand.[93]

Hope and East Ohio were started together by Standard Oil and were intended to work together as supplier and distributor of natural gas. They continued to work together closely for the next several decades. The gas industry was booming, as were other industries at the time. At this time it was still centered in Appalachia, especially in Ohio, Pennsylvania, and West Virginia. Over the next few years both Hope and East Ohio started to grow although, as might be expected, there were some growing pains. In this sense they could be seen as representative of the many new gas firms that had sprung up in recent years.

Incorporated in 1898, East Ohio had 3,874 customers by 1900. When it sought a franchise to operate in Cleveland in 1902 it was opposed by the two companies providing manufactured gas, the Cleveland City Gas Light and Coke Company and the People's Gas Light Company.[94]

This was probably one of the early battles between manufactured gas companies and natural gas companies. The former had been operating successfully since Baltimore first got gas light in 1816. At that time natural gas was known but not exploitable because of the uncertainty of supply, the lack of distribution and storage capability, and safety issues (there was no control of the pressure of the source, for example). Now natural gas had become a viable competitor. It was cleaner, less odiferous, and perhaps most important, cheaper. Around this time manufactured gas was selling at 75 cents per Mcf whereas natural gas was 30 cents per Mcf.[95] (*Mcf* stands for 1,000 cubic feet. This is a common unit in the early natural gas industry, but does lead to confusion because the prefix "M" now usually stands for "mega" or one million. Possibly the "M" in this unit is derived from the Roman numeral M, meaning 1,000.) Customers had complained to the council about the high prices of the manufactured gas. The battle in the city council was bitter, with one member waving a handful of money he claimed had been offered him by opponents of the franchise. Mayor Tom Johnson, although a proponent of municipal ownership of these types of utilities, backed East Ohio, and the franchise was granted on June 23, 1902.[96] Construction of the distribution service started immediately, and Cleveland had gas starting January 1, 1903.[97]

East Ohio expanded quickly after that. The expansion was such that in 1903, East Ohio constructed an 18-inch line from Cleveland to the Ohio River, where it was met by a 20-inch line constructed by Hope from Pine Grove to Round Bottom.[98] By 1905 it had 280 business and 30,000 residential customers.[99] In 1907, only four years after it first received gas, it laid down still another 18-inch line to the river.[100] The expansion included the acquisition of other companies. By 1907 East Ohio had 150,000 customers.[101] In 1908 East Ohio purchased Mahoning Gas Fuel. In 1910 the two manufactured gas companies threw in the towel. At 75 cents per thousand cubic feet, manufactured gas could not compete with the natural gas rate of 30 cents per thousand cubic feet. Both Cleveland Gas Light and People's Gas Light were incorporated into East Ohio. In the process, East Ohio gained approximately 765 miles of distribution system and 65,000 customers. It included all the manufactured gas equipment, holders, buildings and land.[102] This is when it took possession of the Number 2 works in the St. Clair–Norwood area—the site of the 1944 fire. However, East Ohio did not completely convert to natural gas in Cleveland at that time. They continued for a while to supply manufactured gas to those who wanted it. As late as 1938, Stotz and Jamison did not list Cleveland as one of the cities that had converted completely to natural gas, as Dayton had, for example.[103]

By the time of his death in 1926 the second president, Martin Daly, had shaped East Ohio into the largest gas distribution company in the world.[104] Martin Daly took over the East Ohio presidency from Elizur Strong in 1906. He is the one credited with making East Ohio a large, quality company. Earlier he had worked for Strong as a tool dresser in Pennsylvania. He himself was a pioneer in the business. He had applied gas metering as a superintendent at the Buffalo Natural Gas Fuel Company and later introduced metering to the Standard-controlled Northwestern Ohio Gas Company. It was Martin Daly's salesmanship that convinced Mayor Johnson to allow the East Ohio franchise into Cleveland. As president of East Ohio, he was aggressive in pursuing more supplies for northeast Ohio. When there was a proposal to take some of the Standard-controlled Mountain State gas over the Blue Ridge Mountains to the Baltimore area, Daly convinced the Mountain State producers that Cleveland was a better market.[105] He was the source of other innovations that benefited the employees. He established a system of annuities and insurance benefits that was later adopted, with modifications, by Standard itself. He was a civic leader and also known for his loyalty and kindness to the employees. When he died at his desk in 1926 one of the Cleveland newspapers said of him, "When Mr. Daly took charge of the East Ohio Gas Company almost a quarter century ago, its lines reached only a few towns and cities. He left it the largest natural gas company in the world.... His kindness, his absolutely inviolable rules of courtesy, his open heart and hand made him one of the best known personalities in Cleveland and a man who never lost the affectation of his opponents.... This city sorrows for the death of an intimate friend, as in fact, he was."[106]

The industrial cities in northeast Ohio continued to expand, using the gas from West Virginia supplied by Hope. Hope Natural Gas Company expanded similarly to keep up with the demand.

Because Hope was the supplier to the East Ohio, they had to continue to find new sources of gas. In 1902 they drilled 51 wells, mostly in Wetzel and neighboring Marion counties in the northwest part of the state near Ohio. An important event in this year was the construction of the gas compressor at Hastings Station, near Pine Grove in Wetzel County, alongside the Akron 10-inch. Although not the first compressor station, it was a first for Hope.[107] The compressor was necessary not only because of the long lines (~120 miles) but because more and larger pipelines were being used to accommodate the need.

Gas Compressors

When natural gas was first discovered and used, the discharge from the well was powered by the natural rock pressure of the gas underground forcing it to the surface. This could vary significantly and was sometimes a danger if it was too high. However, this was the same pressure that was used to move the gas down a pipeline when eventually lines were built to move the gas to a more useful location. If the pressure was high enough and the distance short enough, no other mechanism is needed to get the gas to its user. However, as gas moves down the pipeline it is slowed by friction and the pressure drops. To get it to the distant user it needs some force to keep it moving to its destination. Think of it this way: Consider the pressure p, in pounds per square inch (psi) in the line at any point acting on the downstream cross-sectional area A, in square inches (in^2) of the line. Pressure times area is a force in pounds (pound-force [lbf]). (The term pound-force [lbf] is used to distinguish it from the weight [mass] of the object in pounds-mass [lbm].) It is this force that moves the gas along. Thus the pressure must be increased at intervals to maintain the force that maintains the gas flow. Compressor stations, like the Hastings Station, have become very common now that the gas network is so extensive.

There are dozens of interstate pipelines crisscrossing the country. Each line contains many stations set at intervals of 50 to 100 miles. Not surprisingly, most of these lines originate in the Southwest and take the gas to different parts of the country. Table 2–1 shows just the 10 largest systems and the number of stations each has.[108]

Table 2–1. Major Pipeline Systems and Number of Compressor Stations

Pipeline System	Starting Location	Number of Stations
1. Texas Eastern Trans Corp	Southwest	75
2. Transcontinental Gas P l Co.	Southwest	47
3. Tennessee Gas Pipeline Co.	Southwest	71
4. El Paso Nat Gas Co.	Southwest	58
5. ANR Pipeline Co.	Southwest	45
6. Nat Gas P L Co. of America	Southwest	50
7. Northern Natural Gas Co.	Southwest	82
8. Southern Natural Gas Co.	Southwest	40
9. Northern Border Pipeline Co.	Canada	17
10. Gas transmission Northwest Co.	Canada	13
Other Systems		703
Total		1201

Most of these compressors, now as then, are fueled by a portion of the natural gas flowing through them. (Remember, the first reciprocating internal combustion engine developed by Otto was fueled by coal gas.) The compressors constructed at that time were natural-gas-fired, high-speed reciprocating engines.[109] This is the most likely design for the Hastings Station compressor. The original installation at Hastings were two 4,500 horsepower (hp) engines; the largest ever, up to that time, to pump gas.

Hope had a big year in 1902 for acquisition reasons also. It acquired Flaggy Meadows Gas Company, South Penn Oil Company, and Carter Oil Company. It thus increased its holdings by 151,000 acres of leaseholds and 202 wells. It was becoming one of the country's largest integrated natural gas systems. It is interesting to note that although gas meters had been invented long before and were used in cities, they were still not economical to install in many of the small towns that were now getting gas. In these cases a flat rate was still used. For Mannington West Virginia the rate for cook stoves was $1.75 per month and for heating a barn it was $3.25 per month.[110]

In 1904 Hope's charter was revised to allow it to sell and supply gas in West Virginia. It was also given the right to exercise the power of eminent domain. These two factors were key to the company's expansion. National Transit was still active in running the natural gas business in that area. They organized Clarksburg (West Virginia) Light and Heat and made E. Strong, former president of Hope and East Ohio, the president, with C.N. Payne as general manager and John Tonkin as treasurer. When the second Hope president, Glenn Braden, left to go to Oklahoma he was succeeded by first Daniel O'Day and then, on his death, by C. N. Payne. All these men were originally from Standard and all helped organize both Hope and East Ohio. Thus Standard, through National Transit, was still controlling all the gas interests in the area.[111]

Hope continued to expand. They expanded the Hastings compressor station by adding nine 1,350-horsepower steam engines and twelve 385-horsepower gas-fired steam boilers. This took three years to complete. They laid another 20-inch pipe to get more gas to East Ohio. They added the Davis compressor station in McWhorter County and continued to drill, averaging about 75 new wells per year. In 1908 they drilled 200 wells, a pace that continued for the next 10 years. By 1909 West Virginia became the leading state in natural gas production and held that position until 1923. This was primarily due to Hope.[112]

Both Hope and East Ohio were founded by the National Transit Company, which was part of Standard Oil. As chronicled previously, Standard became a very large, vertically integrated company controlling much of the oil and gas industry, especially in the Appalachian region. By the late 1880s Standard was starting to feel the pressure from the public, who saw it as a greedy organization that controlled too much of public life through its monopolistic practices. In 1892 the Ohio Supreme Court ordered the trust dissolved. However, the companies took advantage of New Jersey's corporate stock ownership laws and in 1899 established Standard Oil of New Jersey as a holding company to hold all their interests.[113] A holding company is a company that owns enough voting stock in one or more companies to exercise control over them.[114] The capitalization of this holding company was increased from $10 million to $110 million, and it held stock in 41 companies.[115] However, it didn't end there. In 1906 the Roosevelt administration brought suit against Standard Oil of New Jersey under the Sherman Anti-Trust Law. After the suit found its way to the Supreme Court in 1911, the Court agreed that Standard Oil was in violation and ordered a breakup of the company. It was divided into several separate entities, one of which was Standard Oil of New Jersey (later to become Exxon).[116] However, both Hope and East Ohio remained as part of Standard Oil of New Jersey, because Standard Oil's gas activities were not judged to be restraining trade.[117] It wasn't until 1943, when the Public Utility Holding Act of 1935 required Standard Oil to divest itself of its gas utilities, that both Hope and East Ohio were spun off, along with some other companies, into the Consolidated Natural Gas Company (CNG).[118] Thus Hope and East Ohio continued to share the same umbrella.

The first 12 years were ones of extraordinary growth both for the producing company, Hope, and for the distributing company, East Ohio. By 1910 they were ready for another decade of growth, but one that would see the challenges of World War I.

3
Growth to Shortage

The industrialization of America, which got into full swing in the latter half of the nineteenth century, accelerated dramatically in the first two decades of the twentieth century. Nowhere is this better demonstrated than in the use of energy. Figure 3-1 shows the steep increase in total energy use from the turn of the century until 1940, just before the war, interrupted only by the Great Depression.[1]

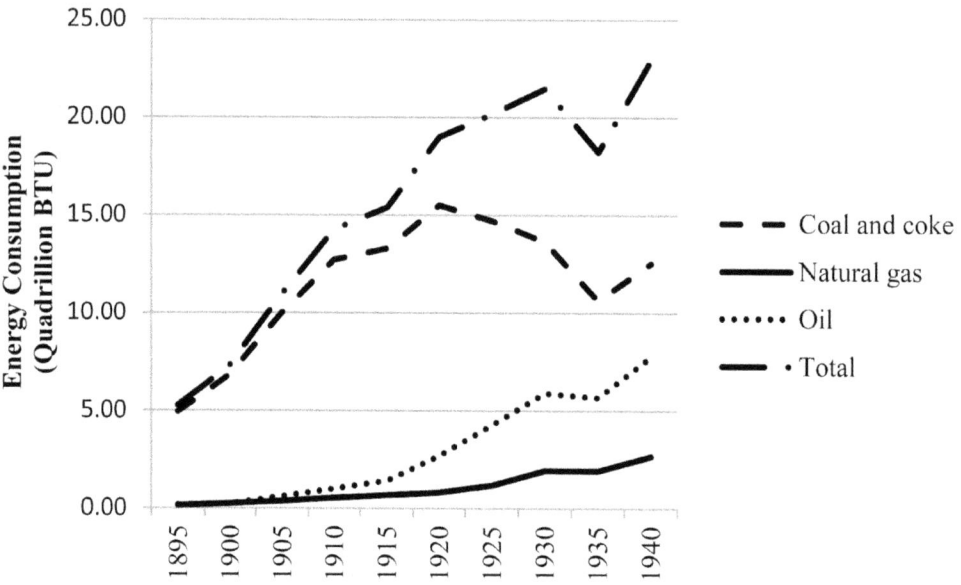

Figure 3-1. U.S. energy consumption, 1895–1940.

Most of the increase, of course, was in coal. However, the more rapid increases in oil and gas and the decrease in coal from about 1920 on clearly shows the trend for the fuels being used. Even more telling is the fact that a good deal of the coal was used for the manufacture of gas. The demand for energy also included the increased use of manufactured gas, although not at the same levels as natural gas (see figure 3-2).

Both charts show the decreased energy use during the Depression. Figure 3-2 also clearly shows that although manufactured gas and natural gas started the century at approximately the same level, the rise in the use of natural gas greatly outpaced manufactured gas only 40 years later, by a factor of five.[2]

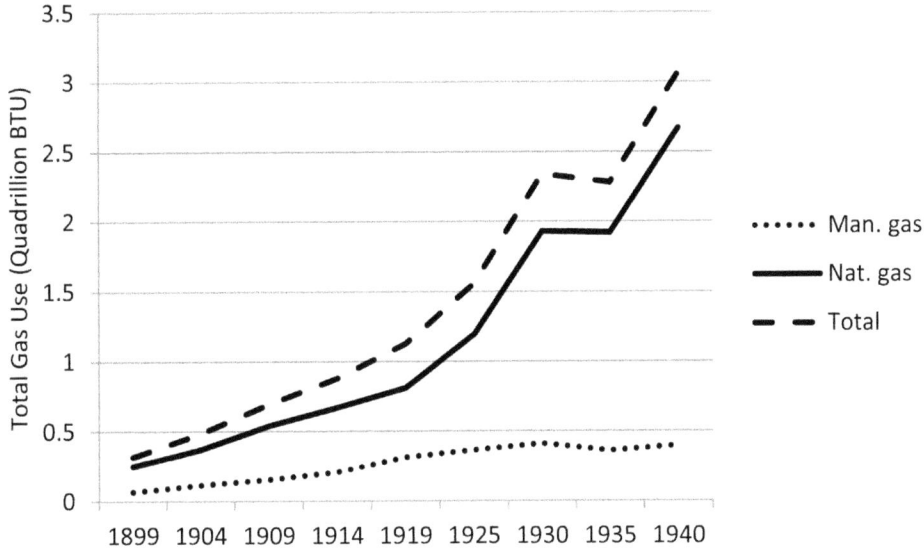

Figure 3-2. Total gas use.

The increase in energy demand came from all sectors of the economy: industrial, commercial, and residential. Coal was still the most used, because it was the dominant fuel for power plants that generated electricity, was widely used in such industrial processes as steel making, and was still the predominant fuel for residential heating. Petroleum use increased rapidly for two reasons: It was becoming easier to obtain because of the relatively recent boom in the oil industry, and it was found to be a more convenient heating fuel than coal. Perhaps most importantly, it was an ideal fuel for transportation, and this period saw the very rapid rise in the automobile industry. By this time the advantages of natural gas were becoming more evident, and therefore it became more popular. It was cheaper and cleaner than manufactured gas, which not only required coal to make but left a lot of messy residues. It also had a higher heating value than manufactured gas. By this time electricity had displaced all types of gas for lighting, so gas lighting was no longer an end use. However, the gas marketers quickly found ways to promote gas for heating for stoves, water heaters, and space heaters. Although it is mostly methane, natural gas is a mixture of various gases. It was in these decades of the twentieth century that processes were developed to extract natural gas products, such as propane and others, and start a whole new industry in liquid petroleum gases (LPG) and natural gas liquids (NGL). These will be discussed later.

What figures 3-1 and 3-2 don't show is the redistribution of the gas supply that started to take place during this period. The Appalachian wells started to go dry, and so shortages started to show up in that region. However, new supplies were discovered in the Southwest, so the total gas supply increased. During this period there were not yet long-distance pipelines crisscrossing the country, so Appalachia had to dig deeper and go farther for their gas until pipelines could get up to that part of the country from the Southwest.

The use of natural gas kept growing. As figure 3-2 shows, it leveled off during the Depression, because the whole economy shrank dramatically at that time. After that it resumed a rapid growth up to the time of World War II. At that point energy demands went up even higher.

The technology used in the field had to keep up with the growth of the industry. This meant a significant growth in pipelines laid. The most important technological advance was the development of electrical welding of large, smooth-bore, high-pressure pipelines, which was a major development in the 1920s. One technology problem that they hadn't yet solved by the end of the 1930s was the problem of storage. Natural gas is an "on demand" fuel; it is needed instantaneously if it is to be used consistently. The only way to be sure you had enough gas all the time was to build pipelines to handle peak loads. This was not practical because then the load factor was low; that is, most of the time the excess capacity of the lines would not be used. If one tried to store it as a gas, the containers became excessively large and still only small amounts could be stored.

By the time of the war in 1940, Hope and East Ohio came up with an idea that would solve the peak load problem without the addition of excess pipelines or very large containers. They came up with an idea for how to store natural gas as a liquid and, in doing so, started a whole new industry.

Increase in Demand

When manufactured gas was introduced in the early nineteenth century, its primary use was for lighting. It soon replaced candles and was a good competitor for whale oil. The superior lighting properties and the reduction of whaling in mid-century made gas the favored fuel for lighting. When kerosene became popular in the 1870s it had some advantages over manufactured gas. There was little danger of asphyxiation, it didn't require a pipeline system, and it burned brighter. This was a major improvement. The real competitor for lighting, however, was the electric light, which was introduced in the 1880s. Edison had helped establish the Edison Electric Light Company in 1878 in order to work on light bulb development. He continued to work on the light bulb into 1879 and was eventually successful with a carbonized thread filament. Just as importantly, however, he worked on an electric lighting system that could be used in a city. He and his family moved to New York in 1882, where he installed the first commercial lighting system on Pearl Street in Lower Manhattan. There were only 400 lamps at first, but the idea grew quickly and the number of lamps in use grew to thousands. His system used direct current (DC), and in this area he competed for years with George Westinghouse, who advocated alternating current (AC). Although Westinghouse's AC eventually prevailed for a number of reasons, Edison had shown the reality of a large electric distribution system. His company eventually merged into what became General Electric.[3]

Although some gas lighting remained until the 1920s, electric lighting essentially ended its use. Therefore, the gas industry was hoping to expand in other parts of the energy market. This effort had been given a significant boost by the invention of the Bunsen burner in 1855. Robert Bunsen (1811–1899) is given credit for inventing it, but it seems most of the work was done by a couple of others including Michael Faraday (1791–1867), whom we will meet later. The burner is essentially a tube with holes around the tip. The gas flows through the tube, drawing in air through these holes and forming an air-gas mixture that is then lit as it exits the tube, forming a pale blue flame. The burner is not an efficient light source, but can produce a hot, soot-less flame that can be used for heating; it was a forerunner of the gas stove.[4] It is still used today in essentially the same form in high school chemistry laboratories, for example. This combination of the loss of the lighting market and the ability to use gas for heating turned the whole industry toward that end. One of the first domestic uses of natural gas was in the gas stove.

One significant indicator of the switch from lighting to heating was the standard by which gas was measured. Originally gas light was measured in candlepower. It was based on the light intensity of a specific standard candle. This now-obsolete unit is an old English measurement of the amount of light given off. It was a crude method of comparing the illuminating power of different light sources. For example, when the kerosene lamp Welsbach mantle was introduced, it improved the light output from three to 20 candles per cubic foot, seven times over what the kerosene lamp could do without it.[5] This gave the kerosene lamp at least a temporary boost. However, as the switch from lighting to heating took place, the standard for comparing gases and other fuels switched to British Thermal Units (BTU). This is another old English unit, although it is still in common use today. It is a measure of energy equal to 1,055 joules in the metric system (see table 4-3). As stated in Chapter 2, a BTU is the heat energy needed to raise the temperature of one pound of water one degree Fahrenheit. It can be used to measure the heating value of a substance, that is, how much heat is produced when a unit of the substance is burned. The value of natural gas compared to carbureted water gas, the manufactured gas most commonly used since the 1880s, becomes clear when the heating values are compared. Natural gas typically has a heating value of 1,020 to 1,100 BTU per cubic foot, which is about twice the value of the carbureted water gas heating value of about 550 BTU per cubic foot.[6] This, plus the fact that natural gas was becoming more common, that is, more sources were found and the supply could be considered to be steady, contributed to the growth of natural gas compared to manufactured gas.

Table 3-1 shows the increase in natural gas production and customers in the early twentieth century.[7]

Table 3-1. Natural Gas Consumption, 1906–1923

Year	MMcf of Gas Produced	Domestic Users	Industrial Users
1906	388,842	879,994	9,074
1916	753,172	2,195,081	18,358
1921	724,052	2,630,915	20,989
1923	1,008,135	3,232,800	18,000

The table shows a dramatic increase in gas production, over two and one-half times, and domestic consumption, over triple, in just 17 years. The industrial increase was not as dramatic. Note, however, that the increased use of coal during this period was even greater than the increase in the use of gas. This most likely went to the continuing increase in industrial capacity. The dip in production between 1916 and 1921 was probably caused by shortages during that time caused by the war. This could also account for the slower acceptance by industry; that is, a reluctance to depend on what might become a scarce resource. Stotz and Jamison reported that a few years earlier (1891) Brown's *Directory of American Gas Companies* omitted for that year a list of natural gas companies because "natural gas companies were turning even more than their accustomed somersaults, and the gas was disappearing so rapidly that it was next to impossible to prepare a list of such companies, that would be reasonably correct for any length of time."[8]

INDUSTRIAL DEMAND

When natural gas was first discovered occurring naturally in "burning springs" it was just a curiosity. Sometimes an entrepreneur would make use of that which was easily available and nearby. Then it became not just a curiosity but a useful fuel. This was the case in Fredonia, New York, early in the nineteenth century. Even in ancient times, for example, in China in AD 100, when it was used to boil off saltwater to extract the salt, it was more a happy coincidence that one could find the brine and gas nearby and make use of the gas to boil the brine. Later, when it was found inadvertently, it could become a nuisance or even a danger. Early in the century it was common to dig or drill for brine. The salt extracted was used for food preservation and leather tanning, for example. In the Appalachian region the brine wells would often produce gas, or gas could seep from an existing brine well. In this case discovery of gas was not appreciated but cursed. Still later, when drilling for oil became popular, gas might be discovered and the well abandoned because there was no oil. In some cases these abandoned wells caught fire and burned for months, if not years. Some enterprising folks used the gas to boil water or cook food.

This early natural energy resource was not seen as useful in any manner approaching an industrial or commercial scale. Its source was unpredictable, unsteady, and non-transportable, and it could be dangerous, so it remained untapped for decades. This was in contrast to manufactured gas. In this case once it was discovered, about the same time early in the century, its uses were recognized and exploited. It was predictable, containable and could be manufactured near where it was needed. It was therefore produced, priced and distributed. The main problem with manufactured gas continued to be its high price; this limited its widespread use. Another problem, toxic residues that had to be cleaned up, was not recognized right away.

The early growth in the use of natural gas for industry was hit and miss. Oil started getting big in the 1860s and by the 1870s was a booming industry. It followed that some entrepreneurs found uses for the supposed waste product, natural gas, which often accompanied oil. For example, "in 1873, two Venango County, Pa., gas wells supplied all the boilers on the Columbia farm on Oil Creek that were used for drilling and pumping oil." Previously coal had been used to drive these pump engines, but they found that "waste" gas from the oil wells could do the job more cheaply. Early natural gas developers sold initially worthless and discarded gas as a fuel to oil fields.[9] Similarly, in East Liverpool, Ohio, pottery manufacturers started using natural gas in their industry in 1873.[10] These uses were all in areas that were close to the source wells and did not require long transportation systems. About the same time several western Pennsylvania companies started using gas as a coal substitute to make iron, glass, and pottery.[11]

As more uses were found for natural gas, more searching was done for it as well as for oil, which at the time was making some people rich. Some finds were bigger than others. In 1878 on a farm near Pittsburgh, near Murrysville, Michael and Obediah Haymaker tried to drill for oil but instead found gas, a lot of it; a real gusher. According to Brignano and McCullough,

> in Michael's words, "There was a terrific roar and rumble that was heard 15 miles away. Every piece of rigging went sky high, whirling around like so much paper caught in a gust of wind. Instead of oil we had struck gas. It was being shot out under such enormous pressure that it continued to shake the ground and roar for months rattling windows for miles around. Nobody knew how to stop it." One night people carrying lanterns got too close to the shooting gas. Michael remembered "a blinding flash. There was an explosion. Flames, it seemed were everywhere. Then my ears cleared and I heard the familiar roar of the well. Gradually the flame ... settled to an even 100 feet straight in the air. It burned for a year and a half. World travelers told us they had never seen anything so magnificent. It gave us continuous daylight for miles around."[12]

It took five years but Haymaker finally sold the well to J. N. Pew (1848–1912) and E. O. Emerson (1834–1912), who got the gas to Pittsburgh's glass and steel industries. More than a hundred other wells in the same area were to follow in getting gas to Pittsburgh.[13] More wells were drilled in western Pennsylvania, West Virginia, and Ohio, the gas to be used for both industrial and domestic uses. The pipeline to Pittsburgh demonstrated the feasibility of delivering gas on a large scale to mills and factories. Later, in 1885, Pew and Emerson formed the People's Natural Gas Company to distribute natural gas to Pittsburgh. It was the first one chartered in the state.[14] Impressed by the Pittsburgh lines and acceding to Daniel O'Day's urgings, Rockefeller gave his famous go-ahead to get into the natural gas business: "I am desirous to have our National Transit Company pursue the gas business earnestly."[15]

It was becoming clear that for the industry to prosper it was necessary for three different aspects to grow together. The three were the production of natural gas as exemplified by the Haymaker well, the pipeline delivery system as developed by Pew and Emerson in getting lines into Pittsburgh, and the distribution system of People's Natural Gas in Pittsburgh. A great deal of the natural gas going into Pittsburgh was for industrial plants such as Pittsburgh Plate Glass, the rolling mills of Wilson, Walker and Co., and the Fort Pitt Glass Works. The success of these works could be traced to the rush of gas lines into the city.[16]

The lure of large-scale, industrial use of natural gas was clearly what Standard Oil, through their subsidiary National Transit, had in mind when they set up Hope Natural Gas and East Ohio Gas Company about a decade later. The target was the industrial Mahoning Valley of northeast Ohio, which included the steel manufacturing city of Youngstown. The first target was Akron, but from the beginning they meant to include Youngstown, Cleveland, and other cities in northeast Ohio. They also understood the need for the integration of the production, delivery, and distribution systems of Hope, National Transit, and East Ohio. In fact, the producing company, Hope, was incorporated a few days *after* the incorporation of the distribution company, East Ohio. The pipelines between the two started almost immediately.

Industrial Cleveland had increased its population by 120,000 in the decade from 1890 to 1900, bringing its total to 381,000.[17] It sat at the heart of American industry right between the Mesabi iron ore range in Minnesota and the oil and coal regions of Pennsylvania and West Virginia. The ships brought the ore to Cleveland, where it was off-loaded onto trains for shipment to the steel mills of Youngstown and Pittsburgh. "Cleveland was making more steel wire, wire nails, and nuts and bolts than any other city in the world and building more merchant ships than any other American city. Cleveland would be the jewel in East Ohio's distribution crown."[18]

Figure 3-3 shows the growth of natural gas use in the domestic/commercial and industrial areas. The rate of growth for both is about the same in the first twenty years of the century. The industrial and carbon black use of natural gas took off in the 1920s.[19]

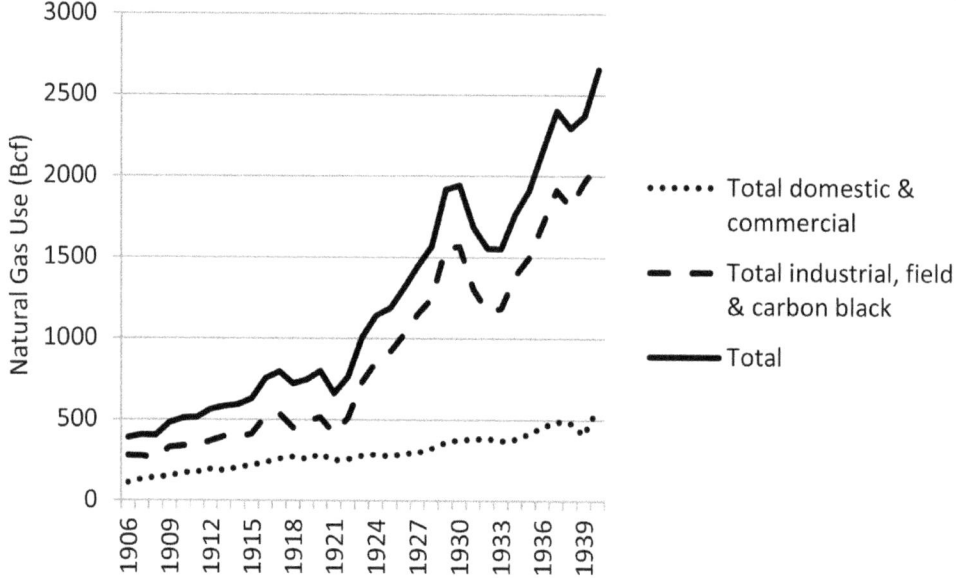

Figure 3-3. Industrial and domestic/commercial natural gas use, 1906–1940.

What is not clear from figure 3-3 is that more than half of the use for industrial purposes is for what is called field use, especially the manufacture of carbon black or lamp black. Carbon black is produced by the incomplete combustion of natural gas. It is used as a pigment in inks, shoe polishes, and paints. It is also used as reinforcement in rubber and plastic products. It helps stabilize the rubber in automobile tires, for example. It was categorized separately from other industrial uses in this period but is included in the total here. Carbon black could be made at the source of the natural gas well, that is, "in the field." It did not require pipelines to move it to an industrial area.

Godfrey Lowell Cabot (1861–1962) was an entrepreneur, inventor, and industrialist born in Massachusetts. His name will come up again later concerning natural gas byproducts and inventions for transporting liquid gas. He founded the Cabot Corporation in 1882 and by 1890 had become the fourth largest carbon black producer in the country. He started in Pennsylvania, but when the gas supplies ran out he moved, in 1898, to Grantsville, West Virginia, just up the Kanawha River from Burning Springs, where gas had been first encountered by George Washington in the previous century. The plant opened in 1900 and at first produced 800 pounds of carbon black per day. It quickly grew to produce 1,400 pounds per day. He soon moved to open other locations in West Virginia. "'In this county Godfrey L. Cabot of Boston, MA has the largest carbon factory in the world, utilizing natural gas for the purpose,' stated the WV Geological Survey about Calhoun County in 1911."[20] Carbon black was used in tires at the time. It took six pounds of carbon black to go into one tire. It was about this time that Henry Ford started on his Model T, which must have been a significant user of Mr. Cabot's carbon black, and which contributed to the rise in natural gas for industrial purposes (see table 3-2). Note that rise in industrial use of natural gas closely matches the rise in Model T production.[21]

Table 3-2. Number of Model Ts Produced

Year	Number of Model Ts Produced
1910	20,200
1912	94,700
1914	248,000
1916	586,000
1918	382,000
1920	1,040,000
1922	1,385,000
1924	1,986,000
1926	1,629,000

More than half the natural gas for industrial uses was going to produce carbon black, which was probably going mostly into tires. The remaining industrial gas was going into what we normally think of as manufacturing; that is, pottery, glass, steel, and other products. In the early years this was not much more than what was going into the domestic market. It seems that since coal was plentiful, the risk of going to gas was not worth it to many early on. This changed in the twenties, as figure 3-3 shows. Of course as Ford's Model T production leveled off, many other car makers were in the business.

Domestic Demand

When manufactured gas became common and started to grow in the 1820s, it was used first for public lighting. It was a real boon to public officials to be able to provide light after dark in major public areas. As it spread it became available to private parties. For example, in Baltimore in 1833 the Gas Light Company of Baltimore owned two miles of gas mains and supplied 3,000 private and 100 public lamps.[22] However, it was expensive, and only the well-to-do could afford it. This remained true for most of the time it was used, even through its continued growth into the early twentieth century. It was never a serious competitor of coal for heavy industrial energy use. Its use was confined mostly to lighting for most of the nineteenth century. Because of the cost it was always under pressure from other sources. When kerosene became popular after 1865, and especially after the introduction of the Welsbach mantle, the kerosene lamp could provide cheaper and brighter light than manufactured gas. Natural gas and electricity could also provide cheaper and brighter light than manufactured gas. The electric light, the brightest and most convenient light source, led to the demise of manufactured gas as a light source. Manufactured gas was expensive because of all the trouble it took to build the plants, buy the fuel (mostly coal), distribute it, and clean up the residue.

As we have seen, natural gas was first seen as a nuisance byproduct of searching for oil, and as a result it was not readily captured and distributed. Therefore, untold millions of cubic feet were either allowed to dissipate into the atmosphere or were flared off into the atmosphere. This happened first in Appalachia, when oil producers didn't know how to handle it or control it. This is somewhat understandable given the first experience with it. However, later, when extensive gas reserves were found in Texas and Oklahoma, it happened again. Again this gas was associated with oil discoveries. At the time there were no local users as there were in Appalachia, so producers didn't know how to use it. Some there wanted to keep it in the area to attract the industry of the Appalachian region, but that didn't work at the time. It was only later, when pipelines were built to move the gas north and east, that the gas became economically useful. This waste would be reduced dramatically later, when conservation efforts were made in the face of shortages and the recognition of gas field depletion. Although there is not an accurate number on how much was wasted, one geologist, L. F. Terry, estimates it could have been as high as 76 trillion (T) cubic feet (10^{12} cubic feet, or 1,000B cubic feet).[23] Table 3-3 shows how egregious that waste was. In many years it was over half of the gas extracted.[24]

Table 3-3. Natural Gas Waste, 1919–1930, in Bcf

Year	Total U.S. NG Waste	Panhandle TX NG Waste	Total U.S. NG Consumption	Total U.S. NG Produced	Percent Wasted
1919	213	n/a	256	469	45.4
1920	238	n/a	286	524	45.4
1921	193	n/a	248	441	43.8
1922	233	n/a	254	487	47.8
1923	416	n/a	277	693	60.0
1924	343	n/a	285	628	54.6
1925	324	n/a	272	596	54.4
1926	417	220	289	706	59.1
1927	444	405	296	740	60.0
1928	412	351	321	733	56.2
1929	589	294	360	949	62.1
1930	553	252	376	929	59.5

Late in the nineteenth century, as the virtues of natural gas for use as a fuel were appreciated, drilling for it, collecting it, and distributing it became an industry. However, in the intervening years when gas was collected and distributed on a smaller scale, the pricing was arbitrary and low. Gas was seen as abundant, at least at first, before the first worries about depletion. In Venango County, Pennsylvania, the Manufacturer's Gas Company (a producer of natural gas) laid lines into Oil City to compete with the manufactured gas company that was already there. There was a rate war for two years, during which time natural gas was offered for 50 cents per month for all the gas one could burn.[25] In another example, "in 1887, in Pittsburgh, gas was delivered in unlimited quantities for cooking ranges for $1 per month; heating stoves or grates at 75 cents per month and for lights at 15 cents per month. A large country house could be heated with natural gas at a cost of 75 dollars per year. The old Duquesne Hotel in Pittsburgh, a modern hotel at the time, was heated for 560 dollars per year."[26] Although meters had been introduced in the 1840s for manufactured gas, they were not yet used for natural gas. When they were introduced around the turn of the century the rates were still low. At that time, natural gas in Pittsburgh was about six or seven cents per 1,000 cubic feet, but by 1890 it had doubled. Table 3-4 shows rates still low in the first quarter of the twentieth century, although they were now rising because of increased demand.[27]

Table 3-4. Natural Gas Rates, 1906–1923

Year	Domestic Rates Per Mcf	Industrial Rates Per Mcf
1906	22.7 cents	7.8 cents
1916	28.3 cents	9.6 cents
1921	44 cents	18.4 cents
1923	51.1 cents	13.4 cents

In Akron in 1898, prior to the East Ohio franchise being awarded there, you could only get manufactured gas at $1.25 per 1,000 cubic feet. Once the natural gas franchise was awarded to Akron by East Ohio in 1898, it took the fitters only two months, from November 1, to lay 22 miles of pipe to supply the first gas for the city.[28] There must have been a good number in the queue to hook up to the mains.

Late in the nineteenth century and early in the twentieth, the competition between manufactured gas, natural gas, and electricity for lighting use was settled by the electric light bulb, although gas lighting held on into the 1920s in some areas. As natural gas faced diminishing use for lighting, the focus was on increasing its use in other areas such as cooking, water heating, and space heating. However, coal dominated the cooking and heating activities at the turn of the century, so there was competition in these areas as well. The Franklin "Pennsylvania Fireplace" coal stove, invented by Ben Franklin in 1744, was still the choice for cooking.[29]

Of course as soon as gas was discovered, people started using it to cook. Cooking was done with gas in Fredonia when gas was installed there in 1825. Cooking was not a major use at that time, and it is not clear what the burners looked like. Cooking stoves, as appliances, first started in England as replacement for coal stoves. James Sharp developed one in Northampton, England, in 1826. It was a while before these stoves reached the U.S., but by 1859 they were for sale here. At first they were for use with manufactured gas. The invention of the Bunsen burner in 1855 made the use of natural gas for stoves more practical. American manufacturers copied the English designs and then advanced the stove design themselves. In 1879 William W. Goodman and Company introduced the "Sun Dial" stove. It had most of the features that are familiar in today's ranges. Henry Doherty of the Madison Gas and Electric Company gave an address at the American Gas Light Association meeting in 1898 in Niagara Falls entitled "How Can We Make Use of Gas for Cooking." This talk set the tone for many merchandising ideas used by the gas industry in later years.[30] In the 1920s the phrase "Cook with gas" became well known and eventually changed into the slangy phrase "Cookin' with gas," which indicated that things were going well for the person who said it. There were some hitches in the conversion to natural gas from manufactured gas. Natural gas, at twice the heating value of manufactured gas (1,050 BTU per cubic foot compared to 500–600), did not burn right in the stoves. The burners had to be adjusted, and this process took time, which slowed, but did not stop, the conversion. By the 1920s it was clear that natural gas was the superior fuel.

As gas became more plentiful and more competitive there was a natural tendency to expand its uses. One obvious use was in heating water. Early gas water heaters were difficult to use because they were not automatic. As early as 1867, water was heated by applying a burner under a tank of water. This took a long time to operate and was not practical for small amounts of heated water. The whole tank had to be heated to withdraw hot water from the top. By 1883 a circulating tank was devised that used a tube to take the heated water at the bottom to circulate it to the top. As natural gas became common and cheap more work was done to improve water heating. By the turn of the century most tanks were constructed of sheet metal jackets surrounding first, iron pipes, and then (because iron rusted) brass pipes. Copper coils followed that.[31] However, all these designs were manually operated. The user had to go into the basement to light the burner prior to heating the water and then go back down to turn it off. Not only was this inconvenient, it could be expensive or dangerous if you forgot to turn off the heat afterwards.

As might be expected when a useful resource becomes plentiful and available, the entrepreneurial spirit encourages innovation. In 1885 H. A. Tobey developed a heater with thermostatic control of the gas. In 1895 J. C. Beckfield made a heater that used a copper coil for the heating surface and gas controlled by a water pressure valve. Edwin Ruud invented a heater in 1897 using a copper coil with a thermostat in the circuit of the coil to control the fuel. By 1899 Ruud combined the water pressure control with the thermostatic control in one heater. A water heater close to what we know today came from an invention by R. W. Robertshaw in 1899. He made a mechanical device that controlled the flow of gas to maintain an even temperature in the water. Since it was thermostatically controlled there was no gas burned until hot water was withdrawn and incoming water had to be heated.[32]

Gas was also considered and used for home space heating, although this use did not come as quickly as the use for cooking and water heating. Part of the reason was the abundance of coal, especially in the Appalachian region of Ohio, Pennsylvania, and West Virginia. Although this was also the region with the most gas supplies, gas was still more expensive than coal. It was also a relatively costly conversion to gas from coal. Oil, which was also becoming more common, made its bid for home heating and therefore competed with gas also. Despite the expense, the convenience of gas was recognized early. A family using coal for the furnace had the coal they used delivered by "chuting" it into the basement coal cellar. They had to shovel it into the furnace, light the fire, keep it going throughout the day and fill it to burn through the night. In the cold morning it would be out and someone had to start it again. Following all this, the ashes had to be emptied and taken out for pickup or you had to dispose of them yourself. (I can attest to this process, which was still in place with coal furnaces in the mid–1940s.) So despite the expense or lack of access, the advantages of natural gas were well recognized. As early as 1886 an alderman in Buffalo said, "Where it [natural gas] has been used it has proved a great benefit to both rich and poor in the way of convenience, comfort, and economy."[33] An Akron editorial commented, "We all remember in the past how we banked our coal fires when we went to bed, and found it necessary to get up an hour early in the morning in order to shake out the ashes and renew the fire. As we stop to think about it we feel the hardship it would be if we had to do this in the present time. Gas has done away with all that trouble."[34]

Well, almost. Akron, having received gas early as the first East Ohio Gas company customer, was ahead of most areas.

The popularity of natural gas soared in the early century, as evidenced by the numbers. From a value of 215,000 dollars in 1882, mostly in Pennsylvania, it increased to 54.6 million dollars in 1908 in over 21 states and territories.[35] Nevertheless, upcoming shortages, expensive conversion from coal to gas, and the relatively cheap coal competitor delayed widespread conversion into the 1940s and 1950s. The market was there, so the gas companies continued to expand their pipelines and wells and to promote the use of natural gas. When people could convert, they did.

Extracting Byproducts

Natural gas is a mixture of gases, as discussed previously. This is not surprising considering that natural gas production is the result of abiogenic or thermogenic processes deep underground. It is also not surprising that it is found with other natural substances such as oil, water, and sand. In fact, the early Appalachian gas wells usually resulted when the seeker was looking for oil or brine. For the very early uses it didn't much matter that all these things were mixed. When oil was sought and it came with gas, the gas was usually just flared off. It was fairly easy to separate water and gas. The other gases in the mixture were simply burned with the primary constituent, which is methane, usually 70 to 90 percent. The early uses were also close to the sources, so there were not many pipeline problems except leakage. However, as the industry matured it became more important to pay attention to these other constituents, both for economic reasons and safety reasons.

Natural gas is termed "wet" when it is found with other hydrocarbons such as propane, butane, and ethane. If it is not found with these other hydrocarbons, it is called "dry." In this latter case the gas is almost pure methane. The gas is often "wet" when it is found together with oil. Wet gas can also contain natural gasoline in either the liquid or vapor form. Natural gasoline can be a hazard or nuisance if it is in liquid form or condenses to liquid form in a pipeline. It can clog a pipeline or deteriorate the rubber couplings between pipes. Thus it needs to be removed from the gas before piping it. Removing it, however, was not a wasted process. Gasoline came into its own as an automobile fuel just as the automotive industry was starting. For the vapor form of gasoline, it was discovered that compression and cooling could be used to extract the gasoline from the natural gas. This process was first used around 1904 at a well near the original Drake oil well at Titusville, Pennsylvania. The gas was condensed by running it through coils in a barrel of cold water. It produced as much as six gallons of gasoline from 1,000 cubic feet of natural gas. This was a major source of gasoline for the burgeoning auto industry before the oil industry started fractionating gasoline from oil.[36]

Others started extracting gasoline from natural gas through other means. In 1906 George Saybolt and Roger Chew started extracting natural gasoline using an adsorption process Saybolt developed and patented. They started this work at the Hope Hastings plant. Hope didn't start production until 1913, by which time others had started to do so. The gas was brought into contact with a heavy absorbing oil, and later the gasoline was distilled by heat. This process was less volatile and more stable than the compression one and would spread quickly. The Carter Oil Company had increased their output of gasoline considerably by 1911 using the Saybolt process.[37] Saybolt's patent was for extracting naphtha.[38] However, naphtha was a generic term at that time (at one time it meant crude oil), and according to Saybolt's patent, "it may be defined generally as including all hydrocarbons, and each of them, which are liquid at atmospheric pressure and temperature, and which have lower boiling points than the normal hydrocarbons of burning oil (kerosene)." This definition includes gasoline: "By 1920, seven percent of the gasoline in the United States was obtained from natural gas. But the market for natural gasoline accelerated with the American adoption of the family car. In fact, in 1930, several times more natural gas was processed for gasoline in the United States than was transported for use in households."[39] These increases contributed to the rapid growth in natural gas use prior to 1930, as shown in figure 3-3. It also helped contribute to the shortage of Appalachian gas in the 1930s.

Natural gasoline was not the only byproduct of natural gas to become profitable and find a useful niche to fill in the fuel industry. Dr. Walter O. Snelling (1880–1965) found others. Snelling had advanced degrees from Harvard, Yale, and George Washington universities, one of which was a doctorate in chemistry. In 1908 he and others moved to Pittsburgh to set up what became the U.S. Bureau of Mines.[40] It turns out that there were some gases that were dissolved in this gasoline extracted from natural gas that refused to stay dissolved. Dr. Snelling got involved with these gases in 1910 when an irate motorist came into his office in Pittsburgh and complained that the gasoline he purchased was evaporating at a rapid and expensive rate. He felt the government should look into these disappearing fumes. When Snelling put some of the gasoline into a bottle in his lab the cork blew out. He realized that dissolved gases were coming out of the gasoline solution and thus reducing the remaining fuel in the tank. When he analyzed these gases he found propane and butane.[41] Apparently the gasoline mixtures at the time contained propane, which was very volatile and could evaporate one-half a tank of gas in one day.

Ethane was first synthetically produced by Faraday in 1834 but was misidentified as methane. It wasn't until 1864 that Carl Schorlemmer correctly identified it as ethane.[42] Ethane, propane, and butane, like methane, are all gases at room temperatures and pressure. However, unlike methane, these three gases can be liquefied at normal temperatures just by reasonable pressures. This means they can be stored in these tanks and moved around where the fuel is needed. Reasonable tank pressures, from 100 to 200 pounds per square inch, allow reasonable-size containers, which are also safe to handle. There are other attributes of these gases that are useful. For example, propane has a heating value of about 2,572 BTU per cubic foot, while that of methane is about 1,050 BTU per cubic foot. Thus there is more energy in propane than methane. Because they are easily liquefied, they are known collectively as liquid petroleum gases (LPG). After his 1913 patent for producing propane from natural gas, Snelling and some colleagues went into business to produce, bottle, and sell propane. This was the start of the industry we know today, in which bottled propane is used for heating, drying, cooking (barbequing), and other uses. By the 1930s the LP gas business totaled 2.8 billion gallons in the United States. The American Gas Association started testing propane appliances in 1938.[43]

Hope Gas got into the business of bottling a propane-butane mixture around the same time. They found they could liquefy propane just by the use of pressure. They set up an operation to do this at their Hastings plant in 1916. The product was charged into cylinders and sold to steel mills in Pittsburgh as a safe substitute for hydrogen and acetylene when used with oxygen to cut steel.[44]

By the first two decades of the twentieth century natural gas was considered to be a good heating fuel in and of itself. But it also had value for its other uses and byproducts. Carbon black, for example, was shown to be a valuable product of burning natural gas, as discussed previously. The value of the natural gas was also enhanced by the removal of the heavier hydrocarbons such as propane, ethane, butane, and natural gasoline. These are not only more valuable as separate products, but their removal facilitates the movement of the remaining almost-pure methane through the pipeline system. The heavier propane is more difficult to move through a pipeline system. This dramatic increase in uses for natural gas is reflected in the steep rise in its use, especially in the 1920s (see figure 3-3).

Growth, War, and Shortage

As figure 3-2 shows, natural gas use more than doubled from 1904 to 1919. Both Hope and East Ohio, firmly embedded in the heart of the Appalachian gas country, shared in this expansion. After the 1911 breakup of the Standard Oil Trust both Hope and East Ohio were still under Standard Oil of New Jersey. They continued to expand. Hope obtained gas wells from Manufacturer's Light and Heat Company, and the Freehold Oil and Gas Company. They also obtained several thousands of leaseholds from these and other companies including property in Calhoun, Doddridge, Gilmer, Ritchie, Tyler, Braxton, and Wirt counties in West Virginia. According to Dominion, "By the end of 1911, Hope had 1,646 producing wells in 14 West Virginia counties, 2,416 miles of pipelines, and 11 compressor stations, three of which—Cove Lick, Lightburn and Marts—were constructed that year. Hope, Peoples, and East Ohio were serving a combined total of 228,450 domestic consumers and many commercial and industrial customers."[45]

In these early years of exploring for both oil and gas, it was discovered that production could be increased by using well-placed explosives in the well to loosen the sand. This activity was the expertise of "shooters," who handled the nitroglycerin that was used. It was a dangerous job and often resulted in accidents after which not much was left. There is one story of a Paddy Darling, a shooter who had violated rules and driven his explosive-laden rig through the center of Oil City, Pennsylvania. He was stopped and arrested, but he did have a card to play. As he stepped down from the rig he said words to this effect: "Go ahead and arrest me, but if you do, it's going to be up to one of you guys to drive this rig out of town." Needless to say he wasn't arrested but got back on his rig. Ironically, later he was killed while blowing out tree stumps on his farm, presumably by using nitroglycerin.[46] This was just one of the very difficult jobs that the workers in the field had to perform in expanding the system. To lay gas lines in the mountains of West Virginia and Pennsylvania they had to haul cast iron pipes over very rough terrain, cutting trees to get through. The pipes at that time were connected by bolted flanges, which were connected by hand, not welded as they would be later. The mule- or horse-drawn wagons often were in mud axle-deep. Despite this and wages around $2.50 per ten-hour day, the pipelines got laid very quickly. The seven-day work weeks didn't leave much time for other activities. It was said that when there was a wedding coming, "It wasn't the bride that set the date ... it was the chief engineer."[47] The difficulty was just as great in stringing the telegraph lines the companies used in parallel with the gas lines. They had to go through the same forested mountains the pipelines traversed.

By mid-decade, in 1915, Hope was serving 15,000 residential and commercial customers. The prices remained low at 18.8 cents per 1,000 cubic feet for residential and commercial, and 8.21 cents for industrial users.[48] At the same time, as the industry was pumping more gas from Appalachia it was looking ahead for how to be able to continue to provide gas on a regular basis. To do this producers would have to be able to even the supply; this meant storage. Storing natural gas would become a major problem in the future. Unlike oil, which can be pumped out of the ground and stored in reasonably sized tanks, natural gas could not be. The gasholder tanks described in the previous chapter would be prohibitively large to store this gas. Yet the storage problem had to be solved for the industry to be reliable. Changes in demand from season to season or industry to commercial had to be accommodated. The industry could not afford to run out of gas for its customers just because it was difficult to store. This was one of the factors that eventually led to the process of liquefaction of natural gas, that is, to store it in a reasonable volume.

East Ohio, as Hope, also expanded. In 1911 it purchased the Canton Gas Light and Coke Company, a manufactured gas producer, and in 1913 it acquired the Mohican Oil and Gas Company of Akron. Another 20-inch pipeline was laid to the West Virginia gas fields that year. By the time of World War I, East Ohio was thriving with a capitalization of over $29 million and a workforce of over 1,900.[49] Ohio at this time was the nation's largest importer of natural gas and West Virginia was the nation's largest exporter of natural gas.[50] By 1916 the majority of homes in Cleveland had gas heat. In Akron, East Ohio's L. B. Terry reported he had a stack of extension orders "one foot high." East Ohio told its customers it was now furnishing the cheapest and best gas service in the world: "If you could but realize the vast treasure and big army necessary to produce, transport, and deliver natural gas, you would wonder how it could be sold for 30 cents per thousand cubic feet."[51]

Then came World War I. The war had major impact on industry and on both Hope and East Ohio. Hope sales reached a new high of 102.6 billion cubic feet, a total that was not hit again until 1946. Sales to East Ohio were 45 billion cubic feet and to People's, 26 billion cubic feet. The average sale price was slightly under 12 cents per 1,000 cubic feet.[52] The industrial demand was high, around the clock, but the commercial and domestic demand increase was comparatively low. Fortunately Hope had drilled many wells just before this, and many were in northwest West Virginia, near the industrial centers of Cleveland and Pittsburgh, areas served by East Ohio and People's.[53]

There were some early indications of shortages even during the war. Conservation, not usually a concern of natural gas interests in the past, started to get consideration. Ironically, this showed up in a change of fuel at the Hope Hastings Compressor Station in 1916. In order to conserve gas for the industrial war production, the fuel for the boilers was changed from gas to coal. So a natural-gas-producing firm had to switch back to coal so it could continue to produce gas for more intensive industrial operations. The coal was first mined at the Hastings site itself.[54] The gas wasted in the early Appalachian fields was now starting to hurt. Because it was cheaper and cleaner than manufactured gas, and easier and cleaner than coal to use, it was in demand so more and more customers came on line. Appalachia was running out of gas; at least the easily obtainable gas: "As early as 1916, low-pressure problems and shortages were common during the winter months, as Appalachian wells could not keep up with the demand, and utilities began curtailing industrial customers."[55] The Pennsylvania wells were the first to decrease output, but it was happening in West Virginia also. Between 1909 and 1919 an average West Virginia well that had yielded daily 21 million cubic feet declined to 620,000 cubic feet per day.[56] Shortages existed or were predicted in Cleveland, Ohio, and Pittsburgh, Oil City, and Sharon in Pennsylvania, and Fredonia, Cuba, Warsaw, and Dunkirk in New York. By 1921 it took an average of three wells to produce the same amount of gas a single well had produced ten years earlier, while production costs soared six times for the same amount of gas produced.[57]

Companies sought new sources and extended pipelines farther into West Virginia. Hope contracted with Godfrey Cabot to use gas that formerly had been used farther south in Calhoun County for making carbon black. A new pipeline and compressor station were constructed to get the gas up to the Hope distribution system.[58] More compressor stations had to be constructed in other places to move the gas longer distances. Because of these shortages, manufactured gas made something of a comeback; this happened in Buffalo. Despite some new discoveries south of the city in 1918 and 1919, the supply to Buffalo was barely sufficient to meet customer demands on very cold days. Francis C. Brown of the Buffalo Gas Company (1919) said later, "General opinion at the time was that the gas industry was a dead end enterprise and it was common advice to gas company employers to get out before it was too late."[59]

The easy gas in Appalachia had been taken in the first two decades of the century. In the region, production declined from 1917 to 1934. Old wells that used to have head pressures of 1,000 pounds per square inch now had these pressures drop to 100 or 200 pounds per square inch. Because the Pennsylvania wells were being depleted West Virginia stepped up production. The state hit a high point in 1917 with 308 billion cubic feet being produced. All of Appalachia hit a peak that year of 522 billion cubic feet. West Virginia was still an exporter at this time but officials were getting concerned about the supply. They considered keeping it within the state. The 1919 Steptoe bill in West Virginia prohibited interstate sales unless the gas was unmarketable in-state. They were trying to avoid a third straight winter of shortages that closed factories and schools. The Supreme Court later (1923) ruled against it, saying it had interfered with interstate commerce.[60]

There had been warnings from experts for years on the waste of natural gas. Waples notes that in West Virginia Dr. I. C. White, the official West Virginia state geologist, pleaded for conservation of natural gas over the years. Early in the century White said, "This precious fuel has not only been used for the crudest forms of heat and power at a nominal price right in the midst of great beds of coal, but many towns, two or three decades ago, actually advertising free gas to all concerns, and as a standing advertisement permitted great torches of the same to burn up millions of cubic feet both day and night." He told the Council of Governors in 1908 that people didn't recognize the value of the gas and it was becoming exhausted:

> The average business man assumed that the supply of natural gas was unlimited, and while turning a deaf ear to the geologists who always warned him that the supply would eventually fall through use and waste, he listened willingly and apparently approvingly to the fakers in the science who assured him the supply of natural gas would never fail, that is was being manufactured at a rapid rate deep down in nature's vast laboratory.[61]

A little later he became a little more optimistic. In 1917 he said, "Quite recently there has been a general awakening to the enormity of this inexcusable waste of the best fuel in the world, and hence it is hoped that much of it may soon cease."[62]

Similarly, Dr. J. A. Bownocker, state geologist of Ohio, gave an address to the Natural Gas Association meeting in Cleveland in 1919 that was also pessimistic. He had studied the gas production of Ohio, Pennsylvania, and West Virginia. The company he studied in West Virginia was Hope. Among the many data he showed was a chart showing the decrease in the average open flow of new wells (figure 3-4).[63]

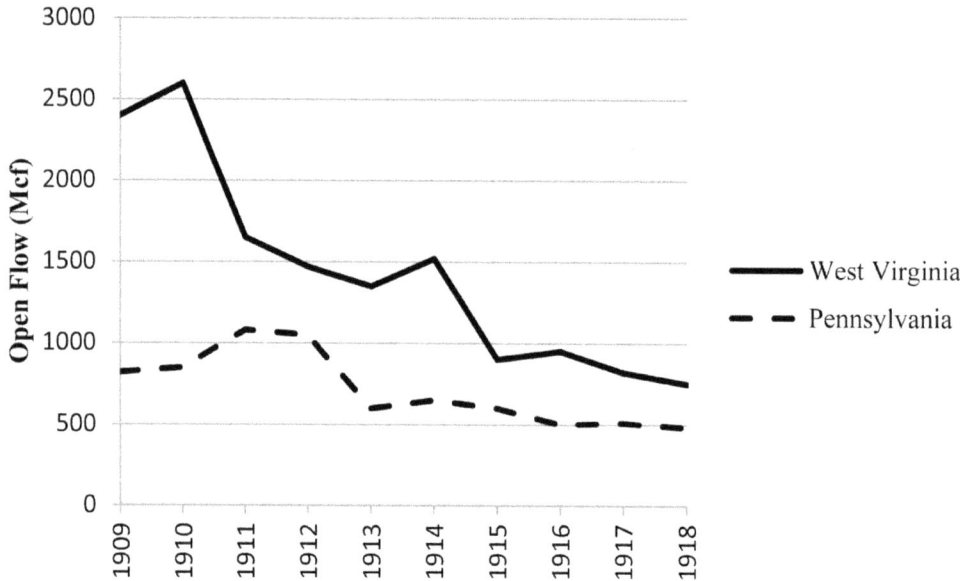

Figure 3-4. Average open flow of new wells.

He opened his talk by saying, "I do not mean by this that our gas supply will suddenly terminate, though we have reached the stage where it appears necessary to notify certain cities and towns that they must return to coal or at any rate not rely on natural gas."[64] He closed it by saying, "All depends on finding new territory in large area, and for reasons previously stated the prospects of such discoveries are very poor. At best the supply on the present enormous scale will last for only a few years."[65]

This pessimistic prognostication on Appalachian gas was born out by later data as shown in figure 3-5.[66] This figure shows how the nation's gas supply coming from Appalachia would continue to decrease as a percentage of the total U.S. supply. It also shows that new sources were found in the Southwest. Figure 3-6 shows the increase in total supply in the following years after the Southwest gas started to become available.[67] At the present time new methods of extracting natural gas are improving our ability to extract more gas from areas that were once thought to be depleted. The transition between Appalachian and Southwest gas is shown in figure 3-3 as a relatively flat production curve between 1917 and 1921. Also, as will be seen later, although most gas was used in the industrial areas of Ohio and Pennsylvania at that time, there were not extensive pipelines between the Southwest and these industrial areas. Therefore, shortages were experienced at this time in the Northeast.

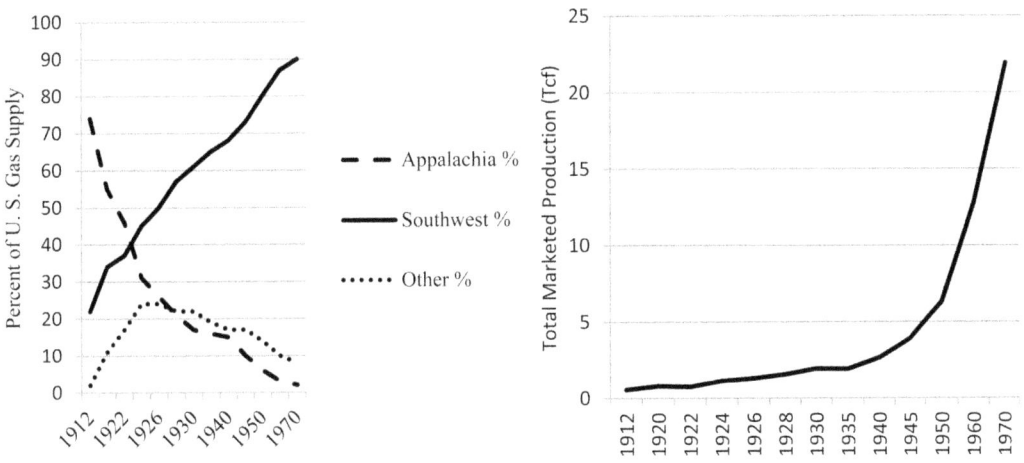

Left: Figure 3-5. Appalachia-Southwest gas supply. *Right:* Figure 3-6. Total marketed gas production.

Because of both the dwindling Appalachian gas supply and the intense industrial demands of the war, Hope and East Ohio were both faced with some struggles from 1917 through the early 1920s. At the end of the war, in 1918, the total gas Hope handled was to drop to 90 billion cubic feet from the high of 108 billion cubic feet handled during 1917. Also, during the war their gas reserves dwindled such that they had a shortage going into the 1920s. It was necessary to extend lines farther south into West Virginia to southern Gilmer County to assure a continuous supply. A total of 500 more miles of pipe were laid and more compressor stations were built. Despite this they handled only about half as much gas in 1921 as in 1916.[68]

East Ohio was having its own troubles. Besides receiving gas from West Virginia, they had drilled some of their own wells in Ohio. But the biggest pool East Ohio had developed, the Lakewood pool, was 95 percent depleted by 1918. At this time they had to tell their customers that they should be prepared to use dual fuel systems, coal or gas, because a continuous gas supply could not be assured. Industrial loads that had accounted for 40 percent of East Ohio's sales in 1916 plummeted to just seven percent in 1921. As table 3-5 shows, the industrial use of gas fell dramatically after the war because of shortages.[69]

Table 3-5. East Ohio Industrial Gas Sales

Year	Industrial Gas Sales—MMcf
1915	24,400
1916	28,800
1917	15,900
1918	11,100
1919	6,930
1920	8,980
1921	2,690
1922	8,110

Between Wars

When Connecticut was chartered as a colony in 1662 its lands were defined as extending from "sea-to-sea." This was typical of many colonies. By the time of the Revolution, Connecticut still claimed a strip of land from the Pennsylvania border across northern Ohio to the Mississippi River. However, by 1786 (still under the Articles of Confederation) the state ceded most of the territory back to the U.S. However, it maintained a small strip of northeastern Ohio, which was designated the Western Reserve. In 1795 Connecticut sold most of the Western Reserve to the Connecticut Land Company. Moses Cleaveland was one of the founders of the Connecticut Land Company, and in 1796 he was sent to the Western Reserve to survey it. He founded the settlement as the "capital city" of the Western Reserve at the mouth of the Cuyahoga River. The surveyors later named it Cleaveland.[70] (Soon after the founding he returned to Connecticut and never returned to Cleveland. Somewhere along the line the extra "a" in Cleaveland was dropped.) The population didn't grow fast at first. In 1800 it was listed at seven persons; even in 1820 it was only 606. However, as it started to grow (Ohio became a state in 1803), it became a regional center for commerce with craftsmen in small shops producing farming tools, barrels for shipping flour, salted meat, and other items. By 1837 it was reported to have four iron foundries making steam engines and other products. It had candle makers, carriage makers, breweries, a pottery, and other manufacturers. The Cuyahoga Steam Furnace Company, founded about the same time, was probably the largest employer, making iron ore, charcoal, and limestone in its blast furnaces. By 1860 the city's most valuable product was iron.[71]

This set the stage for the industrial boom years of 1860 to 1930. The heavy industry, steel and iron, was boosted by the needs of the Civil War. It was just before this, in the 1850s, that the mineral resources, such as iron ore, from the upper Great Lakes were starting to be exploited. After 1860 many industries took hold in Cleveland, making it a manufacturing city. These included iron and steel, machine tools, clothing, chemicals, paint manufacturing, and the electric lighting and automotive industries, which came later. It was here Rockefeller incorporated Standard Oil; he had many refineries here also. By 1930 Cleveland was second only to Detroit among American cities in the percentage of its workers employed in industry.[72] Cleveland lost the automobile industry to Detroit in the early part of the century. However, it still retained a large share of companies that were building parts for the auto industry. As figure 3-7 shows, as industry grew in Cleveland so did the population. Most of the increase was due to eastern European immigrants, who tended to have large families once they immigrated.

The very rapid growth in industry came to an end about 1930. This is indicated in the population chart also. The 1930 population of 900,000 was just slightly below the highest-ever peak of 915,000 in 1950.[73] The industrial growth was not limited to Cleveland but encompassed the whole of northeast Ohio including Youngstown, Akron, Canton, and others.

Clearly this growth of both industry and population was one demand factor for the increased use of U.S. energy (figure 3-1) during this period. The demand from industry was greatest in oil and natural gas, but even the use of coal increased until it peaked around 1925 (figure 3-1). Industry was going to gas, and the domestic demand was for gas cooking, water heating, and space heating, caused by the population growth.

The intense use of natural gas during the war, which drew down reserves, and the

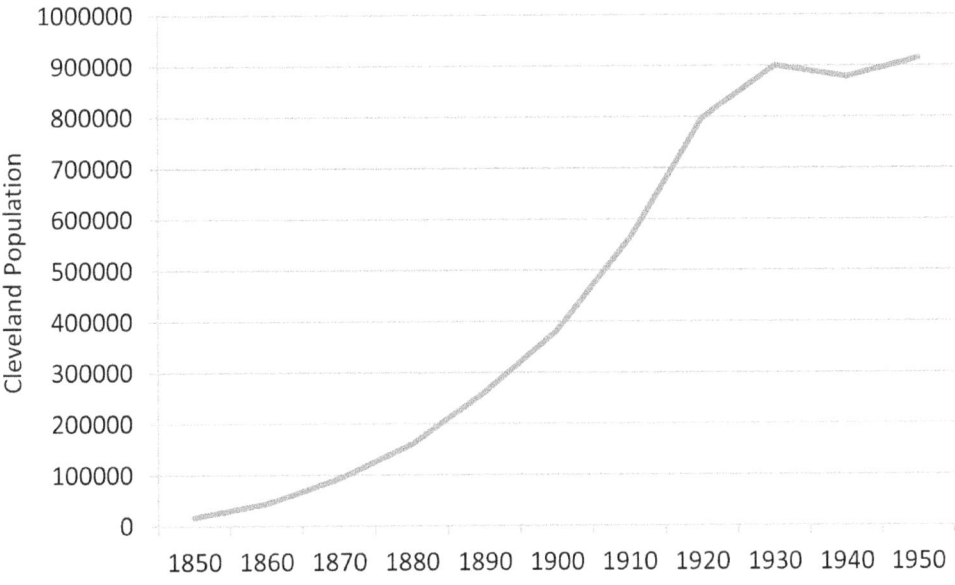

Figure 3-7. Cleveland population.

declining supply of Appalachian gas, made things tight. The 1920s still saw growth but it was not as robust as previously. Many homes had to retain the use of coal for heating, and industry still used coal. Some Clevelanders were still using manufactured gas into the 1930s. It wasn't until 1934 that the remaining consumers using manufactured gas in Cleveland were converted to natural gas.[74] Gas that had been obscenely wasted just a few short years ago now was seen as a valuable resource, so conservation efforts became more widely used. Ohio's governor issued a special proclamation that "special attention be given this matter in all institutions of learning so that there may be carried home suggestions and methods of conserving the supply of gas."[75] Because of the lower supplies, and to encourage conservation, East Ohio raised rates from 30 cents per 1,000 cubic feet in 1917 to 38 cents in 1920, then to 57 cents in 1925 and as high as 67 cents by 1930. This caused many customers to return to coal, especially for heating.[76] Conservation and price increases started to take effect. Each of East Ohio's domestic customers, in 1917, used 128,847 cubic feet of gas annually, on average. By 1930 this figure had dropped to 73,274 cubic feet, a 43 percent reduction. It would drop further in a few years, but that would be due to the Great Depression. Although 142,000 new customers would be added to East Ohio in the 1920s, it wouldn't be until 1946 that gas sales would top the 1917 peak of 38.07 billion cubic feet.[77]

Even as shortages started to take effect, the industry grew. Gas was used by many different people and organizations. As the competition between appliance makers grew, there were many different ways to get customers to use the gas. In cooking, for example, gas stoves were designed to be more appealing:

> This new range was a thing of beauty, ... Gone were the ungainly high ovens, the exposed burner tops and the stereotyped lines of the old cabinet ranges. Top burners and ovens were enclosed in a streamlined artistic cabinet. Thereafter the developments were still more rapid and the efficiency of the gas range made still further strides with the addition of insulated

ovens, the thermostatic time and temperature oven control and an improved automatic lighter which operated by the simple expediency of turning on the gas.[78]

Despite these changes, however, the designs varied, and many were wasteful of gas, poorly designed, and of cheap construction. There were also no standards. As the industry grew, starting with manufactured gas, various associations formed to promote the industry. Regional associations started as early as 1871; one example was the New England Association of Gas Engineers. Two national organizations came into existence between 1905 and 1918, the National Commercial Gas Association and the American Gas Institute, the former concerned with sales and public relations and the latter with technical matters. These two organizations consolidated in 1918 to form the American Gas Association (AGA).[79] It was in the early 1920s that the AGA started looking into the issue of standardization, safety, and compatibility of household appliances such as gas stoves. In 1927 a temporary testing laboratory was set up within space provided by East Ohio. In 1928 a permanent building was erected on East Ohio property at the Number 2 Plant.[80] This AGA testing laboratory on East 62nd Street, just south of the Number 2 Plant, was impacted by the 1944 fire. The testing laboratory set appliance standards and issued a seal of approval for meeting these standards. This contributed to improving the efficiency and safety of gas appliances.

Hope also had to react to the shortages. There was a slight recession in 1921, after which there was increased gas demand. Hope was not able to keep up right away. The company volunteered to increase the price paid to contract vendors if they would drill additional wells and clean out old ones. Hope drilled to deeper formations and in new areas, the Oriskany Sands, for example. This was an unexplored strata with sufficient porosity that might prove useful in the future. For now there was a lack of incentive to risk expensive, deep exploratory drilling. The company purchased more wells from Godfrey Cabot, ones in other counties that had been used for carbon black manufacture. In 1925 Hope spent seven million dollars on extensive construction activity. Part of the construction was for two new compressor stations. The John J. Cornwell Station was constructed on the Elk River at Corton, West Virginia, a few miles from Clendenin.[81] It was at this station, a few years later, that Hope would make history by building the first pilot plant to produce liquid natural gas.

Even as gas use was growing in the 1920s, it was still difficult to get around in the mountains to do the business of supplying natural gas. Stories talk about using sternwheelers on the Kanawha River and taking a day and one-half to make trips that now take two hours. One trip by the Hope general superintendent and attorney was described as follows: "They had a tax problem that had to be taken care of in Granville. It was right in the middle of winter and gosh-awful cold and they could only get as far as Ellenboro on the train. From there they used a buckboard and team to drive some 40 miles on mud roads. Their only comforts were a buffalo robe and a big lantern that they kept burning underneath it, and they nearly froze." Later some solid-rubber-tired trucks and Model T Fords helped them get around a little easier. Despite these difficulties, by 1925 Hope was operating 3,257 wells, with 50 compressor stations, and had 8,777 miles of pipeline of three inches or greater.[82]

Interrupted by the Great Depression

Despite the struggle with some shortages in the Appalachian region, the industry, including Hope, did grow during the 1920s. This was aided by going farther afield, by the introduction of seamless welded pipe, and by the use of other approaches such as consolidation. However, neither Hope nor East Ohio could escape the impact of the Great Depression, which lasted roughly from 1930 to 1937, and some say all the way to World War II. This economic disaster has been covered well elsewhere, so only a few numbers are necessary to illustrate its impact. Table 3-6 shows the Gross National Product (GNP) dropping from a high in 1929 to a low in 1933 and not returning to the 1929 level until 1937.[83] Clearly the high rate of unemployment in 1939 supports the view that it wasn't until the war started that the Depression was over.

Table 3-6. U.S. GNP and Unemployment

Year	GNP in 1929 Dollars	Percentage Unemployed
1928	98.5	
1929	104.4	3.14
1930	95.1	8.67
1931	89.5	15.82
1932	76.4	23.53
1933	74.2	24.75
1934	80.8	21.6
1935	91.4	19.97
1936	100.9	16.8
1937	109.1	14.18
1938	103.2	18.91
1939	111	17.05
1940	121	14.45
1941	131.7	9.66

Industry was hit particularly hard. The Index of Industrial Employment, a measure of industrial output, fell 52 percent in 1930 and 1932. The Wholesale Price Index fell 37 percent in the same period.[84] The impact on the GNP and industry as a whole is reflected in figures 3-1 and 3-2, which show a reduction in the use of energy in these years. There is a significant reduction in the use of coal and a reduction or flattening in the use of natural gas; certainly not an increase.

During this ten-year period Hope experienced a substantial reduction in sales and so sought to reduce expenses. However, it did make an effort to maintain its properties and extend its facilities in anticipation of better times. In the five years prior to 1931 the demands on Hope had remained around 60 billion cubic feet per year. However, in 1931 that had dropped to 56 billion. The Appalachian field yields continued to decrease, so they had to go farther from their major markets to obtain the gas, mostly farther south in West Virginia. Earnings reached a low point in 1932 of only 40,500 dollars, and sales declined to 37 billion cubic feet because industrial activity had been drastically reduced. Hope got its gas from many sources but had to cut back its own production from company wells to seven billion cubic feet, the lowest since 1907. The average price actually *increased* to a new high of 38 cents per thousand cubic feet. This is unusual for a low demand situation but was reversed later when regulation was imposed. Consistent with its philosophy of looking ahead, between 1932 and 1936 it added to its gas reserve and the ability to move this gas to market; that is, it increased capacity despite the lack of demand. This paid off in the cold winter of 1940 when the demand was back up to 50 million cubic feet. By 1939, as the war started, the gas demand that had decreased over the past decade started to rise again.[85]

The distribution company, East Ohio, experienced trouble as everyone else did. When the Depression hit, some customers had trouble paying their bills and had to be cut off. Between 1930 and 1933 East Ohio lost almost 25,000 domestic customers. People were using less, also. In 1930 each domestic customer had used about 73,000 cubic feet annually; by 1933 it fell to 59,000. Gas was also competing now with electricity, which also had a range of appliances available. East Ohio, like Hope, did make progress, however. By 1935 it had regained the lost customer base and by 1940 topped the 500,000 mark in customers.[86] By the late 1930s more and more northeastern Ohioans were looking to switch to cleaner-burning natural gas from coal.

Despite the lingering effects of the Depression, such as the high unemployment through the 1930s, the gas business picked up at the end of the decade for both Hope and East Ohio; they had weathered that storm. They also had to weather another one, one that mostly impacted Hope: regulation. In the early days of natural gas use the gas was used close to its source. This is because the producer had to depend on the wellhead pressure, which is the natural pressure of the gas from the well. This meant it couldn't be moved far; the pressure would drop along the line. This, of course, was a disadvantage it had when competing early with manufactured gas. This changed as the industry matured. Pipes were laid over longer distances, and compressor stations were built to boost the pressure so it could be sent long distances. The pipeline from Hope's West Virginia station to northeast Ohio was over 100 miles long. It also crossed state boundaries. As this was becoming more common, especially with the very long pipelines from the Southwest, more and more state lines were crossed. As discussed in Tussing and Barlow, and in Peebles, Congress found it necessary to pass (unanimously) the Natural Gas Act of 1938. This gave the Federal Power Commission the power to regulate interstate gas transmission.[87] This impacted Hope, as will be discussed below. Natural gas regulation is discussed in Chapter 8.

New Fields and New Technology

As much of the data shows there wasn't really a gas shortage in the 1920s and 1930s; it was just in the wrong place, as far as Hope and East Ohio were concerned. The dip in gas use through the 1930s was clearly due to a lack of demand because of the Depression. As figures 3-2 and 3-3 show, there was actually a nationwide boom in the increased use of natural gas up to that time. Figure 3-5 shows what was happening. Most of the new gas was coming from the South and Southwest of the country. Before, and just after the turn of the twentieth century, gas was discovered in Louisiana, Texas, Oklahoma, and Kansas. Often, as in Appalachia, this was while someone was looking for oil. Likewise, as in Appalachia, this was considered a nuisance, and because there was no ready market, the gas was wasted, mostly by flaring it off. There were attempts to draw some industry to the area to use the gas, but these were unsuccessful. At that time there were no long-distance pipelines. The longest at that time were in Appalachia, such as the Akron 10-inch from Hope in West Virginia to East Ohio in Cleveland, which was about 120 miles long. The pipe was cast iron, heavy, hard to move, lossy (rough inside, causing pressure to drop as the gas flowed through it), small diameter, and hard to install; it used mechanical couplings.

As the industry grew the pipeline technology necessarily had to improve to keep up. This would have been true even if all the gas remained in Appalachia. It was necessary to go to smoother, high-strength pipe that could withstand high pressures. Smoother pipe was necessary to cut down on losses so the number of compressor booster stations along a pipeline could be minimized. High pressure is also necessary to keep the gas moving, especially for long distances; it also minimizes the number of compressor stations. Leaks had always been a problem (especially when hollowed-out pine logs were used for pipelines early in the industry) and are more serious for longer lines with higher pressure. A leaky gas line, as contrasted with a leaky oil line, can be a source of an explosion. Of course new equipment that would allow mechanization of the pipe laying process was necessary to be able to economically lay long lines of pipe. A lot of these improvements were made in the first two decades of the twentieth century and became available around 1925. For example, U.S. Steel had developed 16-inch seamless pipe twice the size of previous pipes around 1925. They were thin-walled, and high tensile strength compared to previous pipes. These new pipes allowed the increased pressure necessary to move the gas. By 1930 they were 20 inches in diameter and operating at 500 pounds per square inch, and by 1948 the pressure was up to 800 pounds and the diameter up to 26 inches. The new pipelines were all welded. Oxyacetylene welding was developed around 1910 and acetylene welding around 1925. There was some electric welding around 1922 but it became more common around 1940.[88]

The pipeline boom started in 1925. The first long-distance line, 217 miles, was laid by the Magnolia Gas Company of Dallas and went from northern Louisiana to Beaumont, Texas. It had pipe diameters of 14, 16, and 18 inches. Other pipeline companies started to develop other routes and lay lines. The first 1,000-mile line was laid in 1931 by the Natural Gas Pipeline Company of America. It was 24 inches in diameter and went from Panhandle, Texas, to Chicago.[89] Between 1910 and 1920 there were many gas finds in the Texas Panhandle and a large one in Hugoton, Kansas. So these were the origin of many pipelines in the late 1920s and early 1930s.[90] Brignano and McCullough quote an enthusiastic *Business Week* in the late 1920s on this boom: "America's gas industry has suddenly developed pep.... The 80,000 miles of natural gas pipelines already laid will look like a garden hose in the back yard when the projects for extending them are completed.... The gas industry, modern Rip Van Winkle, has at last awakened."[91] Even Hope got into the new pipeline business. Although it was only 94 miles long and all in Appalachia, they installed an all-welded, 12-inch, high pressure line between their Cornwell Station near Corton, West Virginia, to their Hastings Station.[92]

Despite this flurry of activity there was a notable absence of new pipeline activity into Appalachia, though there were many miles of old pipelines in that region starting from early in the century. These old lines were the highway that was supplying gas to the major industrial users of the time, Cleveland and Pittsburgh. One can see this on map 3-2 of Tussing and Barlow, which shows pipelines from the Texas, Kansas, and Louisiana fields to places like Minneapolis, Chicago, Indianapolis, St. Louis, Atlanta, and Denver.[93] It appears that many who had never had gas before were probably clamoring for it, which made it worthwhile to connect these cities and these fields. The assumption probably was that sending gas to Cleveland, Pittsburgh, or Appalachia would be like sending coals to

Newcastle, that is, redundant, because they had had Appalachian gas for decades. However, as has been shown, the Appalachian fields were being depleted and these major industrial areas were suffering from shortages. Of course during the Depression the pipeline industry suffered as all the rest, and not much was built until the war started. This left the Pittsburgh-Cleveland-Appalachia triangle struggling through the 1930s until the war came.

Once the war started, the industrial areas of northeast Ohio and Pennsylvania increased their energy demand to ramp up production for the war. Something had to be done, and something was done to get the Southwest energy up to these areas. This happened in two ways. On February 4, 1943, East Ohio contracted with Panhandle Eastern Pipe Line Company to bring gas into its system from the Southwest fields. They built a 20-inch line, 112 miles long, from Maumee, Ohio, near Toledo, which was an area Texas Panhandle served, to the Brush Farm Station near Cleveland.[94]

Hope also concluded something had to be done. As early as 1940 the gas demand started to increase. Hope responded to the call for more energy by drawing on reserves but knew this could not continue because of the dwindling reserves. The company started to formulate plans for a long-distance pipeline to the Southwest. It began surveying and acquiring 826 miles of pipeline right-of-way from the Cornwell Station to a point in Louisiana. In 1942 it applied to the Federal Power Commission (FPC) to build a line from the Cornwell Station to Perryville, Louisiana, a distance of 772 miles. In the meantime a new company, Tennessee Gas Transmission Company, formed in 1940, had proposed a 20-inch line from Arcadia Parish in Louisiana to Nashville. That was turned down by the FPC because it didn't conform to the Natural Gas Act, which required the destination to be an existing market; Nashville was not. The application lingered. For whatever reason—some imply it was because of a connection between the White House and Tennessee Gas—the FPC unexpectedly awarded the proposed Hope pipeline route to Tennessee Gas over Hope in 1943. The line, 1,228 miles, went from Driscoll, Texas, to the Hope Cornwell Station. It was completed quickly, and Southwest gas now was flowing into Appalachia and then to the industries of Ohio and Pennsylvania, where the gas was needed. Early in the war, prior to the new pipelines, Columbus, Cleveland, Dayton, and Cincinnati experienced shortages. The priority was to provide gas to domestic heating. As a result it was estimated that more than 300,000 tons of steel were never produced.[95]

About the same time in early 1942 there was a devastating German U-boat operation targeting U.S. shipping, mostly oil, along the East Coast from Florida to New York.[96] This operation lasted several months in the spring of 1942. Thousands of tons of shipping were lost in plain sight of coastal cities. This had a dramatic impact on the movement of oil, which led to the construction of two pipelines to counter this emergency. The "Big Inch" pipeline was started in 1942 and completed in record time. This 24-inch line connected the oil fields of Longview, Texas, to Linden, New Jersey. A second line, the "Little Big Inch" (20 inches), went from Beaumont, Texas, to Linden, New Jersey. These were originally constructed to move oil. Later they were converted to natural gas lines.[97] The prolific Southwest gas fields were now connected to all parts of the country; the trend would continue as natural gas was about to hit a period of rapid growth.

In the late 1930s all of these new pipelines from the Southwest were still in the future. The Ohio and Pennsylvania industrial areas were still experiencing periodic shortages. The gas that was available in Appalachia could not be moved fast enough. There had to be some way to collect it and store it for when it was needed.

Storage

Ever since natural gas was discovered the problem was "use it or lose it." There was no practical way to store it as there was with wood, coal, or oil. That is one reason so much of it was wasted at first in Appalachia and even later in the Southwest. It was flared off if the driller who was looking for oil or brine found gas instead. Manufactured gas had an advantage in this area. You could build the plant near where it was needed, make as much as was needed, and then store a reasonable amount, to smooth out the delivery process, in the gasholders discussed previously. The first users of natural gas tried to find sources close to them so they wouldn't have to move it so far in the original, primitive piping systems. This is one problem the carbon black users of natural gas didn't have. The capital investment for a carbon black plant was low, so they could go to remote areas to build a plant near the source of the well. Most industrial and domestic users could not do this. The wellhead pressure also varied dramatically from well to well, so each source had to be handled differently. Perhaps one of the greatest constraints on the growth of gas use was the uncertainty of the supply. It wasn't known how much gas each well contained, so there was a reluctance to build a large infrastructure that might be useless when the well ran dry.

After a while enough gas was discovered in Ohio, Pennsylvania, and West Virginia that the effort to lay long pipelines, such as the Akron 10-inch, made it practical to move the gas to where it was really useful. Eventually there were thousands of wells in these states supplying gas, so the fear of any one dry well did not take down the system. However, this transportation system did not solve the storage problem. To assure a continuous supply it was obvious the pipeline network had to be extensive so gas could be moved as necessary to where and when it was needed, but there was a practical limit to this expansion because laying pipelines was expensive. The demand for gas also varied dramatically with the season. In many cases the amount of gas needed in winter was twice the amount needed in summer. This kept many men busy along the network, turning gas valves on or off as necessary. It wasn't practical to size the system for peak loads at all times; load factor was a problem. Thus when it got very cold for a stretch, there might be gas shortages.

The obvious solution to this problem was to move the gas near to the user and store it for use when it is needed. The gaseous form of this energy makes this difficult. You have to either have a large volume or store it under high pressure to be able to store a reasonable amount of energy. This is unlike oil, which is easy to store. For example, one gallon of heating oil has an energy content of 139,000 BTU. Contrast this to natural gas, which has about 1,100 BTU per cubic foot. For one gallon of natural gas, as a gas at atmospheric pressure, the energy content is about 147 BTU. So it takes about 900 times as much volume to store the same amount of energy in natural gas as it does in oil. Gasholders that store natural gas under pressures near atmospheric have been used for a long time and are still used, especially in Europe. The gas volume inside can vary throughout the day as the need for gas varies during the day. The top rises or falls depending on the amount of gas stored or distributed (see figure 2–1). One gasholder was built for manufactured gas in 1853 by the Erie Gas Company in Pennsylvania with a capacity of 30,000 cubic feet. However, they only had 150 customers. Later, in 1878, the Oil City Gas Company constructed a roundhouse gasholder. It was 141 feet in diameter and 19 feet high. This had about the same capacity, that is, about 30,000 cubic feet.[98] Gasholders continued to increase in size.

As the systems grew the size of these gasholders could get out of hand. One gasholder in Los Angeles in 1906 was 210 feet high, over 35 feet higher than the tallest building. A later one in downtown Los Angeles was 300 feet high.[99] See the photo in figure 3-8, which shows gasholders in downtown Los Angeles circa 1945, the large cylinders in the center of the photo.[100] A gasholder 200 feet in diameter and 300 feet tall would hold about 10 million cubic feet of gas. It sounds like a lot, but when Cleveland was nearing its wartime capacity it was using about 400 million cubic feet per day.[101] Even now a medium to large city will use 80 million cubic feet per day. Thus 10 million cubic feet would only last a few hours if it were used for storage. Before the war the largest gasholder was in Gelsenkirchen, Germany. It measured 262 feet in diameter, was 443 feet high, and held 21 million cubic feet of gas.[102] Clearly this was not the way to go for a large amount of storage.

Figure 3-8. Los Angeles natural gas storage tanks (courtesy University of Southern California, on behalf of the USC Libraries Special Collection).

Another way to store it is under high pressure. This way the gas could be stored in much smaller volumes. The problem in this case is the strength of the container needed to store it under high pressure. Again, for example, to store a volume of gas that is 17 cubic feet at atmospheric pressure in a volume of one cubic foot would take a pressure of 250 pounds per square inch. This is certainly doable (gas is often stored at much higher pressures), but it is not practical for large volumes. A large tank would require an excessively heavy steel container. This is both uneconomical and potentially unsafe.

Over the years two other methods for storing natural gas have been developed, both of which are used extensively and effectively today. One is underground storage.

In retrospect, it seems that underground storage would be an obvious idea for natural gas storage. In some ways it was. However, in the very early days storage was not an issue. Natural gas wells often had a high wellhead pressure, and the gas that was discharged was often wasted. The early concerns were with just capping the wells and collecting what seemed, at times, to be an unlimited supply. When it was finally recognized as a valuable resource in the late nineteenth century the focus was on getting it to market and keeping the lines ready for use. Since most of the wells were not near the ultimate users, it was necessary to build a delivery and distribution system. As Appalachian gas supplies started to deplete, conservation became popular; the previously wasted gas became a regret. Storage became both a tool for the gas delivery regulation problem, that is, how to keep the gas flowing under various load conditions, and a way to conserve gas that wasn't needed immediately.

The first recognized underground storage experiments were in Welland, Ontario, in 1915. A few years prior to this W. J. Judge, an executive with the National Fuel Gas Company, experimented with using an old salt mine in Ohio near Cleveland for storage. Northeast Ohio has a lot of salt reserves and old mines. These tend to be underground cavernous areas where the salt was extracted, not the porous rock formations that are the normal source of gas. Apparently he had trouble getting the water out of the mine, so he was unsuccessful in storing gas. However, he tried again later to store gas in an old gas-producing well and was successful. His method was repeated the following year, successfully, in a field near Buffalo, New York. This was considered to be the first U.S. underground storage. This appears to be a logical means of storing gas. If a well has been depleted of its original gas and the wellhead pressure is down to some low value of 50 to 100 pounds per square inch, the well can be turned into storage. It is known to be a good storage area because it held gas in prior years. Gas to be stored is simply pumped into the old well under pressure and withdrawn as necessary. The fields around Buffalo were injected with more gas until they reached almost 200 million cubic feet around 1926. As much as 40 million cubic feet per day were withdrawn to meet periods of demand. A peak winter day can require as much as fifteen times as much gas as a summer day, so the storage areas can be filled in summer to be used in the winter. The porous rock formations in Appalachia were well suited to this type of storage, so this method expanded in use. Hope started experimenting in 1932 and was storing gas by 1937 near its Bridgeport Station.[103] East Ohio opened its first underground storage at Chippewa in 1941 and its second at Stark Summit in 1942.[104] So in this innovation Hope and East Ohio were not early adopters.

Underground storage is now common, but it did not develop that fast before the war. By World War II there were 51 storage pools across the country. The needs of the war motivated the creation of 24 more in the early 1940s (including East Ohio's two).[105] The Southwest gas that finally arrived in the Appalachian region didn't come until later in the war. That included East Ohio's hookup with Panhandle Eastern at Maumee, Ohio, in 1943 and Hope's Cornwell Station hookup to Tennessee Gas in 1943. This meant that in the late 1930s the depletion of the Appalachian gas fields was putting a strain on the supplies for that area, especially the industrial areas. They were still looking for ways around the problem of high demand for extreme temperature conditions.

Another Way to Store

Although the natural gas production, transportation, and distribution systems were now well developed and able to supply gas on a continuous basis, there was still a problem with peak loads. There were times in winter, during cold snaps lasting several days, when the temperature would drop very low compared to the average. This was common in the northeast part of Ohio. The shortages had already precluded a lot of people from converting to gas heating; they remained on coal. However, a lot had converted, so they were vulnerable. When supply was short the decision was usually to meet domestic demands and curtail industry until supply was again sufficient for both. This even happened early in the war when industrial production was critical.

Howell C. Cooper, the president of Hope in 1937, had an idea for how to solve the peak load problem. Cooper had been with Hope for a long time, including during the years of strong growth and the years when they were experiencing the depletion of the gas wells in West Virginia. In 1911, working with John Pew, he had invented the orifice gas meter, a less expensive version than previous ones. He became Hope's general superintendent in 1912, during a period of very good growth for Hope. In 1918 he resigned as general superintendent and was appointed chief engineer. He became vice president of Hope in 1927, vice president and general manager in 1932, and finally president in 1933.[106] He was certainly familiar with all aspects of the natural gas business. This would have made him familiar with the 1915 patent of Godfrey Cabot for storing and transporting liquid gases at low temperatures, and the U.S. government's actions taken in 1917 to recover helium from liquefying natural gas, which will be discussed in Chapter 5. He was also aware of Lee Twomey's patents from the 1920s up to 1937 on liquefaction processes for natural gas, which will also be covered in Chapter 5. What undoubtedly occupied much of his time in 1937, however, was the problem that Hope and East Ohio were having supplying enough gas for peak loads in the winter. Because they couldn't supply enough for these peaks, some customers were being shut off during the peak winter cold snaps.

Putting all these things together, he saw a possible solution to the peak-shaving problem: store enough gas on site to be able to shave these loads so no one would have to be shut off during the cold snap. They way to do this, he figured, was to store the gas more compactly. The answer to that, he decided, was to store it as a liquid. He knew that natural gas takes up less than $1/600$ the volume if it is stored as a liquid rather than as a gas. Moreover, if it is stored at a low temperature ($-260°F$) it can be stored at a low pressure, less than one atmosphere, and therefore would not require high pressure tanks to store. At that point he started to take steps to implement this idea.

This 600-to-one storage ratio has a dramatic effect on tank storage size. For example, if you used the gas holder discussed above that was 200 feet in diameter and 300 feet high, which held 10 million cubic feet of natural gas, and kept the diameter at 200 feet, but stored the gas as a liquid, you could reduce the height to about six inches! Of course you would not build that same type of container, because of the insulation that would be needed; but this comparison does provide perspective on the advantages of liquid gas storage. The short story is that Cooper built an LNG pilot plant, which East Ohio used as a model for a full-size commercial plant. East Ohio did a study and concluded that this plant would be less expensive than adding another pipeline from West Virginia to Ohio. This is the plant described in Chapter 1.

Three years after the Cleveland plant was built, James O. Jackson, chief engineer of the Pittsburgh–Des Moines Steel Company, the company that built the LNG storage tanks for East Ohio, did a short study on storing natural gas above ground. Table 3-7 provides a simple comparison for that time in 1943.[107]

Table 3-7. Relative Cost and Weight of Gas Containers

Type of Container	Approximate Maximum Size (cubic feet)	Per Million Cubic Feet of Capacity	
		Cost	Weight of Steel Required (Tons)
Spherical-Pressure Container	10 million	$108,000	543.0
Water-sealed Holders	10 million	$89,000	440.0
Waterless-Gas Holders	30 million	$47,600	238.0
Liquefied-Gas Holders	200 million	$1,314	4.3

The spherical-pressure holders are heavy, thick-walled tanks holding the gas under high pressure. These were never considered as a long-term solution for storing large amounts of gas for reasons obvious in the table. The water-sealed holders, as pictured in figure 2–1, were commonly used for both manufactured gas and natural gas to smooth the load during the day, going up or down as gas was received and distributed. However, as has been discussed, they could not hold large amounts without being excessively large themselves. The waterless holder is similar to the water-sealed holder in shape except as the gas is piped into the tank the roof rises and the sides extend up, much like a folding water cup or telescope. These were, and still are, very common but have the disadvantage of the water-sealed holders: size. Liquefied-gas holders clearly have a cost, size, and weight advantage because of the 600-to-one ratio of gas to liquid.

The challenge in storing gas this way is that the storage temperature of liquid natural gas is about −260°F. Initially it seems that storage shouldn't be that much of a problem if one uses a double-walled, insulated container, much like a thermos bottle. This eventually turned out to be the greater of the two challenges. However, the first challenge is the conversion of the gas to a liquid, that is, gas liquefaction.

The liquefaction problem had been solved a few years before. It had taken scientists about 200 years to learn how to liquefy a gas, especially the so-called "permanent" gases such as oxygen, nitrogen, and methane. For that we look to the history of gas liquefaction in the next chapter.

4
Discovery of Gas Liquefaction

Science or what went as science in the centuries preceding the Renaissance of fourteenth century Europe, was dominated by the Aristotelian approach. In this approach one "philosophized" or speculated on a model of the natural world and then tried by reason and philosophy, not experiment, to deduce how the natural world worked using this model. Based on this approach, the natural world model was considered settled. For example, the four basic elements comprising the world were thought to be air, earth, water and fire. Few challenges were made to the model since the time of Aristotle (384–322 BC).

The Renaissance, as they say, changed everything including science, or, as it was known then, the study of natural philosophy. Settled views were no longer settled. Curiosity and doubt took over where there once had been certainty. In the late fifteenth and early sixteenth century, observers such as Copernicus started making their own measurements of natural phenomena. This is the acknowledged start of the Scientific Revolution. One characteristic of the Scientific Revolution was to experiment and then to induce general conclusions about how the world worked based on these experiments. Everything was fair game; all materials—solids, liquids, and gases—were subject to study and analysis. One now had to *measure* things to see how they worked rather than speculate on a model and declare it a description of the world. The work was almost all experimental; that is, the observer would try this or try that in order to learn how the world works. This revolution essentially ended the Aristotelian approach to natural philosophy and was the start of science as we know it today.

The scientific method flowed from the Renaissance and contributed significantly to the Enlightenment of the seventeenth and eighteenth centuries, and to the Industrial Revolution of the eighteenth and nineteenth centuries. The linking of science to the liberal ideas of the Enlightenment is covered by Timothy Ferris in his book *The Science of Liberty*.[1]

Matter

We recognize three states of matter: solids, liquids, and gases. Solids have a fixed shape, are not easily compressible, and do not flow. Gases and liquids, however, do have the property that they can flow easily, hence the name fluids; their particles can move past one another easily. This leads to the property that they assume the shape of their containers. Although both are fluids, liquids are not very compressible, whereas gases can be compressed easily. In liquids and solids the particles are close together, so they are often called condensed phases of matter.[2] Because they are condensed, liquids have a well-defined surface, whereas gases do not. Therefore gases will expand to fill a closed container or expand beyond the container if it is not closed. Figure 4-1 shows the relative bonding or separation of these three phases of matter.

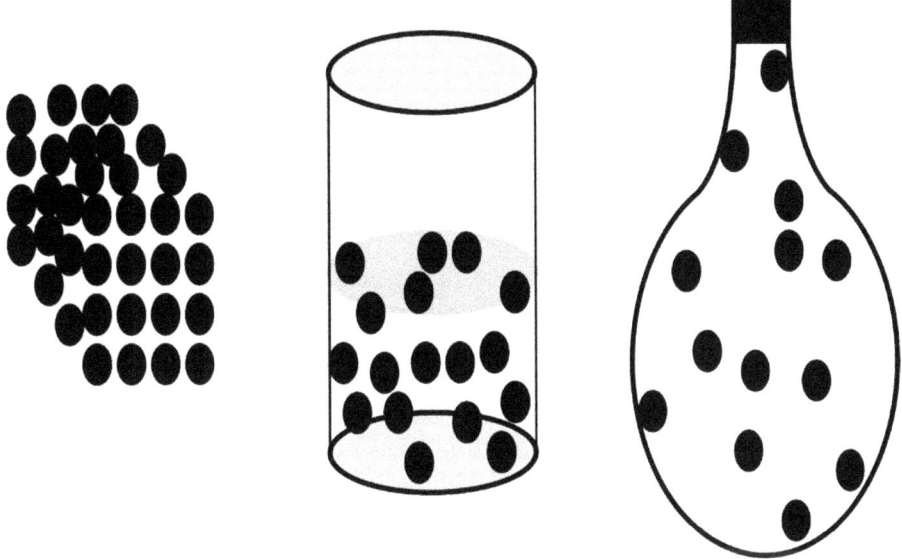

Figure 4-1. Three phases of matter: solid, liquid, and gas.

It turns out that gases can be liquefied; that is, they can be changed from a gas to a liquid. It is also possible to go one step further and solidify gases. The motivation for doing this the first time is not clear. However, it most likely came as a natural extension of the study of gases, which started early in the seventeenth century with the experiments of Jan Baptista van Helmont (1580–1644) and Robert Boyle (1627–1691).

By then the properties of many fluids, including water, water vapor, and steam, were well known, and probably were discussed well before the actual liquefaction of gases was started. It was probably the similarity of gases and liquids as fluids that sparked the curiosity to study the behavior of gases. It took the sophisticated development of gas laws, starting with Boyle, the kinetic theory of gases, thermodynamics, and especially the study of cold temperatures, to set the stage for the liquefaction of gases. In the early thinking about gas liquefaction, cold temperature and pressure were thought to be important to the process. This was well before the actual processes were developed.

Once the interest in the study of gases took hold, the subject was picked up by a number of curious scientists, not yet known by that term, and the work continued apace. (The term scientist was first proposed by William Whewell in 1834 and accepted by the OED by 1840.)[3] But still it took over 200 years of experimentation, until the late nineteenth century, before these gas liquefaction processes were developed and well understood. It was only in the twentieth century that gas liquefaction became commercially useful.

Early Gas Pressure and Temperature Experiments

The classical Greeks recognized air as one of the four basic elements along with earth, water and fire.[4] Although one could not see air, the effects could easily be seen and felt in the wind, in the breathing process, and in other effects, for example, erosion. Air is formless, taking up all the space around solid and liquid objects. It is a gas, a substance possessing perfect molecular mobility and the property of indefinite expansion, as contrasted to a solid or liquid. This property of a gas to assume the shape of any container, or being everywhere without a container, would seem to fit the description of the Greek word "chaos," which referred to the formless state preceding the creation of the universe.[5] So the behavior of air or other gases was linked to chaos.

The analogy to chaos led, in one story, to the word gas; *gas* being a neologism first used by the early seventeenth century Flemish chemist Jan Baptista van Helmont. The word appears to have been simply a phonetic transcription of the Greek word *khaos* (chaos)—the *g* in Dutch being pronounced like the Greek *kh*.[6] Van Helmont was one of the first persons to work with gas; he was the discoverer of coal gas. In one of his experiments he weighed, then burned, 62 pounds of coal, and then found the weight of the ashes to be one pound. He declared the difference to be "wild spirit or breath" that he called "geest," which was later to become "gaz," and then gas, thus leading to another possible derivation of the word gas.[7] Van Helmont was also the first to understand that there are gases that are distinct in kind from atmospheric air. Besides coal gas, he recognized that carbon dioxide, given off by burning charcoal, was similar to the gas emitted in the fermentation process, in wine fermentation for example. Van Helmont was also a medical doctor and did many experiments in biology and botany. He was a transitional figure, having one foot in the new science and the other in the Aristotelian world. For example, he still believed that air and water were primitive elements.[8]

During the seventeenth century others started experimenting with gases, and knowledge expanded rapidly. Evangelista Torricelli (1608–1647) was the first to experiment with the "weight of the air." A scientist and mathematician, he did an experiment in 1643 in which he filled a tube with mercury, held his thumb on the top, and inverted the top (and his thumb) into a dish of mercury. The mercury column immediately fell to 76 centimeters (cm). He had demonstrated the first barometer. He claimed the weight of the air on the mercury in the dish supported the column of mercury: "We live submerged at the bottom of an ocean of the element air that by unquestioned experiments is known to have weight."[9] The science, or natural philosophy, community of the time was not extensive. Many of the experimenters knew one another. Prior to this discovery in 1641 Torricelli had moved to Florence to study with Galileo.[10]

Robert Boyle (1627–1691) also had an interest in pneumatics (pertaining to air). Born into a wealthy family in Ireland, the fourteenth son of the first earl of Cork, he had the time and resources to experiment in the natural sciences. He was educated first at home and then, starting at age eight, at Eton College. He and his brother started traveling abroad in 1637; he returned to England in 1644 and settled in Stalbridge in Dorset. It was a difficult time for him because his family was split; his father was a Royalist and his sister was a Parliamentarian. His circle of friends included Galileo, whom he met in Florence in 1641–1642; he was in Florence when Galileo died in 1642. Undoubtedly he met Torricelli there also. This was also the time he started to study mathematics. Although he was a member of the Church of England, he was sympathetic to Galileo because of Galileo's treatment by the Roman Catholic Church. His study of Galileo's works may have been the start of his interest in science. When he returned to London he frequently met with friends who discussed scientific issues. This "invisible college" eventually became the Royal Society, chartered by Charles II in 1662. Boyle moved to Oxford in 1654, although he did not hold any university post. However, this is when most of his scientific work was done. His extensive experiments and writings took place in tumultuous times, including such events as the English Civil War, 1642–1646, and the beheading of King Charles I in 1649.[11] See the Gas Liquefaction Timeline, table 4-2, at the end of the chapter to help put Boyle's work in the context of the times and the context of the Scientific Revolution.

Boyle started collaborating with Robert Hooke (1635–1703), who was well known for his own discoveries in mechanical systems. His most well-known one is that the deformation of a material (steel, for example) is directly proportional to the force causing the deformation. In 1655 Boyle commissioned Hooke to construct an air pump along the lines of the Otto von Guericke (1602–1686) air pump, developed a few years earlier. In 1650 Von Guericke had developed an air pump, or vacuum pump, that could be used to pump air into or out of a glass vessel, that is, to evacuate it. In using it to evacuate the vessel he had directly challenged the adage, around since Aristotle, that "nature abhors a vacuum." Von Guericke used his vacuum pump in 1654 to evacuate a metal sphere (about 50 centimeters in diameter) composed of two hemispheres. They were called the Magdeburg hemispheres after his home town in Lower Saxony. In this way he demonstrated that the air pressure holding them together, the force of a vacuum or the weight of the air, was strong enough that teams of horses could not pull them apart.[12] This phenomenon, "the weight of the air," would be used years later in the Newcomen steam engine.

In 1659 Boyle and Hooke improved the Hooke air pump. The Boyle-Hooke pump was constructed out of a spherical glass container, a piston and cylinder that were hand cranked by a rack and pinion. This pump allowed a person to pump air out of the glass container. This pump allowed them to experiment with air pressure, vacuum, and other aspects of pneumatics. Boyle then began a series of experiments on the properties of air, including its role in combustion and respiration. These properties were covered in his first publication, *New Experiments Physico-Mechanicall, Touching the Spring of Air, and its Effects (1660)*.[13] In the experiments described in the book, Boyle first likened the "springiness" of air to that of a fleece of wool. The fleece can be compressed easily but immediately springs back when the pressure is released.[14]

Using this air pump Robert Boyle was the first to recognize the inverse relationship between the pressure on a gas and its volume (1662). This became the well-known Boyle's Law, which can be stated simply as[15]:

$$p_1 V_1 = p_2 V_2 = \text{constant}$$

In other words, the pressure p times the volume V of gas in a closed container remains constant even if you change one or the other; if the pressure goes up the volume goes down and vice versa. (In the metric system of units pressure is in pascals [Pa], volume is in cubic meters [m³], and the constant is in joules [J]. Another unit of pressure that will be used is an atmosphere [atm], which is the air pressure we feel at sea level because of the weight of the air in the atmosphere. See table 4-3 on units.)

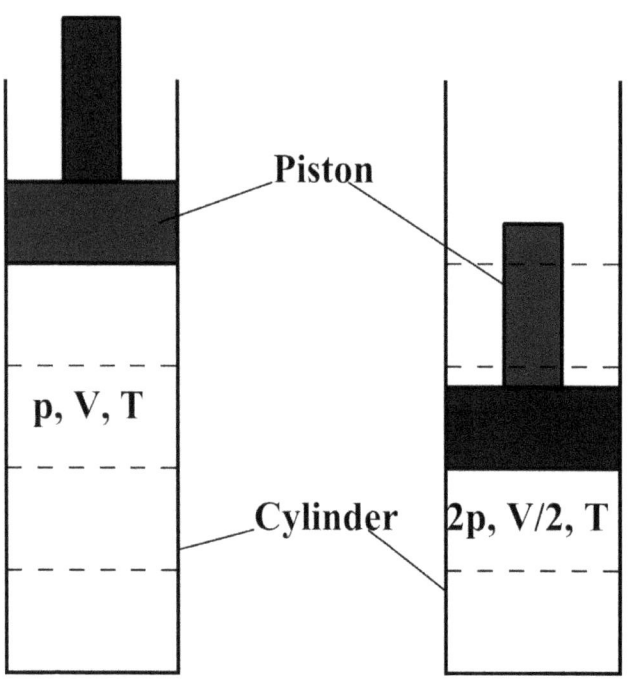

Figure 4-2. Boyle-Hooke air pump demonstrating Boyles's Law.

For example, if one changes the pressure p of a volume V of gas from p to $2p$, the volume will change from V to $V/2$, all at a constant temperature. This is shown figure 4-2. The system on the left is at one unit of pressure and four units of volume, so the constant is four units. On the right the pressure has been increased to two units. By Boyle's Law, then, the volume is reduced one-half as shown, so the product of pressure and volume remains constant at four units. Note this has been done isothermally, that is, at a constant temperature T. This inverse relationship will hold for any ideal gas for all pressures and volumes, and comes close for a real gas except at low temperatures or high pressures. It can be expressed in the pressure-volume (p-V) diagram of figure 4-3. As the pressure increases the volume decreases. The lines of constant temperature (T_1, T_2) are defined as isotherms. For Boyle's Law to hold, the temperature must be held constant, that is, one must move along an isotherm. This means that heat must be added or removed in the process to maintain the constant temperature, although this constraint is not intuitively obvious. The differences between real and ideal gases will be considered later in the chapter.

If Boyle's Law holds only

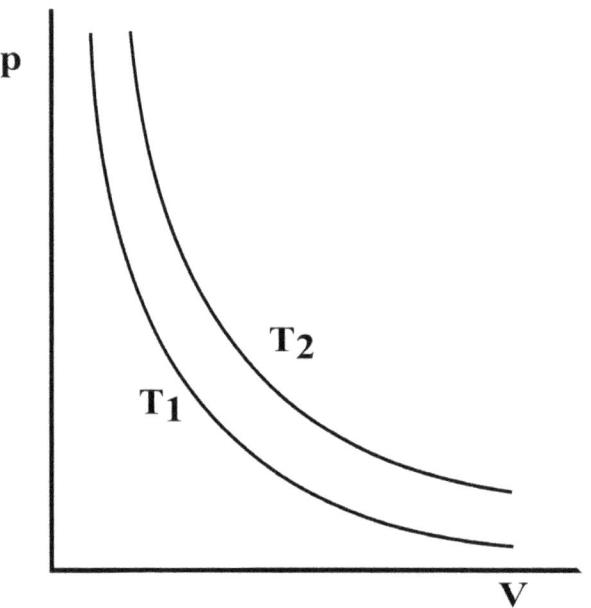

Figure 4-3. P-V diagram for Boyle's Law.

when the temperature is kept constant, what happens when the temperature is changed? One might logically ask, what is the relationship between gas pressure and temperature and/or between gas volume and temperature?

Guillaume Amontons (1663–1705), a French instrumenter and physicist, was one of the first to experiment with gas temperature. His instrumentation was crude so the results were more qualitative rather than quantitative. Nevertheless, around 1702 he discovered that the pressure of a fixed mass of gas, at a constant volume, increased in proportion to a temperature increase.[16] On the other hand, Joseph Louis Gay-Lussac (1778–1850) was, in 1802, the first to make an accurate measurement of the change in *volume,* at a constant pressure, with a change in temperature.[17] Jacques A. C. Charles (1746–1850) was credited with this work earlier, around 1780, but Gay-Lussac is now given credit for it. The Gay-Lussac Law shows a linear relationship with temperature and can therefore be stated as

$$V = V_o + k_o T$$

where V is the gas volume, V_o is the initial gas volume (a constant), T is the temperature in degrees Celsius (°C), and k_o is a constant. The experiment was originally done using the centigrade (now Celsius) temperature scale. The results showed an initial volume offset V_o when the temperature is zero degrees Celsius. This suggests a need for a different temperature scale, one that starts at zero degrees. This scale, the Kelvin scale, was developed later, in 1848, by William Thomson (1824–1907), Lord Kelvin. (His process in developing this scale is covered below.) The Kelvin scale is defined by the following:

$$T_K = T + 273.2$$

where T_K is the temperature in kelvins (K) and T is the temperature in degrees Celsius. This would redefine the Gay-Lussac formula as

$$V = kT_K$$

where T_K is the temperature in kelvins (K), and k is a constant but different from k_o.

The Kelvin scale is one in which one can define absolute zero as zero kelvin (K). Absolute zero is the temperature at which all kinetic motion of gas molecules ceases and the thermal energy of matter is zero. From the equation this would put absolute zero at −273.2°C. Clearly this would not hold as one approaches absolute zero, because volume would not go to zero. Instead the gas molecules would come closer together and the gas would become a liquid or solid. This is one instance where the ideal gases and real gases would not be equivalent. The laws of thermodynamics, developed later, preclude the achievement of absolute zero, although one can come very close.

The Boyle and Gay-Lussac experiments were on real gases but were in moderate temperature and pressure ranges where these simple laws hold. They had not yet pushed the gases to extreme conditions in which the change of state from gas to liquid would occur.

The work on the relationship of pressure, volume, and temperature started in the mid-seventeenth century with Boyle, continued to the late eighteenth century through the work of Charles, Gay-Lussac, and others, and eventually led to a general gas law for ideal gases. This law is derived by combining the Boyle and Gay-Lussac Laws.[18]

$$pV = nRT_K$$

where p is the pressure (Pa), V is the volume (m³), n is the number of moles of the gas, R is the gas constant (8.31 J·K⁻¹·mol⁻¹), and T_K is the absolute temperature (K). (A mole [mol] is a measure of the number of molecules in the gas volume.) It is important to note that although this holds quite well for real gases, it only holds exactly for ideal gases. The behavior of real gases can be related to the behavior of ideal gases through a compressibility factor, which is derived through experiment.[19] As one gets closer to liquefying real gases this ideal gas law equation no longer holds. It also does not hold as T_K approaches absolute zero. One can see in the equation, however, the pressure/volume relationship as defined by Boyle's Law, and the volume/temperature relationship as defined by Gay-Lussac's Law.

Kinetic Theory of Gases

The gas laws discussed have been observed by experimentation; that is, by working with the gases at a macroscopic level. However, there is eventually a need to explain the physical model that gives rise to this behavior. The explanation of the gas laws produced different physical models. In ancient times, matter was explained as consisting of tiny, invisible atoms in constant motion. This model was revived by Boyle in his experiments with gases. One of his postulates was that air is composed of elastic particles that repel each other like coiled pieces of wool or springs. This seems to be an evolution from his earlier model in which he likened a gas to a large, compressible fleece. The more contemporary model is that of a small elastic particle like a billiard ball, rather than pieces of wool or springs. These particles, or molecules as they later became known, took up only a very small fraction of the volume of a container; gas is mostly empty space. This accounts for the compressibility and low density of a gas. These molecules act like small elastic billiard balls moving at high velocity, bouncing off one another and the walls of the container. The forces of attraction of gas molecules are very small because they are so far apart. Thus they have no potential energy, only kinetic energy; the energy in a gas is therefore only due to kinetic energy. The molecules travel in a straight line until they impact the wall and transfer momentum. This is what accounts for the pressure in the container. The energy before and after a collision is the same, so energy is conserved.

In 1738 Daniel Bernoulli (1700–1782) was the first one to explain the pressure/volume relationship, Boyle's Law, from a molecular point of view. He envisioned a closed container of gas with a piston and weight on it compressing the gas. He described the inside of the cylinder:

> Let the cavity contain very minute corpuscles, which are driven hither and thither with a very rapid motion; so that these corpuscles, when they strike against the piston and sustain it by their repeated impacts, form an elastic fluid which will expand of itself if the weight is removed or diminished.[20]
>
> He derived Boyle's Law for gas pressure by computing the force exerted on a movable piston by the impacts of n particles moving with speed v, in a closed volume V. If V is smaller the pressure will be greater because the particles strike the piston more frequently. If the space occupied by the particles themselves is small compared to the volume V, the pressure should be inversely proportional to V; so, as stated, the product PV is constant.[21]

Using this model Bernoulli went on to show that the pressure of the gas is directly proportional to the kinetic energy of the gas molecules.[22]

We know the general gas law for ideal gases relates the product pV in direct proportion to absolute temperature T_K. Since the product pV can be derived as above from kinetic gas theory mechanics as a function of the kinetic energy of the gas molecules, "the energy of an ideal gas is proportional to the Kelvin temperature and depends on temperature only, independent of the pressure and of the volume."[23] If heat is added to the gas, the gas molecules move faster and the temperature increases; the reverse is true also. As the temperature increases, the product pV increases.

Thus one can derive the ideal gas law from the mechanics of the kinetic theory of gases based on the following assumptions:

- An ideal gas consists of rigid, elastic molecules.
- The molecules move with uniform linear motion between impacts.
- The molecules exert no force on one another except during impact.
- The average kinetic energy per molecule is proportional to the Kelvin temperature.[24]

The only difference between an ideal gas as described here and a real gas is that an ideal gas cannot be liquefied because all of the assumptions do not hold; for example, the molecules in a real gas exert attractive forces on one another especially at low temperatures, where they are closer to one another. Thus at low temperatures other equations come into play.

Although these kinetic theory equations do not hold at very low temperatures, one can do a thought experiment in which a gas container is lowered in temperature, thus slowing down the particles; that is, reducing the kinetic energy. As the temperature gets very cold these gas molecules slow down and coalesce at the bottom of the container, becoming closer and closer together, eventually interacting so the fluid becomes a liquid rather than a gas.

Thus the kinetic theory of gases can be used to imagine a bridge between the gaseous and liquid states.

Low Temperature Investigations

About the same time that Van Helmont was starting his experiments with gas, Francis Bacon (1561–1626) expressed curiosity about low temperature. In 1626 he started experimenting with how long a dead chicken might last if one stuffed it with snow. Bacon is credited with the whole concept of understanding the natural world by experimentation and induction of experimental results to general conclusions. Therefore, he is considered one of the founders of the Scientific Revolution; that is, he helped give it its philosophical underpinnings.

> In his works, Bacon saw himself as the inventor of a method which would bring to light the "secrets of the universe." This method involved the collection and interpretation of data, and carrying out experiments to learn the secrets of nature by organized observation. Bacon's method had a powerful influence on the development of science in seventeenth century Europe.[25]

Robert Boyle was born a year after Bacon died, and became an experimenter like Bacon, and because of Bacon. One of his most important works, *New Experiments and Observations Touching Cold,* covered many of the experiments he did on cold temperatures. He investigated the expansion of water as it freezes, and measured the expansive force of freezing water. Water is one of the few substances that expand when cooled from a liquid to a solid; most contract. This causes problems, such as when ice in road cracks causes damage to the roads when the ice expands. He experimented with freezing other liquids such as salt, spirits and various oils. He concluded that only substances that included water could be frozen; spirits and oils could not be. He considered freezing salt water as akin to distillation, that is, a way of separating pure water from the salt. As an experimenter a lot of his focus was on refuting Aristotelian theories.[26]

By the early eighteenth century absolute zero temperature became a topic of interest. Amontons's experiments led him to speculate that a sufficient reduction in temperature would lead to zero pressure, a clear violation of Boyle's Law. Although Amontons didn't realize it at the time, this was the deviation from ideal gases that would eventually lead to the liquefaction of gases; all molecular gas motion would cease and the molecules would condense to liquid or solid form as suggested by the kinetic theory of gases. He was one of the first researchers to discuss the possibility of absolute zero. His calculation put absolute zero at about −250°C.[27] The present value for absolute zero is −273.15°C.

Although absolute zero temperatures were discussed by Amontons, it was only in 1848 that William Thomson, later Lord Kelvin, defined an absolute thermometric temperature scale, discussed above. He was concerned that existing temperature scales were somewhat arbitrary and depended on the system and substance being used; that is, there was no absolute scale. He drew on the work of Nicholas Leonard Sadi Carnot (1796–1832), a pioneer in the field of thermodynamics, on his ideal steam engine. Carnot had shown that the work done in an ideal steam engine depended only on the original and final temperatures: the change in temperature. It did not depend on the particular substance (gas) used in the engine. Kelvin claimed,

> The relation between motive [mechanical] power and heat, as established by Carnot, is such that *quantities of heat,* and *intervals of temperature,* are involved as the sole elements in the expression for the amount of mechanical effect to be obtained through the agency of heat, and since we have independently, a definite system for the measurement of quantities of heat, we are thus furnished with a measure for intervals according to which absolute differences of temperature may be estimated [emphasis in the original].[28]

In other words, he wanted to relate a specific amount of heat to a specific temperature rise, independent of the type of thermometer used. He based his work on the experiments of colleagues who had used mechanical work to generate heat and then measured the corresponding temperature changes. The amount of heat used per temperature unit was independent of the substance used, according to the results of Carnot. Kelvin used the Celsius temperature interval as the unit. He then went on in a footnote to define an absolute zero temperature:

> That infinite cold must correspond to a finite number of degrees of the air-thermometer below zero; since if we push the strict principle of graduation, stated above, sufficiently, we should arrive at a point corresponding to a volume of air being reduced to nothing, which would be marked as −273° of the scale ... and therefore −273° of the air-thermometer is a point which cannot be reached at any finite temperature, however low.[29]

This led to the equation above that relates the absolute scale, Kelvin, to the Celsius scale.

With the pressure, temperature, and volume characteristics of gases now defined, and the properties of cold being explored, the stage was set for pushing the state of the art in the science of gases, that is, liquefaction.

Beginnings of Gas Liquefaction

In the late eighteenth and early nineteenth centuries interest in gas liquefaction increased. This probably was a result of the curiosity about the implications of the recent work of Charles, Gay-Lussac, and others on gas volume and temperature interactions, but more importantly, the continued desire to push the limits of the understanding of nature. The Scientific Revolution was now almost two hundred years old, and the scientific method was well understood. Some liquefaction examples had been known for a long time, for example, the condensation of steam into water when it came into contact with cooler air or a colder surface.

The first liquefaction of a gas besides steam is attributed to two French physicists: Gaspard Monge (1746–1818) and Jean Francois Clouet (1751–1801). Around 1783 or 1784 they liquefied sulphurous acid gas (H_2SO_3). Thomas Thomson, a lecturer on chemistry in Edinburgh, stated in 1803, "According to Clouet and Monge, when this gas, in a state of condensation, is exposed to the temperature of −18°, it is condensed into a liquid."[30] Another report by Frederick Accum of the Royal Institution in 1803 indicated that pressure was also necessary: "Monge and Clouet affirm that by extreme cold and a strong pressure exerted at the same time, they rendered sulphureous [sic] gas fluid."[31] These early efforts were of the, "look I can do it," variety, that is, qualitative efforts to see what could be done. The intense activity on liquefying gases started a few years later, early in the nineteenth century, and continued until air was finally liquefied just before the end of the century.

Michael Faraday (1791–1867) is credited with the early systematic efforts on gas liquefaction. He had an intense interest in science in general, and although he is better known for his work with electricity, he did work in certain periods of his life on gas liquefaction. He started in 1813 at the Royal Institution in London as an assistant of Sir Humphrey Davy (1778–1829), head of the Royal Institution. Early on he recognized the work of Monge and Clouet and was convinced that they had liquefied sulphurous acid gas (although he acknowledged he could not find the processes by which they did it). He also acknowledged that Thomas Northmore (n.d.) had liquefied chlorine in 1805–1806.[32] Faraday chose to work on chlorine. Perhaps this was because of his knowledge of Northmore's work or because Davy had suggested he do so: "Davy had considered chlorine to be *his* gas—he had been the first to show it was an element.... Davy was inordinately proud of chlorine."[33] It was well known that Davy didn't get along with Faraday and treated him poorly. He was said to be jealous of Faraday. There was speculation that he had encouraged Faraday to do a particularly dangerous experiment with potassium chlorate that resulted in an explosion. This resulted in many pieces of glass in Faraday's eye, which his wife had to remove.[34]

His first attempts to liquefy chlorine using heat only were unsuccessful. He tried a different tack in 1823 when he heated hydrate of chlorine in a sealed glass tube. At first, with a low temperature of 60°F, nothing happened. (Although the existing Celsius temperature scale was adopted in 1744, Faraday seems to have consistently used the Fahrenheit scale.) With a higher temperature of 100°F, chlorine gas was produced in the tube and eventually some liquid chlorine, a yellow oily liquid.[35] As will become clear later, this was because of the increased *pressure* obtained by heating the tube, not the temperature itself. Later he repeated the experiment using an L-shaped, sealed tube to heat a substance in one end to generate the gas and increase pressure while cooling the other end with ice, for example, to achieve a low temperature and liquefy the gas. The combination of high pressure and low temperatures was seen as the key to liquefaction. Figure 4-4 shows a sketch of the tube.[36]

Chlorine was the first gas Faraday liquefied. He did this in 1823 and presented it in a paper the same year. He went on to liquefy many other gases—sulphurous acid gas (H_2SO_3), carbonic acid (H_2CO_3), ammonia (NH_3), and others—in the same timeframe. (Carbonic acid is a weak acid formed by dissolving carbon dioxide [CO_2] in water. However, it is also an archaic name for carbon dioxide.) These results were presented in the same paper.[37] Faraday then took a break on investigating gases to work on other things, mostly electricity, for which he is better known. He returned to gases in the 1840s to work again on liquefaction.

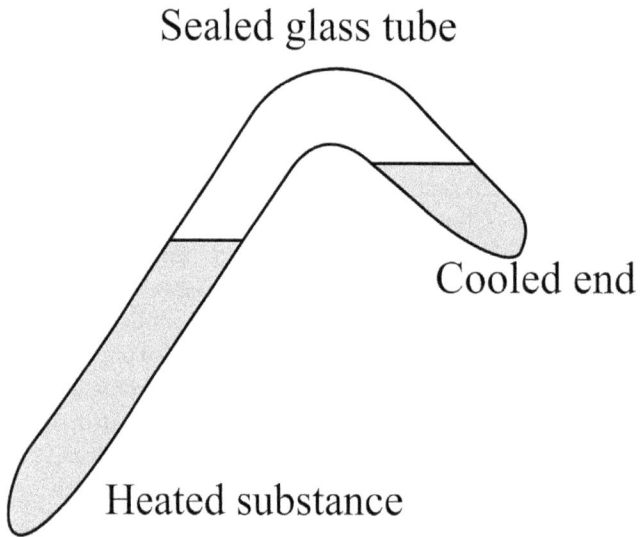

Figure 4-4. Liquefaction apparatus.

In 1824 A. A. B. Bussy (1794–1882) liquefied sulphurous acid gas without raising pressure but by just lowering temperature to around −20°C. The −20°C temperature can be reached by using a saltwater-and-ice mixture. This was a major change from the way it was done by Faraday, who used the L-shaped sealed tube described above to achieve the pressure and temperature necessary to liquefy sulphurous acid gas. At this point Bussy made a couple of critical observations. First, he observed that when the liquid sulphurous acid gas was allowed to evaporate in air, the temperature dropped to −57°C. Second, if the evaporation took place under reduced pressure, the temperature dropped to −65°C.[38] Vaporization from a liquid to a gas is a change of state. He had observed that heat is removed from the liquid, that is, the temperature drops, when this state change (liquid to gas) takes place, and that the effect is intensified under reduced pressure. This phenomenon was to be used extensively in the future to help liquefy gases.

Gas experiments continued throughout the century. Carbonic acid was liquefied on a much larger scale by Charles Thilorier (n.d.) in 1834, as much as two to three liters. He did this by chemically producing carbon dioxide in a closed pressure vessel, using baking soda, water, and sulphuric acid, and then using the pressure of the gas to liquefy it.[39] Under pressure carbon dioxide can be liquefied at room temperature. At the same time he took it farther and solidified carbonic acid (carbon dioxide), which is now known as dry ice. This became an important coolant for the next round of experiments. He further extended its coolant properties by moistening it with ether. This combination, known as Thilorier's Mixture, was able to produce very low temperatures, as low as −76.7°C.[40]

In 1844, about 20 years after his first round of experiments, Faraday began a second round. Apparently he was inspired by a couple of developments that he thought would help improve the liquefaction process. One was a promise of very low temperatures achievable by using Thilorier's Mixture. The other was a property of gases discovered by Charles Cagniard de la Tour (1777–1859) in 1822, prior to Faraday's first round of experiments. Cagniard de la Tour applied heat and pressure to various amounts of some volatile liquids (alcohol, naphtha, and ether). He found that *regardless of pressure* the substances could not exist in a liquid state above a certain temperature.[41] This was the "critical temperature" characterized in detail later by Thomas Andrews. Faraday saw this, correctly, as important to the process going in the opposite direction, that is, going from the gaseous to the liquid state. In other words it would be necessary to get the gas below its critical temperature in order for it to liquefy. He was anxious to try again to liquefy the "permanent" gases of oxygen, nitrogen, and others. (They were called "permanent" because it was thought they could not be liquefied.) He hoped to do this by the use of considerable pressure and very low temperature. At this time the relationship between temperature and pressure in the liquefaction process was still unknown.

To achieve this Faraday built a two-stage air pump with one inch and one-half inch diameter pistons. The first compressed the gas up to 20 atmospheres; the second to higher, but unspecified, pressures. He used Thilorier's mixture of solid carbonic acid (dry ice) and ether to achieve the low temperature for the gas he was trying to liquefy. He placed the mixture into a couple of earthenware bowls and insulated between the bowls to minimize heat conduction. The tubes of the compressed gas were immersed in this mixture. He further reduced the temperature of the coolant by using a vacuum pump to reduce the pressure above it to 1.2 inches of mercury (Hg) or 0.042 atmospheres. This had the effect of increasing its rate of evaporation. Since the Thilorier mixture was insulated, the heat of vaporization came from the mixture itself, thus lowering its temperature. This apparatus was able to lower the temperature of the coolant from about −106°F (−76.6°C) at ambient pressure to about −166°F (−110°C) at 0.042 atmospheres. He was using the effect observed by Bussy, that is, lowering the pressure above the coolant to reduce its temperature further.[42]

Although using these methods he was able to liquefy some gases (ethylene) and solidify others (ammonia and nitrous oxide), he was unable to liquefy the permanent gases, oxygen for example. He came closer than he thought. The critical temperature of oxygen is −118°C, which means that it can't be liquefied until it is brought below that temperature, no matter what the pressure. So the −110°C he achieved was not far off.

Thus a lot of progress was made in the first half of the nineteenth century. Many gases had been liquefied and some solidified by various combinations of pressure and temperature, although a systematic process model had not yet been defined. The experimenters still did not know the combinations of temperature and pressure that would liquefy the gases. Some gases, as Bussy had found with sulphurous acid gas, could be liquefied by just lowering the temperature without raising the pressure. Others, as Thilorier had found with carbon dioxide, could be liquefied with pressure alone. Faraday was right in observing that some combination of temperature and pressure would be necessary to liquefy the gases and to achieve the "holy grail," liquefaction of the permanent gases oxygen, nitrogen, methane, and others. All the properties of gases under temperature and pressure had yet to be identified. This came in the next few years with the work of Andrews, Joule, Thomson, and others. However, these properties had started to be identified in the previous century with the work of Joseph

Black (1728–1799) and Martin Van Marum (1750–1837). Let us now take a look at some of the critical properties, some of which have been already discussed.

Critical Constants and Changes in the Law

As they achieved the liquefaction of some of the easier gases at the end of the eighteenth century and beginning of the nineteenth century, the experimenters started to understand the phase change of gases; that is, changing the phase from a liquid to a gas or from a gas to a liquid. Liquefaction of a gas is nothing more than the change of phase of that gas from one state to another. In the early work they tried many different approaches to liquefy a gas, just to see if it could be done. Now the approach became more methodical. New laws and new constants were being discovered as they sought to define the boundaries of the processes quantitatively. It was becoming clear that other factors besides temperature and pressure were involved. Some of this work had started earlier.

CRITICAL CONSTANT: HEAT OF VAPORIZATION

One phenomenon that everyone has observed is evaporation. A pan of water left at room temperature will eventually totally evaporate. The process, called vaporization, is the conversion of a liquid to a gas. Ordinary evaporation is a surface phenomenon; some liquid molecules have enough kinetic energy to escape into the air above the surface. These form a vapor of that liquid just above the surface. To provide the kinetic energy for all the water to evaporate, heat must continually be supplied from the surroundings. In a static situation, at normal room temperature for example, the heat comes from the surrounding air. If more heat is added, for example from a stove, the vaporization takes place faster. Joseph Black had examined this process in the mid-eighteenth century in some detail through an extreme temperature range.[43]

In 1761 Black did some experiments in melting ice and boiling water. He found that when heat is added to an ice-water mixture, the mixture will maintain a constant 0°C temperature until *all* the ice is melted, and only then will added heat cause the temperature of the water to rise. He called the heat added to melt the ice (without raising the temperature of the mixture) the latent heat of fusion. It is expressed in calories per gram. (A calorie is the amount of heat needed to raise the temperature of one gram of water one degree Celsius.) Similarly, with water and steam, when heat is added to boiling water, the water remains at 100°C until *all* the water is turned to steam. This heat he called the latent heat of vaporization, or heat of vaporization, similarly expressed in calories per gram. When returning the gas to a liquid the same amount of heat has to be removed, but now it is called the heat of condensation. These constants are unique to the material, and Black measured them. Since evaporation is a phase change it requires the heat of vaporization be added to make the change. If the surroundings do not supply enough heat to do this, or the fluid is insulated from the surroundings, then the heat will come from the fluid itself and the fluid temperature will drop. This is what Bussy had experienced years later with his vaporization of sulphurous acid gas.

The pressure at which a liquid and its vapor can exist in equilibrium is called its vapor pressure at that temperature.[44] For an open pan of water at a room temperature of 25°C this pressure is 0.03 atmospheres, well below normal atmospheric pressure. Because this low vapor pressure is working against the much higher ambient pressure (one atmosphere), vaporization of the water will take a long time. Other liquids will evaporate faster at room temperature. Propane, for example, has a much higher vapor pressure, approximately eight atmospheres at room temperature; it is considered more volatile and evaporates faster. The boiling point of a liquid is that temperature at which the vapor pressure of the liquid is equal to the external pressure.[45] If the external pressure above a pan of water is one atmosphere, the boiling point of water is 100°C. By lowering the pressure above an evaporating liquid you lower the boiling point of the liquid; by raising it you raise the boiling point. If the pressure above this pan of water is lowered to 0.03 atmospheres, the water will boil at room temperature (25°C).

For gas liquefaction experiments this means that the heat of condensation has to be *removed* to change a gas to a liquid. Thus somehow the gas has to be cooled. Bussy liquefied sulphurous acid gas just by lowering its temperature to −20°C, that is, removing the heat of condensation. Conversely, Bussy observed that when he allowed the liquid sulphurous acid gas to evaporate in air, that is, to change back to a gas, the liquid temperature dropped. Since he did not add heat, it had to come from the liquid itself. Thus the liquid temperature dropped as the heat of condensation of the liquid was removed by evaporation. Bussy's experiments demonstrated that for some gases one just had to cool the gas sufficiently (remove the heat of condensation) to change it into a liquid at a constant pressure.

Critical Law Change: Boyle's Law Revisited

Other properties of gases were being discovered around the same time. For example, exceptions to Boyle's Law were found less than 40 years after it was formulated. As early as 1799 Van Marum found that some gases did not follow Boyle's Law. For example, ammonia and carbonic acid were found to be more compressible than air. Other experimenters followed with similar results. In the 1850s Henri Regnault (1810–1878) did some precise measurements and found that the ratio p_1V_1/p_2V_2, which should equal 1.000 for Boyle's Law, was, for most gases, slightly greater than 1.0. For example, for air at a p_1 of atmospheric pressure the ratio was 1.001414. It also changed with increasing pressure. This meant that for increasing pressure the p-V curve deviated inward from a perfect hyperbola, as show in figure 4-5.[46]

Experiments were done on oxygen

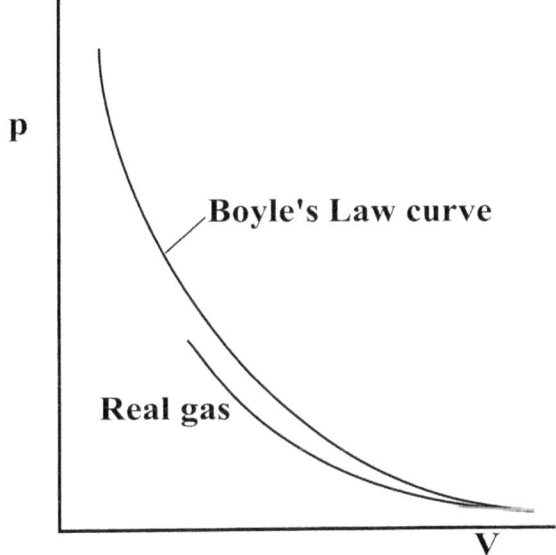

Figure 4-5. Deviation from Boyle's Law.

and nitrogen; they were put under high pressures. Although they did not liquefy, it was shown that under these pressures, some over 1,000 atmospheres, they deviated from Boyle's Law.[47] This was the first indication that Boyle's Law holds for ideal gases but not real gases under some conditions.

CRITICAL CONSTANTS: TEMPERATURE AND PRESSURE

By early in the century the concept of "critical temperature" had been discovered. Cagniard de la Tour and others had determined that there was a temperature above which no gas could be liquefied. Later in the century Thomas Andrews (1813–1885) did the definitive work establishing what happens to the p-V curves of a gas when the temperature is lowered sufficiently.

Thomas Andrews was born in Belfast and educated in Edinburgh. He was a professor at Queen's College in Belfast from 1849 to 1879.[48] He did a lot of work on the phase boundaries of gases. Through his experiments he confirmed (1863) the concept of critical temperature (T_c), showing that it is necessary, among other conditions, to cool a gas below this temperature if it is ever to be liquefied.[49] The pressure required to liquefy a gas at this temperature is the critical pressure (p_c). These critical values are different for all gases and explain why some elements are naturally gas and others naturally liquid. Chlorine gas has a critical temperature of 143.8°C, well above room temperature. Oxygen has a critical temperature of −118.6°C. It is easy to see that chlorine can be liquefied easily at room temperature with the application of pressure, but that low temperature is the key to liquefying oxygen (see figure 4-6).

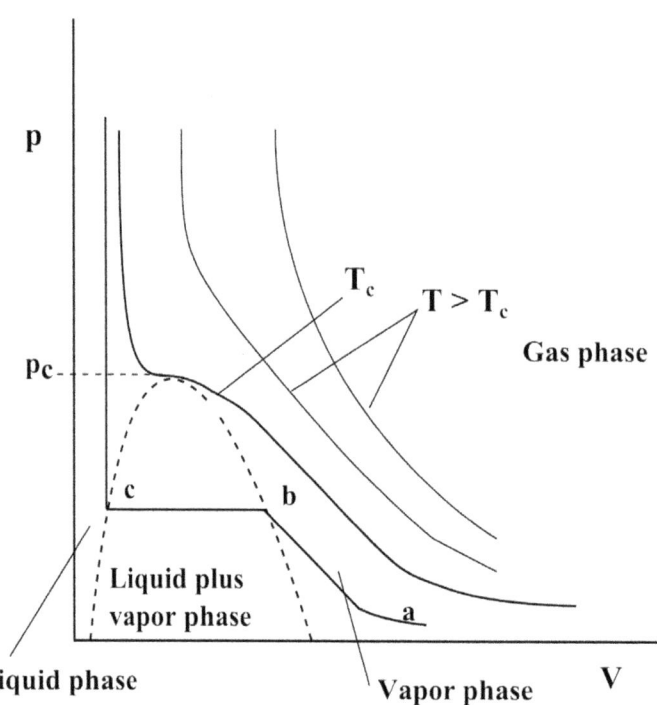

Figure 4-6, developed by Andrews through experimentation, shows the isotherms (lines of constant temperature) of a real gas near the critical temperature.[50] This figure is a close look at the lower left corner of figure 4-5, which shows Boyle's Law and the start of deviations from it. It represents a real breakthrough in understanding of the liquefaction process compared to the earlier laws and attempts. Even in the region above the critical temperature, the gas has deviated from Boyle's

Figure 4-6. Isotherms of a real gas.

Law, as described above and as discovered by Regnault. The critical temperature isotherm, shown as T_c, delineates the gaseous phase from the vapor phase, from the liquid plus vapor phase, and from the liquid phase. The liquid phase, in which the fluid is entirely liquid, is everything to the left of the dotted line parabola, and to the left of the isotherm T_c. (T_c touches the dotted parabola at p_c.) The gaseous phase is everything to the right of T_c. The vapor phase is to the right of the dotted line parabola and to the left of T_c. A vapor is defined as a gas below its critical temperature. It can be condensed to a liquid by pressure alone, while a gas cannot.[51] The area under the dotted line (all below the critical temperature) represents the liquid plus vapor phase, that is, the phase in which the gas is condensing into a liquid and both liquid and vapor can coexist.

Starting at high volume in the vapor phase, point a, and increasing the pressure (at a constant temperature) from a to b will cause the volume to decrease as in a gas, similar to but not exactly following Boyle's Law. At a particular pressure (b) the volume will continue to decrease while the pressure remains constant, from point b to point c. This is because the mixture is now partly liquid, which takes less volume than the vapor, and partly vapor. Molecular motion has decreased and the molecules are closer together in the liquid phase. When the volume becomes all liquid, point c, the curve goes almost straight up. This is because a liquid is essentially uncompressible. Thus in the figure everything to the left of the dotted line and T_c is a liquid. For any temperature below the critical temperature there is only one pressure at which the substance can exist in equilibrium as a liquid and vapor. This is called the vapor pressure for that liquid at that temperature.[52] This is the horizontal line from b to c. As one moves from b to c the gas is being condensed at a constant temperature so the heat of condensation is being removed. As an example, for water at a temperature of 100°C the line b–c is at one atmosphere. Point c is the boiling point of the liquid.

Table 4-1 shows the critical constants for a number of gases and liquids.

Table 4-1. Critical Constants

Substance	Critical Temperature °C (K)	Critical Pressure Atm (kPa)	Boiling Point °C (K)
Ammonia (NH_3)	132.4 (405.5)	111.3 (11,280)	−33.7 (239.5)
Carbon dioxide (CO_2)	32.0 (304.2)	72.8 (7,380)	−78 (195.2)
Chlorine (Cl_2)	143.8 (417.0)	76.0 (7,700)	−36.6 (236.6)
Ether	195 (468.2)	40 (4,052)	35 (308.2)
Ethylene (C_2H_4)	10.1 (283.3)	51 (5,166)	−102.5 (92.7)
Methane (CH_4)	−82.3 (190.8)	45.8 (4,640)	−164 (109.2)
Nitrous oxide (N_2O)	36.6 (309.6)	71.5 (7,245)	−88.5 (184.7)
Oxygen (O_2)	−118.6 (154.5)	49.8 (5,050)	−183.2 (90)
Propane (C_3H_8)	96.7 (369.9)	41.9 (4,249)	−41.7 (231.5)
Sulfur dioxide (SO_2)	157.6 (430.8)	77.7 (7880)	−10 (263.2)
Water (H_2O)	374 (647.2)	217.7 (22,053)	100 (373.2)

Note that a number of gases have critical temperatures above room temperature, such as ammonia and chlorine. It is possible to liquefy them at room temperature by simply raising the pressure; reducing temperature is not required. On the other hand, oxygen and methane require considerable precooling before they can be liquefied.

The discovery of these critical constants in the second half of the nineteenth century more fully characterized real gases instead of ideal gases. Andrews's work, especially, provided the information that indicated the conditions for liquefying a gas. Lowering the temperature below the critical temperature was the key. If this is done, extremely high pressures are not required. How to lower the temperature became the challenge.

Liquefaction of the Permanent Gases

The work of Andrews in characterizing the behavior of gases below the critical temperature gave rise to more attempts to liquefy the so-called permanent gases, oxygen, nitrogen, and methane for example. Although the critical temperature of methane is not quite as low as the other permanent gases it is considered one because its critical temperature is still very low (−82.3°C). Methane, of course, is the principal component gas of natural gas. Previous attempts to liquefy these gases with very high pressures were not successful because their low critical temperatures had not been reached. The importance of critical temperature was not fully realized until Andrews's work.

In December 1877 Louis-Paul Cailletet (1832–1913) liquefied oxygen in his lab. It was announced by him in a letter to the meeting of the French Academy in December 1877: "I have to tell you first, and without losing a moment, that I have just this day liquefied oxygen and carbon monoxide."[53] Within a few weeks, and independently, Raoul Pierre Pictet (1846–1929) also liquefied oxygen. Cailletet also liquefied nitric oxide and methane about the same time. Their approaches differed, and only a few weeks after Cailletet did it, Pictet did it using a more sophisticated method that showed progress in the art.[54]

Cailletet sealed the oxygen in a closed, thin glass tube. He pressurized the oxygen by using mercury at the bottom of the tube, which in turn was pressurized by water using a hydraulic pump. All this was enclosed in a metal container for safety. He surrounded the top of the tube (containing the oxygen) with a solution of liquid sulphurous acid gas to provide the cooling. The apparatus reached a pressure of 300 atmospheres, well above the critical pressure of oxygen at 49.8 atmospheres. The temperature of the gas was only −29°C, well above the critical temperature of −118.6°C. Therefore it could not be liquefied under these conditions. After a steady state was achieved he suddenly released the pressure, opening it to the atmos-

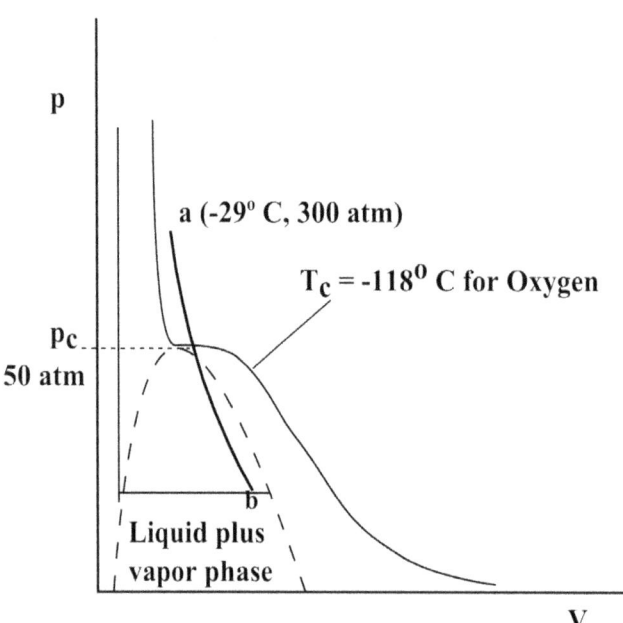

Figure 4-7. Cailletet *p-V* curves.

phere. A mist was formed in the tube, indicating he had liquefied some of the oxygen.[55] In this qualitative experiment the final pressure was atmospheric (one atmosphere), but temperature and volume were not recorded; they were not measureable. However, the sudden release of pressure was equivalent to dropping adiabatically from the steady-state point *a* in figure 4-7 to a point *b* below the critical temperature and pressure, that is, into the range where the liquid and vapor can exist in the same phase. The mist he observed was the liquid at point *b*.

Adiabatic means literally "not to be crossed" or "impassable" in Greek. Thermodynamically it means a process that occurs without gain or loss of heat, that is, without heat transfer. A process can be effectively made adiabatic by insulating it so no heat is transferred during the process or by doing it quickly, because heat transfer is a slow process. When a gas is compressed under adiabatic conditions, say very quickly, the work done on the gas increases the internal energy. We know that internal energy is a function of temperature only; therefore the temperature of the gases rises. It does not rise because of any heat transferred to it; we have precluded that by doing the process quickly. The temperature and pressure have risen *only* because of the work done on the gas, not because of any external heat input. Conversely, when a gas expands under adiabatic conditions, its pressure and temperature both decrease without the gain or loss of heat. It can be shown that an adiabatic expansion of an ideal gas can be described by

$$pV^\gamma = \text{constant}$$

where γ is a positive constant ranging from 1.2 to 1.6 for most gases. It is the ratio of heat capacities, which are discussed in Sears.[56] On a *p-V* diagram these curves are steeper than the isothermal *p-V* curves so they will cross the isothermal curves and the temperature will change during an adiabatic compression or expansion. This is shown in figure 4-8. The adiabatic compression-expansion curves are similar for both ideal and real gases because the temperature of either gas will change the same way during this process. The only difference is that an ideal gas will not liquefy.

Pictet's experiment, done only about three weeks later, was a little more elegant and precise. The apparatus is described in Hardin.[57] Pictet set up a cascade of cooling cylinders through which he ran two liquid gases. These were two separate cooling cycles with two sets of pumps; the first cooling one liquid, and then that liquid was used to cool the second liquid, which in turn was used to cool the oxygen (see figure 4-9).

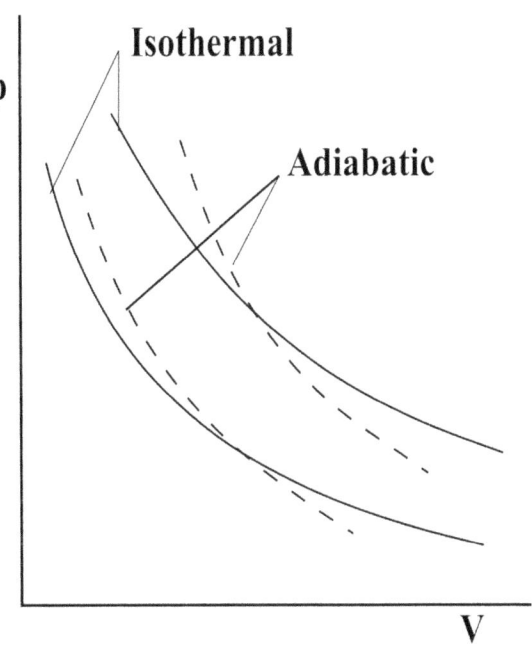

Figure 4-8. Isothermal and adiabatic *p-V* curves.

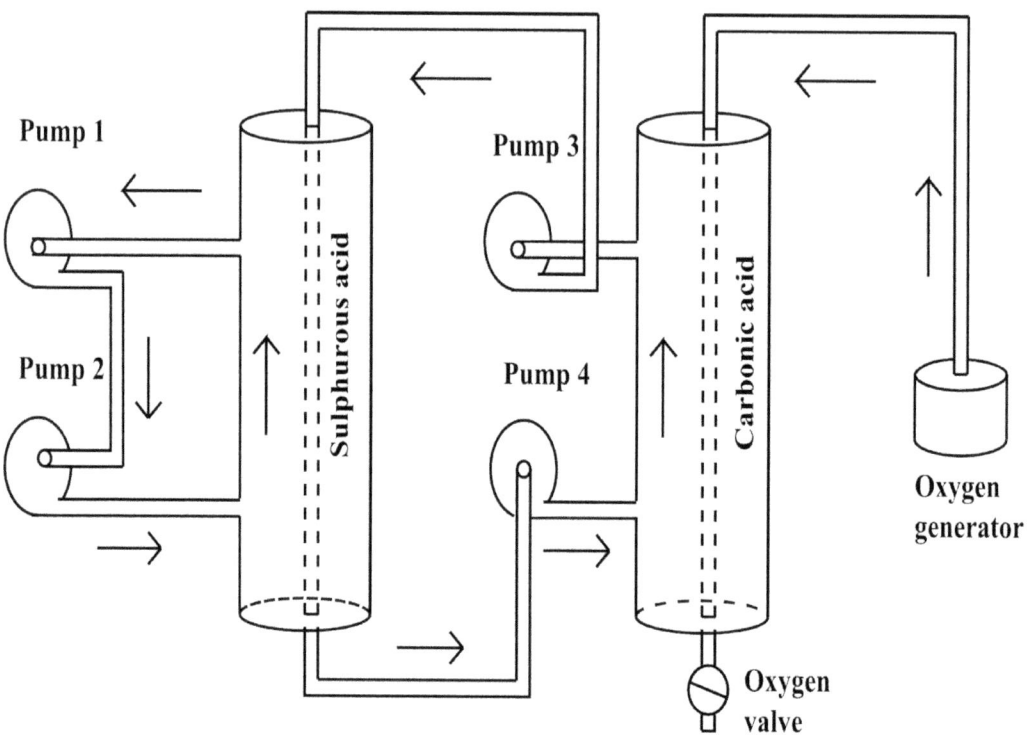

Figure 4-9. Pictet apparatus.

The first was liquid sulphurous acid gas, which reached a temperature of −65°C. Note that to reach −65°C, he used one pump (Pump 1) as a vacuum pump to reduce the vapor pressure above the liquid sulphurous acid gas just as Bussy had done several years earlier to get a lower evaporation temperature. Pictet used this liquid to cool carbon dioxide to make liquid carbon dioxide with which he achieved a cooling temperature range of from −120°C to −140°C. He records −130°C as the temperature of the coolant. Again, one pump (Pump 3) was used to reduce the vapor pressure above the evaporating carbon dioxide liquid/vapor mixture just as Faraday had done previously with the Thilorier mixture. There is an apparent paradox here. Normally at −130°C carbon dioxide would be solid dry ice, yet this fluid cycle was maintained. How? When Pictet started the flow of warm oxygen, the carbon dioxide temperature rose slightly to about −48°C. This clearly put it into the liquid/vapor phase. When he turned on the vacuum pump, the temperature immediately dropped to −130°C. The vapor pressure apparently achieved was near that achieved by Faraday, that is, in the 0.01 to 0.04 atmospheres pressure range. This is enough to keep the carbon dioxide a gas rather than a solid, a very cold gas, but a gas nevertheless. This can be seen in a carbon dioxide phase diagram.

This latter temperature range is below the critical temperature of oxygen (−118°C). Pictet ran a concentric tube through the cold carbon dioxide tube for the oxygen. He generated oxygen in the tube by using a mixture of potassium chlorate (700g) and potassium chloride (250g) at one end in a closed pressure vessel to which he applied heat to generate the oxygen. The other end of the oxygen tube was closed with a valve. As the oxygen was produced the pressure in the tube increased, peaking at about 529 atmospheres, and finally reaching steady state at 471 atmospheres. The pressure drop from 529 atmospheres to 471 atmospheres indicated that the oxygen had indeed condensed in the tube because liquid takes up less room in the tube and therefore the pressure is lower. The oxygen was in the liquid state as shown in figure 4-10. He allowed it to reach steady state at 470 atmospheres and −130°C.

Pictet then opened the regulating valve for the oxygen tube and liquid oxygen spewed out for a few seconds. As he relates, "A liquid jet ensues with great violence, and assumes the appearance of a brilliant white pencil. A bluish halo surrounds the jet,

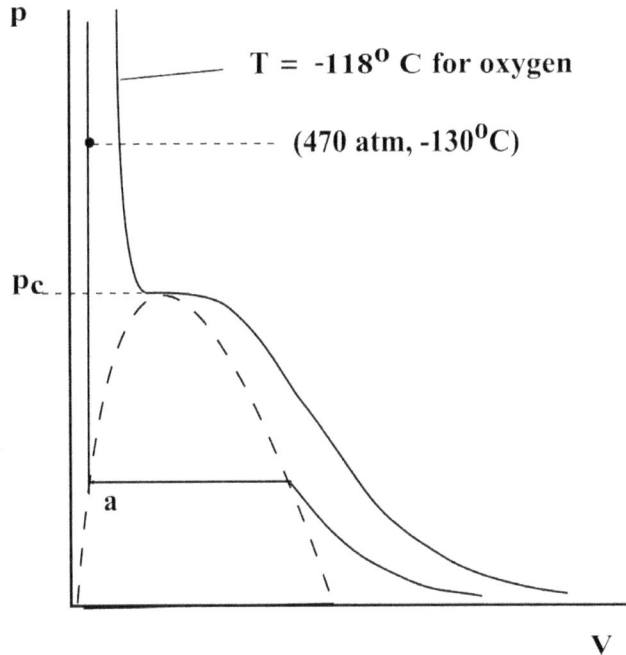

Figure 4-10. Pictet p-V curves for oxygen.

especially the lower part. The jet of liquid is from 10 to 12 cm. in length, and about 1.2 to 2 cm. in diameter. It continues for a period of 3 or 4 seconds."[58] He closed the valve and then repeated this at a lower pressure. Note that in the first test the jet of liquid (lasting three or four seconds) dropped the pressure of the liquid oxygen down from 470 atmospheres to the boiling point (a in figure 4-10) and quickly boiled off into the atmosphere as the latent heat of vaporization from the atmosphere was added to the jet of liquid. The boiling point of oxygen at atmospheric pressure is −183°C. When he repeated it a second time, a few minutes later, the tube was only partially filled with liquid oxygen. When he opened the valve the remaining liquid spewed out as in the first test, but then only gaseous oxygen was released.

Pictet clearly liquefied a significant amount of oxygen, compared to the amount liquefied by Cailletet just a few weeks earlier. These methods, however, were still dependent on transient phenomena: a sudden release of pressure that dropped the gas into the liquid/vapor phase. They could not produce liquid oxygen in a steady-state process. Nevertheless, one "permanent" gas had been liquefied, which was a major accomplishment. Pictet went on to liquefy hydrogen in 1878, using a similar method that depended on the transient reduction of pressure.

Following Pictet's success, other experimenters (Wroblewski [1845–1888], Olszewski [1846–1915], Dewar [1842–1923], and others) continued to devise more sophisticated apparatuses for making larger quantities of liquid gases and measuring the properties.

One important advance was by Olszewski and Wrobleski in 1883. It was the liquefaction of oxygen in a steady state; it did not depend on the transient release of pressure. They achieved this by using a cascade cooling process similar to that used by Pictet. They first cooled ethylene in a freezing mixture, not described, but probably ice or a saltwater-ice mixture. The cooled ethylene was then cooled further by using the dry ice–ether Thilorier mixture that had been used by Faraday previously. The further-cooled ethylene was then used to surround the oxygen. It was evaporated by a vacuum pump as had been done previously by Pictet, which of course cooled the ethylene much further. They achieved a temperature of −130°C, which is below the critical temperature of oxygen. In this manner they were able to liquefy oxygen in a steady state. In essence they used the method Faraday had used in 1845 but were able to get 20°C lower in temperature, which was enough to make the difference so they could liquefy the oxygen. They observed the liquid oxygen to be a colorless liquid with a well-defined meniscus. Later, in 1886, Olszewski liquefied methane and measured its boiling point and density. Methane, of course is the major constituent of natural gas.[59]

Regenerative Cooling for Liquefaction

In 1852 James Joule (1818–1889) and William Thomson did some experiments on the flow of gas (air and other gases) through a tube containing an obstruction to impede the flow of the gas. They used a hand pump upstream to maintain a pressure of two to three atmospheres. Downstream of the obstruction, the pressure was atmospheric. They used various materials such as leather, cotton, and silk as the porous plug between the high upstream pressure and the low downstream pressure. A simple orifice can be used also. The work was a follow-up to work Joule had done in 1845 on the free expansion of gas. They were trying to determine if the pressure drop across the orifice also resulted in a temperature change. Under their carefully controlled temperature conditions, it was an adiabatic expansion; they *did* discover a temperature drop as the fluid passed through the porous plug or orifice. This effect has come to be known as the Joule-Thomson effect, also called a throttling process.[60]

Figure 4-11 shows the gas flow through the pipe with the orifice. The mass of gas ahead of the orifice at p_1, V_1, T_1, is the same mass after the orifice at p_2, V_2, T_2, but the downstream pressure, p_2, is lower. Joule and Thompson had measured the change in temperature as a function of the pressure: $(T_2 - T_1) / (p_2 - p_1)$. This ratio is called the Joule-Thomson, J-T, coefficient.[61] If this coefficient is positive the gas cools on expansion; if negative it warms. For most gases and temperatures it is positive, so most gases cool on expansion. Thus gases throttled through an orifice can be cooled significantly. For example, for air at 300°K (27°C), the J-T coefficient is about 0.2. For a change of pressure from 200 atmospheres to 20 atmospheres the temperature drop is 36°C after passing through the orifice. (Although Joule and Thomson did measure $[T_2 - T_1] / [p_2 - p_1]$, the use in this example with the J-T coefficient is approximate.) Physically what happens is that as they pass through the orifice, the molecules get farther apart and the kinetic energy decreases. This results in a decrease in temperature.

What if one could repeat this, that is, pressurize the air and cool it again over and over by sending it through the same orifice? In the late nineteenth century Carl von Linde (1842–1934) devised a regenerative process based on the Joule-Thomson effect that would continue to maintain an upstream pressure while operating on increasingly cooler air. By running the cold air that had passed through the orifice through a concentric tube around

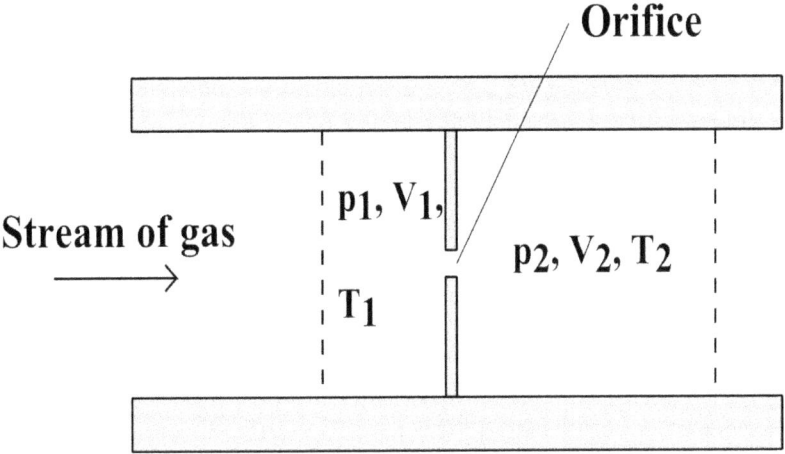

Figure 4-11. Joule-Thomson effect.

the pressurized air prior to the orifice, he "regenerated" the cooling effect. The circulated air eventually was cooled to the point where it became a liquid. As stated previously, the temperature drop associated with an adiabatic expansion will occur for both real and ideal gases; however, only a real gas will liquefy. He achieved the liquefaction of air in 1894. Following that he was able to devise a process to separate liquid oxygen and liquid nitrogen. It was now possible to generate large quantities of liquid air, oxygen, and nitrogen for refrigeration and scientific research.[62]

Figure 4-12 is a simplified diagram of a Linde machine in which air leaves the compressor A at high temperature and pressure (B). It is cooled (to remove the heat of compression) in C by water but is still at high pressure. It passes through the countercurrent cooler G, which contains cold gas, and then through the orifice or nozzle (E) where it is throttled (Joule-Thomson effect) and thus cooled and reduced in pressure. The compressor A keeps a low pressure in the path H from the liquid container to the compressor. This continuous process regenerates itself until the air becomes cold enough upon expansion at E that it liquefies. The liquid F can then be drawn off.[63]

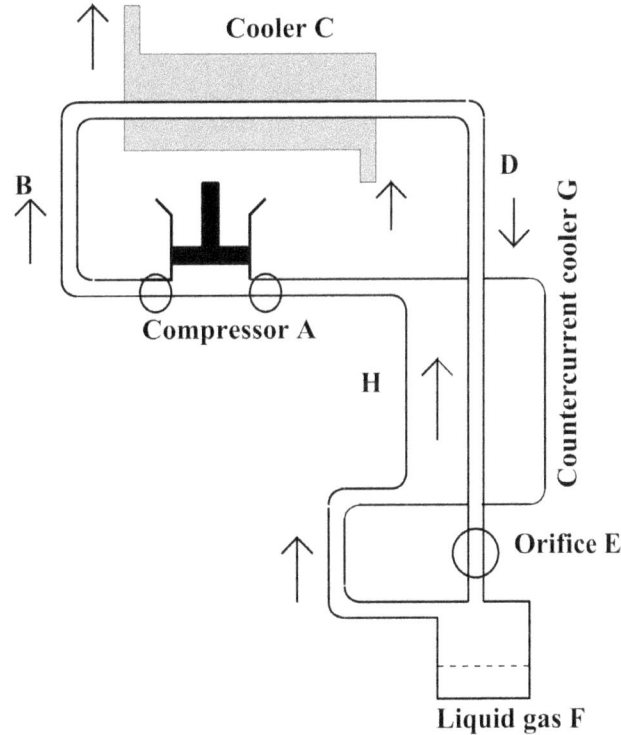

Figure 4-12. Linde process (courtesy Linde Group).

The Linde process, while simple, has a low efficiency and requires a high pressure. The low efficiency is due to the fact that no work is recovered during the adiabatic expansion. As an example, a system might require a pressure of 200 atmospheres and yield an efficiency of ten percent. However, it does not require the cascaded pre-coolers that previous processes used. The high working pressure requires high power and robust equipment.

In 1902 the French engineer Georges Claude (1870–1960) came up with a competing method that used some of the energy of the compressed gas to do work by expanding against a piston.[64] This removed energy from the gas stream and lowered the temperature further. This was used in a loop to further cool the gas, which resulted in a more efficient system. Apparently Claude implemented the work suggested years earlier by the French chemist J. Armengaud. He was the one who proposed the expansion of air, like steam in an engine, doing work. Claude was trying to produce cold, not power.[65] The Claude process can use a lower pressure, for example 40 atmospheres instead of 200. It also results in a higher yield, in one example twice as much liquid gas. The Claude process uses both the Joule-Thomson effect (used by Linde) and isentropic expansion into the cylinder to move the piston.[66] Isentropic means having constant entropy (see any chemical thermodynamics textbook).

Figures 4-13 shows the Claude processes. The fresh gas intake near the compressor is not shown. The cooler after the compressor uses water and is used to remove the heat of compression. The countercurrent heat exchanger is not physically as shown, but is concentric tubing in which the inner tube going to the expansion valve is inside the tube leading back to the compressor. The Lindes used over 100 meters of tube to assure sufficient regenerative cooling. The Claude machine shown is similar to the Linde machine in that it also uses Joule-Thomson expansion through an expansion valve. However, additional cooling is achieved by having some of the gas do work by expanding into the piston. The input to the piston expansion is tapped just after the cooler. About 80 percent of the gas is diverted to the piston; the remaining 20 percent goes through to the expansion valve.[67] The gas cooled by doing work in the piston is fed back to the countercurrent heat exchanger and goes back for recycling

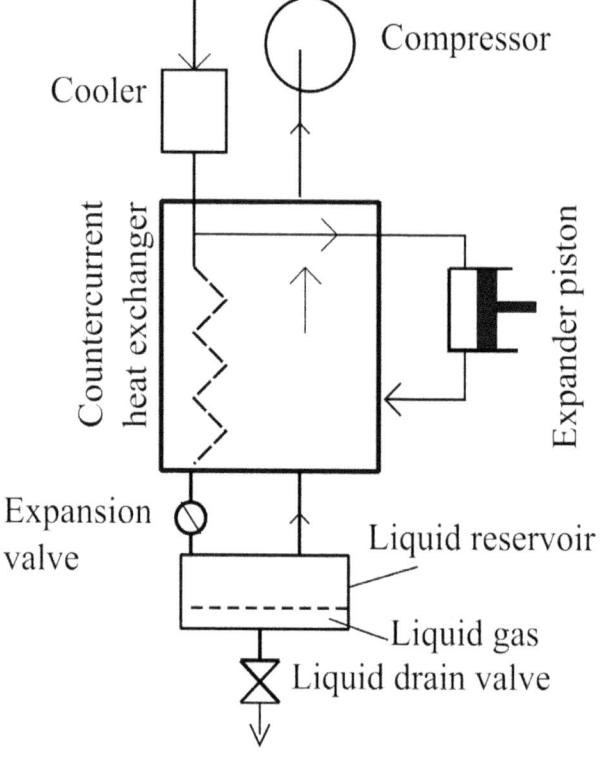

Figure 4-13. Claude process.

through the compressor. Although work can be done by the piston, the object here is to use the cold produced by the removal of the kinetic energy of the gas. It is an extension of a Linde machine with the piston tapped about point D in figure 4-12 and exhausting back into the countercurrent cooler G.

Summary

Experimentation with gases started in the seventeenth century with the fundamental gas laws formulated by Robert Boyle. An ideal gas that follows Boyle's Law has an inverse relation between pressure and volume at a constant temperature. This defines a hyperbolic p-V curve for any value of temperature, as shown in figure 4-3. However, it gives no hint of how to liquefy a gas, if they even thought about that at the time. Interest in the other gas variable, temperature, especially low temperature, started even earlier, in the sixteenth century with Francis Bacon's experiments. Guillaume Amontons in the early eighteenth century did the initial research on gases and temperature, and he found that gas pressure, at a constant volume, increased when its temperature increased. Gay-Lussac is credited with finding the relationship between gas volume and temperature in 1802. When the Boyle and Gay-Lussac Laws were combined, in the middle of the nineteenth century, to form the universal gas law, the behavior of gases (at least ideal gases) was fairly well defined.

Although these gas laws were originally derived experimentally on real gases, they only hold for real gases in a moderate pressure, temperature, and volume range. They are gas laws for ideal gases. There is no suggestion through these of how to liquefy a gas. Liquefaction only becomes possible when one drives down into the lower left corner of the p-V diagram, especially when the temperature is driven down. When this is done the extreme non-linearity of the p-V curves becomes apparent, and the ideal gas equations do not hold (see figure 4-6). In other words, liquefaction of a gas can only be done on a real gas, not an ideal gas.

The idea to look into the region of low temperature probably was suggested by considering the properties of steam, which had been known for a long time. It was known, for example, that steam would condense when it was cooled or was in contact with a cool surface. Whatever the reason, the experimenters between the late eighteenth century and mid–nineteenth century subjected gases to various combinations of temperature and pressure in an attempt to liquefy them. It was generally thought that low temperature and high pressure were necessary to liquefy gases. There were some successes for some of the easier gases to liquefy (chlorine and ammonia, for example). It was hit and miss at first as they experimented with different temperatures and pressures. The data was not available to suggest a process to liquefy gases. There was no early understanding of what was going on down in that lower p-V-T region. There was no success with the "holy grail" of liquefying the "permanent" gases such as oxygen and nitrogen.

All this changed in the mid-nineteenth century when Thomas Andrews published his results on critical constants. He expanded on the work of Charles Cagniard de la Tour, who had discovered the critical temperature of a gas. The critical temperature (T_c) is the temperature above which a gas can never be liquefied regardless of pressure. Andrews collected the data that defines the conditions for gas liquefaction, shown in figure 4-6. The variable T_c turned out to be the critical parameter. It was now possible to see clearly the roles temperature and pressure play in the liquefaction of gases. Extremely high pressures were no longer necessary. One way or another the gas must be dropped below its critical temperature (T_c) for it to be able to liquefy. Achieving the low temperature became the goal.

Various experimenters (Faraday, Cailletet, Pictet, Wroblewski, and Olszewski) used elaborate methods to achieve these cold temperatures and try to liquefy oxygen. Faraday just missed it, but the others were successful. The "permanent gases" had now been liquefied, but only in small amounts.

Another discovery made in 1852 by James Joule and William Thomson made an important contribution to making liquefaction more practical. Their discovery was that if an orifice, an obstruction, is placed in a continuous stream of gas, the pressure drop across the orifice will be accompanied by a temperature drop of the gas. This Joule-Thomson effect could now be used to lower the gas temperature. Toward the end of the nineteenth century Carl von Linde used this effect in a regenerative manner to make liquid air in a continuous process. In 1902 Georges Claude developed a competing process to the Linde process that was more efficient for liquefying gases, although it was slightly more complex.

By the end of the nineteenth century the processes for the liquefaction of gases, including the so-called "permanent" gases, were well known. All known gases except helium had been liquefied. Helium was eventually liquefied in 1908 by the Dutch physicist Heike Kamerlingh Onnes (1853–1926).[68]

In the latter half of the nineteenth century refrigeration machines were built that would make ice.[69] With the advent of these refrigeration machines and the ability to liquefy large quantities of air or other gases, the stage was set to take advantage of these processes in the twentieth century.

Table 4-2. Gas Liquefaction Timeline

1543	Copernicus publishes *Revolutionibus Orbium Coelestium* (On the Revolutions of Celestial Bodies). Start of the Scientific Revolution.
c1609	J. B. van Helmont discovers a gas, other than air, by burning coal and measuring the mass before and after. He coins the term *gas*, probably derived from the Greek word *chaos*.
1626	Francis Bacon starts experimenting with cold temperatures to preserve dead animals.
1642–1646	English Civil War
1650	Otto von Guericke invents the air pump, or vacuum pump, which can be used to evacuate a vessel.
1654	Von Guericke demonstrates the "weight of the air" with the Magdeburg hemispheres.
1655	Boyle employs Robert Hooke to construct an air pump.
1659	Hooke and Boyle improve the Von Guericke air pump.
1660	Hooke discovers his law of elasticity, in which the stretch (deformation) of a body, wood or metal, is proportional to the force applied to it.
1660	Boyle publishes "New Experiments Physico-Mechanicall, Touching the Spring of Air, and Its Effects."
1662	Using the Hooke-Boyle air pump, Boyle's Law is formulated: $pV = $ constant.

4. Discovery of Gas Liquefaction

1662	Royal Society is formed.
1665	Boyle publishes "New Experiments and Observations Touching Cold." He is one of the first to discuss an absolute minimum temperature, i.e., absolute zero.
1702	Guillaume Amontons discovers that the pressure of a fixed mass of gas, at constant volume, increases in proportion to temperature. He also speculates that a sufficient reduction in temperature will lead to zero pressure.
1709	Daniel Gabriel Fahrenheit constructs an alcohol thermometer. In 1714 he constructs a mercury-in-glass thermometer.
1742	Anders Celsius creates an inverted centigrade, or Celsius, temperature scale, in which 100 represents the freezing point of water.
1744	Carl Linnaeus inverts the scale to the present Celsius scale, in which 100 is the boiling point of water.
1761	Joseph Black discovers the heat of fusion and the heat of vaporization of water and steam.
c. 1780	Jacques A. C. Charles does work measuring the change in gas volume, at a constant pressure, with a change in temperature.
c. 1783–4	Gaspard Monge and Jean Francois Clouet achieve the first liquefaction of gas when they liquefy sulphurous acid gas (H_2SO_3).
1799	Martin van Marum finds that some gases deviate from Boyle's Law under significant pressure. More precise measurements in the 1850s by Henri-Viktor Regnault confirm this.
1802	Joseph Louis Gay-Lussac formulates the law that carries his name, i.e., the change in volume of a gas, at constant pressure, with a change in temperature: $V = V_0 + kT$. This builds on the work of Charles.
1834	Emile Claperyon formulates the ideal gas law as a combination of Boyle's Law and Charles's (Gay-Lussac) law: $pV = nRT_k$.
1813	Michael Faraday joins the Royal Institution as Sir Humphrey Davy's assistant.
1822	Charles Cagniard de la Tour experiments and finds that certain volatile liquids cannot exist in a liquid state, despite the application of heat and pressure, above a certain critical temperature.
1823	Michael Faraday liquefies chlorine for the first time. He goes on to liquefy sulphurous acid gas, carbon dioxide, and ammonia.
1824	A. A. B. Bussy liquefies sulphurous acid gas just by lowering the temperature to −20°C without raising pressure.
1834	Charles Thilorier liquefies carbon dioxide at room temperature just by using pressure. Later he solidifies it (dry ice).
1844	Michael Faraday, using new techniques, is able to liquefy more gases (e.g., ethylene) and solidify others (ammonia, nitrous oxide), but still cannot liquefy oxygen or nitrogen.
1848	Lord Kelvin (William Thomson) establishes the Kelvin thermometric scale in his paper "On an Absolute Thermometric Scale."
1852	James Joule and William Thomson discover the throttling process, or Joule-Thomson effect, by which a gas throttled through an orifice decreases in temperature.

1863	Thomas Andrews confirms the concept of critical temperature (T_c) first discovered by Cagniard de la Tour in 1822. He then characterizes the behavior of gases in the liquid, liquid-plus-vapor, and vapor phases. This is the breakthrough for understanding gas liquefaction.
December 1877	Louis-Paul Cailletet liquefies oxygen for the first time.
December 1877	Raoul Pierre Pictet liquefies oxygen only days or weeks after Cailletet, independently, using a different method.
1883	Zygmunt Wroblewski and Karol Olszewski liquefy oxygen in a steady state, that is, without depending on a transient expansion of the gas to liquefy as the Cailletet and Pictet experiments did.
1886	Olszewski liquefies methane and measures its boiling point and density. (Methane is the major constituent of natural gas.)
1895	Carl von Linde liquefies air in large quantities, continuously, using the Joule-Thomson effect in a regenerative manner.
1908	Heike Kamerlingh Onnes liquefies helium, the last of the gases to be liquefied.

Table 4-3. Units

Mass kilogram (kg)	1 kg = 1,000 g = 2.2046 lbm (pound-mass) 1 lbm = 0.45359 kg
Length meter (m)	1 m = 3.28084 ft 1 ft = 0.3048 m
Volume meter cubed (m^3)	1 m^3 = 35.3147 ft^3 = 264.17 gal 1 ft^3 = 2.83169 × 10^{-2} m^3 = 7.8045 gal 1 Mcf = 1,000 cubic feet (ft^3) 1 MMcf = 1,000,000 cubic feet 1 Bcf = 1,000,000,000 cubic feet 1 gallon = 0.1337 cubic feet 1 barrel = 31.5 gallons
Force newton (N)	1 N = 0.2248 lbf (pound-force) 1 lbf = 4.448 N
Pressure pascal (Pa)	1 Pa = 1 N/m^2 1 bar = 100 kPa 1 atm = 101.325 kPa = 1.01325 bar = 14.696 lbf/in^2 = 760 mm Hg (0°C) 1 lbf/in^2 (psi) = 6.8948 kPa
Power watt (W)	1 W = 1 J/s 1 hp = 550 ft·lbf/s = 745.7 W
Energy joule (J)	1 J = 1 Nm = 0.23899 cal 1 BTU = 1.0551 kJ = 778.1693 lbf-ft (BTU = British Thermal Units) 1 BTU is the quantity of heat to raise the temperature of one pound of water by one degree Fahrenheit 1 BTU = 252 cal
Temperature kelvin (K)	°C = 1 K − 273.15 (C = Celsius) °F = 1.8°C + 32 (F = Fahrenheit)
Gas constant R	R = 8.31451 J/(mole·K)

5
Liquid Storage

In the mid–1930s Cleveland was running out of gas. Natural gas was still being delivered through multiple pipelines to the East Ohio Gas Company in Cleveland from the sister company in West Virginia, Hope Natural Gas, but the demands were increasing such that these pipelines could no longer deliver enough for peak loads. These peak loads would come during cold snaps of three or four days, when everyone needed more gas. This meant that gas to some users had to be curtailed to continue the supply to other users. Domestic customers got priority, so some industrial customers had to shut down during these cold snaps. More pipelines would solve this problem, but there was a load factor issue. If the pipelines were sized for a few cold snaps per year, most of the time they would be running under capacity. Sizing pipelines for peak capacity was neither practical nor economical. Nevertheless, East Ohio was thinking about adding more pipelines.

It was about this time in 1937 that Howell Cooper, president of Hope Natural Gas, got the idea to store natural gas on a user's site as a liquid. This idea had two important attributes. First, the gas could be collected and liquefied in off-peak hours, thus precluding the need for any more pipelines. Second, the storage space requirements would be minimal compared to storing it as a gas because of the 600-to-one volume reduction in going from a gas to a liquid. The liquid gas could then be regasified and put into the city gas mains during peak load needs. However, the liquid gas had to be stored at the low temperature of $-260°F$.

We know now that Cooper was successful in developing a system that could liquefy, store, and regasify natural gas. After a successful pilot plant was operated in West Virginia for a while, East Ohio Gas built the first commercial LNG plant in Cleveland. We also know that the system worked in shaving peak gas loads—until it didn't. The result was the fire covered in Chapter 1.

The investigations that followed the disaster concluded that the tank failed because of brittle fracture of the tank 4 steel alloy. The 3½ percent nickel-steel alloy used in the storage tanks, originally thought by Cooper and his colleagues to be adequate, was determined by the investigators to be inadequate for this use. Even worse, the investigators, and follow-on court case plaintiffs, took data on the tank fragments that showed the alloy that was used in tank 4 was much less tough than originally thought. The alloy used for tank 4 was apparently a bad batch of an inappropriate material.

How did all this happen? What led to the failure? Why was 3½ percent nickel-steel chosen? The steps leading to the original design of the plant must be considered in order to answer these questions.

Helium Extraction

Helium is the second most abundant element in the universe, with only hydrogen being more abundant. However, here on Earth it is a difficult to find and extract. Small amounts can be found in the air and in certain minerals, but these are not usually commercially feasible to extract. Helium was eventually discovered in some natural gas: "When helium was discovered in natural gas, all commercial recovery efforts quickly shifted to this new and exciting source."[1] It is not all that common in natural gas, though, sometimes being present only as a trace gas along with argon, neon and others at less than one percent. Helium was only discovered in 1868 as a yellow line in the spectrum of the sun, and only liquefied in 1908, the last gas to be liquefied. Today it has numerous applications including use as a cryogenic material to study superconductivity, as a shield gas for arc welding, as a pressurant for liquid fueled rockets, in scientific and party balloons, and even as a filler for the Goodyear blimp.[2] It is the latter use that made it so valuable early in the twentieth century.

Early in the First World War, Great Britain was anxious to use blimps as weapons. Traditional aircraft were still in their infancy as weapons and did not have the capacity to carry bombs any distance. However, the Zeppelin, or blimp, was seen as a bomber of great capacity. They envisioned bomb loads of 10 tons. The traditional gas used for blimp buoyancy was hydrogen; it was used as late as 1937 in the *Hindenburg*. The British realized that any tracer bullet could quickly set fire to any blimp using hydrogen and destroy it. So the use of hydrogen was impractical for wartime. They turned to helium, which, although not quite as efficient as hydrogen, was more tolerant of single bullets. Their only concern was that an aircraft could ram the blimp and destroy it. They planned to outfit the blimps with several batteries of guns to repel such attacks.[3]

The discovery of helium as a component of natural gas is an interesting story. Natural gas was discovered in the West and Southwest in the early twentieth century. In 1903 a real "gasser" was discovered in Dexter, Kansas; nine million cubic feet escaped before they could cap the well. When they did cap it, the town planned to celebrate by lighting a stream of gas from the well. When they tried to do this the flame fizzled out. Each time they tried, it failed to keep burning. The townsfolk were disappointed and called it "wind gas" or "hot air." Erasmus Haworth, the state geologist, requested and received a steel tank of the gas for analysis. He analyzed the gas and quickly found out that the reason it wouldn't burn was that the flammable methane part was only 15 percent, while non-flammable nitrogen was about 72 percent. He decided to analyze the approximately 12 percent residual inert component. Since coconut charcoal had recently been discovered to remove all the gases in the atmosphere except helium, hydrogen and neon, they immersed glass bulbs of the residual gas with coconut charcoal into a bath of liquid air, which was used to condense out the hydrocarbons. This was advanced chemistry, since air had been liquefied by Carl Linde only eight years before, in 1895. The small amount of residual gas was passed through a tube into a spectroscope on December 7,

1905. Instantly the yellow line of helium flashed in the spectroscope—helium had been discovered in natural gas. The amount in this sample was surprisingly high, 1.84 percent.[4] Thus from 1905 it was known that some natural gas was a good source of helium if it could be extracted.

For the British the need for large amounts of helium for blimp use was acute, so a crash program was initiated to produce the necessary amounts. Unfortunately the natural gas supply available in Britain had a very low percentage of helium, only about one third of one percent. They then turned to their Commonwealth partners in North America. The first functional plant to produce helium was the L'Air Liquide Company in Hamilton, Ontario. It is not clear where their natural gas came from, but Hamilton, Ontario, was not far from the prolific gas-producing region of Appalachia. This experimental plant had difficulties but did produce a small amount of 87 percent pure helium.[5]

When the U.S. entered the war in April 1917, the British appealed for helium production from their allies. The U.S. Bureau of Mines was put in charge of producing it. The bureau decided to develop its own process to produce the helium. This development, however, would have caused an unacceptable delay in a wartime emergency, so the Navy and War departments ordered the Bureau of Mines to use any and all *existing* means to produce the helium. As a result the bureau contracted with the Linde Air Products Company, the Air Reduction Company, and Jeffries-Norton Company to extract the helium.[6] All these companies used essentially the same process, although each had a proprietary version. The approach was to liquefy the natural gas, leaving the free helium, which requires a much lower temperature to liquefy. The Linde plant was ready in four months and the Air Reduction Company plant was ready in five months. Linde, with the best results (92.5 percent helium purity) was contracted in October 1918 to build a large-scale commercial plant in Fort Worth, Texas. Just prior to the armistice, over 150,000 cubic feet of helium was delivered; but it was never used because the war had ended.[7] The Bureau of Mines assumed operation of the Linde plant in 1925. In the late 1920s the bureau erected a helium extraction plant near Amarillo, Texas, at which time the Fort Worth plant was closed.[8]

Thus, from about 1920 on, liquid natural gas was produced in quantities for the production of helium. The process was not described, but presumably it was based on the Linde process for making liquid air, that is, a Joule-Thomson expansion to liquefy the natural gas in a continuous process. The resulting natural gas was not stored but was regasified and put back into the gas mains.

When Howell Cooper started thinking about storing natural gas as a liquid in 1937, he didn't have much history behind him. It was only 50 years earlier that methane had first been liquefied by Wroblewski and Olszewski. Because natural gas has a low boiling point, like oxygen and nitrogen, it was difficult to liquefy and was one of the last gases to be liquefied. However, Cooper did have a lot of information. He was aware of the efforts less than 20 years previously to extract helium from natural gas by liquefying the natural gas to separate out the helium. So Cooper felt confident that a process for liquefying the gas could be developed. More recently, in the mid-1930s, Lee Twomey had obtained a series of patents on the large-scale liquefaction of natural gas. He even suggested the possibility of building a peak-shaving plant. These patents were the most likely source for Cooper's idea to build such a plant. Another series of patents by Godfrey Cabot in the

1910s described methods for storing liquid gases. Cooper knew from these patents that he would also need an insulator around any low-temperature tank to keep the heat loss to a minimum. Although he didn't have the designs for the liquefaction plant and the storage tanks, he did have the starting point.

It is what Cooper *didn't* have that is most important. There were two critical pieces of information that he did not have. First, he didn't have an acceptable material for the tanks. This would be the first time that storage tanks would be used for long-term storage at very low temperatures—−260°F. There was no precedent for this. When natural gas was liquefied in quantity to extract helium it was immediately regasified and put back into the gas mains; there were no storage tanks. Most materials, including normal carbon steel, get very brittle at very low temperatures and can fracture easily. Cooper was aware of this and knew they would have to find an acceptable material for the tank. The second critical piece of information he was lacking was any information on standards and building codes. What material is acceptable for this environment, and how should it be used?

The large LNG storage tanks are both containers and large structures, and they need to be considered from both aspects. As containers of LNG they need to meet certain standards for containers that hold a very cold fluid. The American Society of Mechanical Engineers (ASME) sets safety standards for mechanical containers, so the tank, as a container, must meet these standards. However, the large spherical and cylindrical tanks are structures also; they are as large, or larger, than many buildings, so they must be sited properly and meet the local building codes.

Cooper and his colleagues lacked information in both these areas. There were no standards in place to guide the design of the tanks as containers, and there were no specific building codes that covered LNG structures, although existing building codes could have been used. The following brief discussion on materials standards will highlight the first issue: the lack of standards for the material for an LNG storage tank. Building and fire codes will be covered in Chapter 7.

Materials Standards

Over many years, going back centuries, various codes have been developed for the purpose of providing assurance to a building occupant that the building he dwells in is safe. These usually are the result of some bad experience that people don't want to repeat. Some of these codes could be drastic. The Babylonian king Hammurabi, in 2000 BC, had a performance code based on "an eye for an eye." The builder was responsible in kind for any damages that occurred because of the failure of a building. If someone lost an arm the builder would lose an arm. If someone in the building died as a result of a collapse, then the builder would be killed in retaliation. Modern codes are not quite that drastic. Around the turn of the twentieth century the first building codes were developed on the East Coast. They were intended to protect buildings, not people. The safety of occupants was not emphasized until the 1930s and 1940s, when codes included fire exits and fire alarms.[9]

Similarly, standards were developed for many products and materials. (A code is a collection of laws on a particular subject, for example, building or fire codes. A standard is an approved model, an authority, used as a basis of comparison. A standard can form the basis for a code. Sometimes these terms are used interchangeably, which can be confusing.) If after much analysis and testing a material was determined to be safe it could be listed in some standard as safe. If used in the way specified, the designer could be sure it was safe and use it for his design. He would not have to do basic testing on it himself, because others had done it and certified it. When a house is built, for example, the builder refers to the county building code for guidance on placement and types of electrical and plumbing fixtures. Thus knowledge of, and reference to, a particular code or standard can provide guidance to a designer on the materials he can use with confidence. If that information is not available, the project becomes a new development and entails research on any material to be used in that project.

The Industrial Revolution started in Great Britain in the eighteenth century, and continued in the mid- to late nineteenth century in the U.S. Steam power was used not only for steam locomotives and steamboats but to power factories, especially in New England, and also to provide heat. Steam power meant steam boilers. The number of boilers in use as reported in the 1880 census was 72,304, with 100,000 estimated to be in use by 1890. These were manufactured by many different companies without any standards for construction. As a result there were hundreds of explosions every year killing hundreds of people; in 1901 alone there were 399 explosions.[10] After a particularly deadly explosion at a shoe factory in Brockton, Massachusetts, on March 10, 1905, which killed 58 and injured 117, followed by another shoe factory explosion the following year in Lynn, Massachusetts, the state decided to act. It came out with some regulations regarding the safety of boiler construction. These were successful, and in 1911 Ohio passed regulations similar to those of Massachusetts. There had been a hue and cry from the manufacturers that this was a case of needless government intervention and would put small boiler makers out of business. This might have been true for some smaller manufacturers, but overall the industry was helped, not hurt, and people were safer. Partly to address these types of issues, the ASME started to put together some guidelines for a boiler code. This took a while and required public hearings. Nevertheless, by 1914 they had come up with a code, published in 1915, that was accepted as the standard for safe boiler construction. Entitled "Rules for the Construction of Stationary Boilers and for Allowable Working Pressures," it started to cut the boiler explosion rate dramatically.[11] This was one of the early industrial codes and is still considered a standard reference.

Not surprisingly, the popularity of the code spawned many amendments, starting in 1918, and similar codes. Over the next 15 years various related codes were established, amended, and moved around. A protocol gradually emerged that listed a lot of these related codes as sections under the primary boiler code. A specification for materials moved in and out of various sections and finally ended up as a section of its own. It was in the early 1920s that the need was seen for a code for *unfired* pressure vessels, that is, ones that were not fired to produce steam. The first "Code for Unfired Pressure Vessels" was adopted by the ASME January 15, 1925, as section 8 of the boiler code. Because of the size of some of these codes, some were published as one volume and others as separate volumes. By the early 1930s the *Boiler and Pressure Vessel Code* (BPVC) had the following sections[12]:

- I   Power Boilers
- II Material Specifications
- III Locomotive Boilers
- IV Low-Pressure Heating Boilers
- V   Miniature Boilers
- VI Rules for Inspection
- VII Suggested Rules for Care of Power Boilers
- VIII Unfired Pressure Vessels

This consolidation of the BPVC was less than 10 years before Cooper built his LNG pilot plant. It would seem from this list that the sections most applicable to the construction of large cryogenic tanks over the following 10 years were section 2, on materials, and section 8, on unfired pressure vessels. While this is generally true, it was not at all clear if or how these might apply. This was because of all the changes on these sections, and also because it was not clear if the storage tank conditions were even covered in these sections. One example is the designation *pressure vessel*. A pressure vessel was defined as having at least 15 pounds per square gauge in the vessel. (Pounds per square gauge [psig] is measured by a gauge above atmospheric pressure which is 14.7 pounds per square inch absolute [psia].) When in operation, the pressure in the LNG tanks was only about three pounds per square inch gauge, so technically these were not even pressure vessels. This was a minor point, but it is one example of how difficult it was to classify the design. It is worth remembering that the original BPVC was defined well *after* thousands of boilers had been built, so it was relatively easy to decide what was and was not a boiler.

In the "Materials Specifications Section" (section 2) the change was also rapid over the years, as they added more specifications for materials for various uses. These were labeled with an "S" number. In the 1930 version of the BPVC, section 8, all references to materials were made to section 2, which included the new specification numbers ("S" numbers). By this time, the specified number of materials was up to S-24.[13] In 1934 S-25 was added, and in 1935 S-26 through S-31 were added.[14] None of these, however, included a material specification that would cover the material needed for the LNG storage tanks that were about to be constructed. Note the quick pace of change of the codes as more and more materials were added.

In 1936 and 1937 specifications S-32 through S-41 were added to the acceptable materials in section 2.[15] Some were for high-temperature service, but none were for low-temperature service. So by the time Cooper had started his research on processing liquid natural gas, there were *no* materials listed that he could reference in a code book in which he could feel confidence. More changes were made between 1938 and 1940. In the "Materials Specifications" in the 1940 code, 16 new specifications were added, S-42 to S-57.[16] One of these was "S-43 Specifications for Low-Carbon Nickel-Steel Plates for Boilers and Other Pressure Vessels." This specification included 2.00 to 2.75 percent nickel.[17] Low-carbon nickel-steel with 3½ percent nickel was *not yet* covered in the code, even in 1940 when the Cleveland plant was built.

The other section of the code that bears on this subject is section 8, "Unfired Pressure Vessels." This section, first published in 1927, also had many changes through the years. The ASME code for "Unfired Pressure Vessels," 1935 edition, refers to section 2 for all material requirements. There is nothing in this edition that mentions low temperatures at all. The first time low temperatures are mentioned is when an addendum is added to section 8 by the ASME in August 1936. The following is added:

Rules for Containers for Gases and Liquids at Temperatures from −10 to −150F
 These rules cover containers for non-corrosive gases and liquids which have no deleterious effect on the steel of the vessel, which containers may be used for the liquefaction or gasification of solid carbon-dioxide. They do not apply to temperatures below minus 150 F, or to vessels designed for atmospheric or higher temperatures, nor do they apply to vessels in which thermal stresses imposed by the conditions of operation will be an important factor.[18]

This was added to the 1937 version of the code under paragraph U-140.[19] It was clearly intended only for solid carbon dioxide containers, two of which are shown in figure U-25 of that code. Note also that it specifically limits the temperature to no lower than −150°F. Thus though low temperature use is first mentioned in the 1937 code, it is not close to the use we are discussing for the storage tanks (−260°F).

The next edition of section 8 was in 1940. Under paragraph U-71 it states, "The materials used in the fabrication of any fusion-welded part of a pressure vessel covered by this code shall conform to one of the following specifications."[20] It then specifically lists the S-43 material, which is also listed in tables U-2 and UA-8. This is the first version of section 8 to mention low temperatures in the index (pp. 101–104). However, there are only two noticeable changes from previous editions regarding temperature. One is the removal of −150°F as the lowest temperature limit. This implies that lower temperatures are acceptable. *However, it now requires impact tests be done at the lowest temperatures to which the vessels will be subjected.* These impact tests, Charpy impact tests, are then described in paragraph U-142. For a standard 10 mm by 10 mm specimen it required a minimum impact value of 15 foot-pounds at *operating temperature.*

The experiments on the pilot plant material took place in the 1937–1939 timeframe, which was prior to the Charpy impact test requirements in section 8 of the ASME BPVC of 1940, and prior to the specification of the S-43 material, a low-carbon nickel steel with 2.00 to 2.75 percent nickel, in that same edition. Also, since the East Ohio tanks were designed early in 1940, it is not clear if Cooper and Jackson even saw the 1940 edition of section 8 before the Cleveland plant was built, or while it was being built. Cooper did not have that information in 1939 when he built the pilot plant.

By 1940 the ASME BPVC provided almost no guidance for the designer of a large storage tank for LNG at a temperature of −260°F. The only requirement was that for low temperatures it must pass a Charpy impact test with a value of 15 foot-pounds at those low operating temperatures. In summary, Cooper had no applicable code in which he could have confidence; he was ahead of the curve. He and his colleagues were breaking new ground when they designed the tanks.

Patents on Storing Liquid Gases

On May 18, 1915, Godfrey Cabot (1861–1962) of Boston received a patent titled "Means for Handling and Transporting Liquid Gas."[21] This is the same Godfrey Cabot introduced in Chapter 3 as a major producer of carbon black by using natural gas. At first it appears to be a cart-before-the-horse effort because he doesn't talk about how to liquefy the gas in question, and doesn't say which gas he has in mind. However, he does mention another patent application applied for two weeks after this one but issued two years later that describes "an apparatus for condensing gas under high pressure."[22] In the first patent he describes a system of two large, low-pressure, well-insulated tanks to store liquefied gas at low temperatures and move it on a barge. He says that it would be applicable to the condensed gases he discusses in the second patent. In the second patent he describes "an apparatus for condensing gas but particularly natural gas under high pressure." Although it might appear he is liquefying methane, the primary component of natural gas, this is not the case. A complete reading shows that the gases he is liquefying are the higher hydrocarbons of natural gas, such as ethane, propane, and butane. He uses the expansion of the non-liquefied natural gas, mostly methane, from high to low pressure (the Joule-Thomson effect) to provide a very low temperature gas to liquefy these higher hydrocarbons. Dr. Snelling had separated propane using moderate pressure. This method uses low temperature to separate the ethane, propane, and butane from natural gas.

In Cabot's 1915 patent on storing and transporting liquid gas, he does acknowledge that it is not only appropriate for the condensed gases covered in his later patent but that "this apparatus may be used in connection with any apparatus known for the purpose of forming a liquid gas." This is true because the apparatus he describes is essentially one that can store liquid air or liquid natural gas. Thus by 1915 a method for storing large amounts of a liquid gas such as natural gas had been described, but it hadn't been designed. This is a crucial difference that was recognized by Cooper.

Storage Tank Material

It was in August 1937 that Cooper decided to start research that would prove the concept of liquefying natural gas, storing it, and regasifying it when it was needed. By September 1939 research had progressed to the point that Hope decided to build a pilot plant to liquefy, store, and regasify relatively large quantities of natural gas.[23] The site chosen to build the pilot plant was at the Hope Cornwell Station near Corton, West Virginia, along the Elk River. (The records for the pilot plant, such as specifications, research results, engineering notes, and pictures, no longer exist. The plant that was built in 1939 was dismantled shortly after the concept was proved. Apparently the documentation was also discarded. This account was constructed from articles in the open literature.) The Cornwell Station was an existing Hope compressor station. By this time Cooper was retired. He had retired as president of Hope in early 1939 but was asked (and agreed) to stay on to do this pilot plant work. He oversaw the project, but the Hope engineers did the design and built the pilot plant. The plant was completed and put into operation the middle of January 1940, a relatively rapid development for a new technology.[24]

The first item to be researched was the storage tank. Storing large amounts of liquid natural gas had never been done before, whereas processing the gas into a liquid had been done. Thus they started with the greatest unknown. The Cabot patent information provided a place to start but did not result in a specification. There were two problems to be solved. One was the material to be used, not only for the tank, but also for all the auxiliary equipment including the piping between the components of the plant. The second was the insulation to be used. Again, Cabot mentions the necessity of insulation but does not specify it.

At normal temperatures steel is a very ductile material. It can be stretched or bent or stamped into shape, and it will retain the shape and strength, such as when used in auto body parts. A ductile material can absorb a lot of energy and distortion before it fails. A brittle material, however, does not deform or stretch before failure. Once it reaches its strength limit it will snap. To use an exaggerated example with candy, a ductile material is like taffy that stretches before breaking; a brittle material is like peanut brittle, which snaps easily. Ductility and brittleness are not absolutes. These properties can change with temperature. For example, normal carbon steel, as with many materials, gets very brittle with low temperature even though it is ductile at normal temperatures. At very low temperatures it is so brittle that it can break like glass breaks at normal temperatures; that is, it will shatter. Very exotic behavior of many materials can be demonstrated at very low temperatures. For example, an ordinary object that is normally very elastic, such as a tennis ball, if immersed in liquid air and then dropped will shatter like glass. As soon as the pieces return to normal temperatures they will be just as flexible and elastic as before they were quick frozen, but they will look as though the ball had been cut by a knife. So clearly, toughness at low temperature was a concern when deciding on the materials for the storage tanks. What material could be exposed to −260°F (−162°C)? As shown previously, Cooper had no guidance from ASME standards.

Steel has a well-defined ductile to brittle temperature transition (DBTT) behavior that depends on the composition of the steel and the temperature. A generic DBTT curve is shown in figure 5-1.

A ductile fracture will exhibit a rough end where it fractures, much like the end of a paper clip that has been bent back and forth until it fractures. A brittle fracture will show a clean separation similar to but not as clean as a piece of fractured glass. The transition temperature will depend on the composition of the steel. For a normal mild (low carbon) steel, the ductile-brittle transition might occur at around −60°C.[25] This transition is measured by an impact test. This test is specifically designed to measure the impact resistance of a material, a measure of the energy (foot-pounds) absorbed by impact to cause a piece to fail. The test apparatus consists of a known weight, the hammer, at the end of a rigid, pendulous arm. The pendulous arm is pivoted around the pendulum axis to a calibrated angular position and held there, thus setting the potential energy of the hammer above

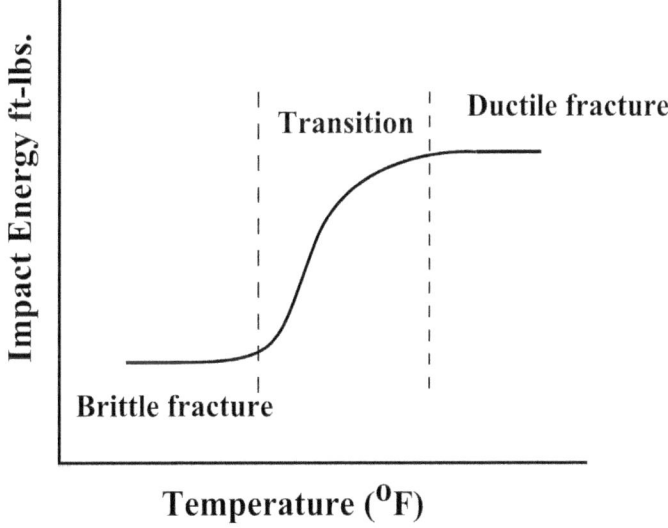

Figure 5-1. Mild steel DBTT.

the nadir. The height of the pendulous weight (hammer) above the nadir of the pendulum motion is a measure of the energy imparted to the sample. The sample to be tested is clamped at the nadir position of the pendulum. The pendulum is then allowed to swing through the sample, thus fracturing it. The sample is notched to assure that each sample breaks at the same point. The weight, length, and hammer angular orientation determine the energy of impact. This test is called the Charpy impact test, after Georges Charpy (1865–1945), who proposed it around 1905.

Determine the DBTT requires testing over a range of temperatures, as shown in figure 5-1, including some very low temperatures. To do this the samples are soaked in liquid nitrogen and quickly (within five seconds) placed in the machine; the hammer is released. A series of these tests over a temperature range determines the transition temperature. Steel in the brittle fracture area might take only a slight tap for it to crack and break like glass; recall the tennis ball example. Steel can be made tougher under low temperature (moving the S-curve to the left) by the addition of nickel. The Charpy impact test is considered to be the best indicator of material performance at low temperatures; that is, the best indicator of brittle fracture.

Although the Charpy impact test had been around for several years it was only in 1933 that the American Society for Testing Materials (ASTM) had finally produced a standard test method for pendulum testing. As was noted much later,

> Impact testing seems to have been a useful technique for evaluating materials, but was not a common requirement in purchase specifications and construction standards until the recognition of its ability to detect the ductile-to-brittle transition in steel. Probably the greatest single impetus toward implementation of impact testing in fabrication standards and material specifications came as a result of the large number of ship failures that occurred during World War II.[26]

In other words, there were no clear ductile-to brittle standards available in 1937, especially over the low temperatures being investigated.

Hope Natural Gas did some laboratory experiments with various metals at low temperatures. They found, for example, that half-inch boiler plate immersed in liquid methane could easily be broken with a small hammer because it was so brittle.[27] What material was tested, whether or not it contained any nickel, and what results were achieved are not known. This was not peer-reviewed published research.

Pilot Plant Tank Material and Insulation

Despite the experiments by Hope there is no clear line from the experiments to the choice of the material for the pilot plant tank. The reason for the choice of the metal for the pilot plant storage tank is quite clear, however. Cooper testified on this choice at the mayor's board of inquiry hearings, which commenced October 24, 1944, only four days after the fire. In responding to a question about the pilot plant tank material, he said,

> Well, this tank was built out of some steel which I got from the Lukens Steel Company and it was not particularly adapted to it [the low temperatures], but it was the *only steel that I could find at the time that had some nickel in it* that was available in the market. We could not have any steel made for such a small job, so I used this steel that was made by the Lukens Steel Company and built the tank out of it[28] [emphasis added].

Thus he was acknowledging the need to use steel with *some* nickel content, though he didn't have a specification for it. He knew that some nickel content would make the steel tougher at low temperatures. He used what steel he could find at the time that contained some nickel. He made no mention of doing DBTT testing on it. The steel he referred to as being available was two percent nickel-steel.[29] He later said, "I had had this experience with the less favorable steel in the Pilot Plant."[30] He never elaborated on what experience he was talking about, so we don't know what trouble he had had with it. The lack of available nickel-steel also suggests he probably did not have a lot of different alloys with which to experiment before the pilot plant was built.

The pilot plant tank was constructed of alloy steel plates. It was a horizontal symmetrical tank 10 feet in diameter and 18 feet long. It held 14,500 gallons of liquid natural gas, which is equivalent to about one million cubic feet of gas.[31] (In his testimony Cooper recalled the tank as being about eight feet in diameter and eight feet long. Since this testimony was almost five years after the pilot plant was built, it is likely this was just faulty memory.) The tank design was adequate for the pilot plant because it, along with the rest of the plant, operated successfully for only four months before it was dismantled. Therefore, long-term durability of this material had not been proved.

The other part of the tank design, as recognized in the Cabot patent, was a means to insulate the tank to maintain the low tank temperature needed to store the liquid. They experimented in the laboratory with a small tank covered with three feet of insulation. Cooper later said the only insulation they tried was cork. They filled and refilled the small tank many times with liquid nitrogen and calibrated the insulation with thermocouples to determine heat infiltration into the tank. They ended up covering the pilot plant tank with two feet of formed cork, which they cemented on and waterproofed with bituminous tar.[32] The tank sat in a horizontal position resting on the cork insulation; there was no outer tank. A thermocouple four inches in from the outer surface showed a temperature of −17°F. Their calculated heat loss was such that only one percent of the liquefied gas would evaporate in any 24-hour period. Further calculations showed that an additional eight inches of cork would reduce this loss to less than one-fourth of one percent.[33] However, when they shut the liquefying process down, that is, stopped liquefying and let the tank sit in a quiescent state, they measured a daily evaporation of 28,000 cubic feet of free gas. For a one-million-cubic-foot equivalent tank, this was about 2.8 percent evaporation loss.[34]

The chief engineer, J. A. Clark, and the research director, R. W. Miller, for Hope co-wrote a journal article about the pilot plant published in October 1940, while the Cleveland plant was being constructed, in which they listed some conclusions they had reached from the pilot plant operation:

> After going below −50°F, the pipe and tank steel becomes so brittle it is entirely unsafe. The metals which retain a safe Charpy impact-test values are, in order of excellence, pure copper, bronze, monel metal, red brass, stainless steel and steel plate with carbon content less than 0.09 percent and nickel over 3½ percent.[35]

They concluded that a nickel-steel alloy that had more than 3½ percent nickel should be used. This might have been the result of their pre-pilot plant experiments, although there was never any mention of having 3½ percent nickel-steel available even for testing. They used two percent nickel-steel in the pilot plant because, as Cooper said, this was the only material available that had some nickel in it, and he could not get a special run of steel for the small amount they used in the pilot plant tank. Another reason for 3½ percent nickel might have been the less-than-favorable experience Cooper said he had with the two percent pilot plant material. In either case, they did not say why they concluded that 3½ percent nickel-steel was acceptable.

In summary, two percent nickel-steel was used in the pilot plant tank because it was the only material they could get with some nickel in it, and they knew some nickel was needed for toughness at low temperatures. There was no reference to any standard. There was no standard that mentioned 3½ percent nickel-steel.

Cleveland Plant Tank Material

Things were moving fairly rapidly. The pilot plant started operation in January 1940. It operated for four months, until May, while Hope collected data on the operation. Most of their questions had been answered, and they considered the plant a success. The decision by the Hope sister company, East Ohio, to build a full-scale commercial plant in Cleveland, based on this pilot plant, was made during the spring of 1940 after a particularly cold January. Originally East Ohio was considering building another 12-inch line from Hope to supply more gas, but after a study, the company concluded it would be cheaper to build the LNG plant.[36] The decision was probably made while the pilot plant was still in operation. The application for the building permit for the storage tanks for the Cleveland plant was made on June 12, 1940, and issued on June 15, 1940.[37] It took only three days to issue the permit for a very novel construction in the middle of the city. Clearly the local authorities had no qualms about the new plant. Construction of the Cleveland plant was started in the fall of 1940. Since the storage tanks for this plant were the cutting-edge technology for the plant, the design had to be done early and, therefore, the material had to be chosen early.

The decision on the material for the large LNG storage tanks for the East Ohio plant is interesting. Cooper said he did research on gas liquefaction and storage from 1937 until 1939, but he didn't say what kind of research. Sometime after he retired, probably in 1939, he also became a consultant for East Ohio Gas, the sister company of Hope Natural Gas, from which he had just retired. He was a consultant when East Ohio decided to build the full-scale LNG plant. They chose the Gas and Machinery Company in Cleveland as the prime contractor. The Pittsburgh–Des Moines Steel Company was chosen to build the storage tanks. Somewhere in that process, early in 1940, the Gas and Machinery Company bought a lot of 3½ percent nickel-steel from Republic Steel on Cooper's recommendation. He did not discuss this choice with the contractors, Gas and Machinery and Pittsburgh–Des Moines, and apparently made the decision before the contractors came on board.

Pittsburgh–Des Moines Steel, and specifically James O. Jackson, their chief engineer, designed the storage tanks for the Cleveland plant and consulted with Cooper, but not on the initial steel buy. There is no indication Jackson worked with Cooper before this contract; that is, no indication he (Jackson) worked on the pilot plant at all. According to Jackson's testimony before the mayor's board of inquiry,

> Q: You were pretty much on an uncharted course outside the pilot plant?
> A: Yes, we were. Mr. Cooper had a pretty good idea of the steel that should be used. In fact the steel for the first spheres was purchased by the Gas Machinery Company, but we wanted to be sure we could weld that steel, so we made quite a few tests jointly with Mr. Cooper and satisfied ourselves in the same way that the welding could be done ...
> Q: Will you explain the research of the materials used in regard to the treatment for the tanks and who was responsible for the selection of these materials?
> A: Mr. Cooper, who was a consultant for the East Ohio Gas Company had determined the kind of steel to use when he came to us, that is, he had made a study of it and had concluded that the three and a half percent nickel steel was the best to use.
> Q: And those were in the specifications?
> A: Well, there were not really any specifications, but that is what the Gas & Machinery Company bought for us to make the tanks from. We had no voice in the matter.
> Q: You never made any research of these materials?
> A: No.[38]

In other words, Cooper was the sole decider on what material to use and Pittsburgh–Des Moines, including Jackson, had no say in the matter. The basic steel material had been chosen without any research by Jackson. There were no tank material specifications by the tank builder Pittsburgh–Des Moines. It appears that Cooper had Gas and Machinery purchase the steel prior to his work with Jackson.

Although Jackson didn't do research in choosing the material originally, he does mention later in his testimony the tests on the purchased steel that he did with Cooper, as mentioned above. They made a jig, welded materials such as regular low carbon steel and the nickel-steel, and bent them around the jig after cooling them in liquid nitrogen. Jackson testified,

> But then we also found that we could take carbon steel and chill it down to the same temperature and finally it would go around the jig. At that we got convinced that the test was not sensitive enough to distinguish between metal that was good at low temperature, and metal that was not, so we went to the Charpy impact method and it was sensitive enough to distinguish between carbon steel and nickel steel welds.... My opinion is that you can with three and a half percent nickel steel, with the proper preheating on the weld, that a weld may be made, that has at least fifteen foot pound impact either on the center of the weld or the fusion zone.[39]

This statement seems to indicate that by the time Jackson started working with Cooper, the 3½ percent nickel-steel was already available and they were doing the testing mainly to verify the welds at the low temperature.

Why had Cooper chosen the material without any research by Jackson and Pittsburgh–Des Moines? He never really answers the question of why he chose 3½ percent nickel-steel. He gives some partial answers in his testimony.

During the testimony they were discussing the pilot plant, when Cooper was asked about the choice of nickel-steel. He started to answer that question with respect to the pilot plant, but then switched and discussed it with respect to the Cleveland plant:

> Q: How did you arrive at the decision of using nickel steel?
> A: I would reply to that by saying that it was a revue [sic] of all the different types of steel and forms of metal in general which presented some possibilities of use at this very low temperature. There were several different metals available, but for the purpose of a large

size tank, which would be required for a commercial plant, the best that I could determine was a steel and carbon, low carbon steel with a three and a half percent nickel in it. This all happened some four or five years ago, and I am trying to think back.[40]

He indicates *he* chose the material after reviewing materials that were available. This testimony corroborates Jackson's testimony, which claimed that Cooper had chosen the material prior to any involvement by Jackson. Cooper didn't say which materials he had reviewed. He was then asked if he had consulted with anyone. He said he did, including with someone from the Mellon Institute. He then continues,

> So when we came to build this plant [Cleveland], I felt that if we could properly weld three and a half percent nickel steel, we better use that. That was the description of steel that was used in the A.S.M.E. low temperature vessels of that period. I think if you will look in your codes of the A.S.M.E. you will see what they designate to use for −150 [*sic*] and for pressure vessels, and I wanted to get a steel which would be as nearly conforming to the steel that they thought was good for pressure to use in making the tank in which no pressure was to exist, but was to be at a lower temperature, and as of that time what seemed to be the best that we could get, and I thought would prove entirely satisfactory.[41]

A couple of things stand out, considering he was remembering this from about five years prior. His memory of −150 was probably the −150°F he remembered from the 1937 edition of the code. His memory was a little incomplete because in that edition the −150 was the *lowest* allowed, well above the operating temperature of −260°F ultimately used. Also he remembered 3½ percent nickel steel as that used by the ASME in low-temperature vessels at that time. This was also faulty memory. As we have seen, the only nickel-steel recognized by the 1940 code was 2.00 to 2.75 percent; 3½ percent was *not* mentioned. Also, we're not sure he ever saw the 1940 version of the code since the material choice was made early in 1940. He also refers to using a steel that was conforming to the steel the ASME thought was good for pressure for a tank in which no pressure was to exist, but was to be at a lower temperature. By this statement he might have thought he was giving himself more margin. He thought that this tank being at low pressure would allow him to go to a lower temperature, that is, trade off temperature and pressure. This may have been his intuition, but there is no engineering reason to justify this trade. He had no reliable guidance from the codes; they just didn't cover these materials and temperatures. It appears he did the best he could in interpreting the ASME codes that were available. After some questions on riveting the tanks, Cooper comes back to the material:

> A: Now may I go a little further with this. Getting back to the steel for this particular plant, the Republic Steel here had a good deal of steel left from a project which they had made of steel of this description that I thought would be proper for use in this tank. It was a low carbon steel with three and a half nickel in it. So we came over here to the laboratory of that company and tested that steel in all of its physical characteristics, that particular steel, and also made bend tests, made the Charpy tests, using nitrogen, which was some sixty degrees colder than the liquid we proposed to hold, and we got very favorable results from these tests, and it was on the basis of steel of that sort that we decided to use it in these tanks and we still had to learn how to weld it properly so we used samples of that steel and worked up our welding, I mean to say the Des Moines Steel Company worked up a technique of welding that particular steel. That was a cut and dried process that covered several months of work.[42]

Cooper's first answer, that he had based his selection on a review of available steels, and the Jackson testimony that the material had already been chosen, is most likely the correct answer, and Cooper ran these two together in his last answer, which was almost five years after the fact. Cooper alone had chosen the steel for the tanks. In the last answer he says they tested the 3½ percent nickel-steel that Republic Steel had *left over from another project,* found it to be satisfactory, and decided to use it. There is no record of the project that Republic Steel had made this run of steel for. Whatever research he had done on materials (unspecified), including the use of two percent nickel-steel in the pilot plant tank, he must have concluded that higher nickel content was a good idea. Remember, he had earlier said that he had had a bad experience with the two percent nickel-steel. He then found access to some leftover 3½ percent nickel-steel and decided to use this higher nickel alloy steel. So for a *second* time he chose a material that was available rather than one developed specifically for cryogenic temperature use.

In summary, Cooper had no applicable code that he could have confidence in; he was ahead of the curve. He and Jackson were breaking new ground when they designed the tanks. Jackson had acknowledged in his testimony that they were in uncharted territory with the tank design. Pittsburgh–Des Moines had done work with tanks as low as −30°F but nothing this low in temperature. Cooper knew two things, though. One was that the higher percentage of nickel in this batch of steel would make it tougher at low temperatures than the two percent nickel-steel he had used previously and with which he had had some trouble. Second, he knew that, since they were breaking new ground, they would have to test this material at low temperatures, especially with various welding materials. He alluded to this in his last answer.

Now consider some events that happened after the fact, after the plant had been built.

Research After the Build

Jackson wrote an article in December 1941, less than a year after the plant opened, in which he describes the testing done. It reads as if the research was done prior to the material choice for the Cleveland tanks, but as we know from the testimony above there was no other testing to choose a tank material after the nickel-steel referred to above was purchased from Republic Steel through Gas and Machinery. Jackson says,

> Experimental work was done to determine suitable materials from which the tanks could be manufactured.... After some preliminary research using liquid nitrogen as a cooling means it was concluded that the Charpy impact test made at low temperatures, using standard key-hole notched specimens, was the best index of the suitability of various materials and weld metal for these containers. Many tests were made of various types of steel with different alloy contents and of a number of non-ferrous metals and their impact values and other characteristics determined at low temperature. After suitable base materials were developed welded specimens were prepared from which low temperature Charpy impact tests were made of the metal in the welds, and in the fusion and heat affected zones. The tanks were made of 3½ percent nickel steel, using stainless steel welding electrodes, having an analysis of 25 percent chromium and 20 percent nickel. Charpy impact values of 20 ft.-lb. or more were consistently obtained in the weld metal and in the fusion and heat affected zones.[43]

It seems likely that the original 3½ percent nickel-steel that Cooper had Gas and Machinery purchase, a purchase that Jackson had no voice in, was used as purchased; it was not the result of "many tests were made of various types of steel with different alloy contents." that Jackson claims ex post facto in his 1941 article above. However, it is possible the tests he is referring to are those of Cooper in his 1937–1939 research. The tests he refers to seem to confirm that the 3½ percent nickel-steel alloy used for the first three tanks *did* exceed the Charpy impact requirements of 15 foot-pounds. He filed patents over the next three years that showed how his view evolved and how he settled on the 3½ percent nickel steel as the appropriate one, even though he had been presented with that material before the tanks were built.

Jackson filed a patent on August 6, 1941, after the Cleveland plant had been built, in which he talked about "spherical liquid air storage tank constructed of suitable alloy steel sheets."[44] On November 21, 1941, he and Cooper filed a patent in which they said that an object of the invention "resides in a double-walled container for low temperature fluids, the inner wall of which is composed of an austenitic material such as chromium-nickel steel, particularly one containing approximately 18 percent chromium and 8 percent nickel, and the outer surface is highly polished."[45] This 18-8 is stainless steel. Finally in a patent filed January 6, 1942, Jackson acknowledges that the 18-8 stainless steel is too expensive for this use, and he searches for a material that will be satisfactory for these low temperatures but has a more reasonable cost than the stainless steel. He uses the Charpy impact test criteria. He claims that it is generally accepted by engineers that a structural steel must have a Charpy value of at least 10 foot-pounds before it can be used in structures. So, he says, "another object of my invention resides in producing welded structures which have a Charpy impact value of at least 10 ft. lbs. at temperatures as low as −260°F, and which the composition of the base metal or alloy and the composition of the weld metal are predeterminedly correlated." Why he claims that 10 foot-pounds Charpy impact is acceptable at −260°F is unclear. By this time the ASME standard required 15 foot-pounds at low temperatures. He goes on to say he is really looking for 18–20 foot pounds Charpy impact at −260°F. He then goes on to describe "steel having the following composition":

	Percent
Carbon	About 0.10 to 0.30
Manganese	About 0.30 to 0.50
Silicone	About 0.10 to 0.20
Nickel	About 3.0 to 4.0
Sulphur	Up to about 0.04
Phosphorous	Up to about 0.04
Iron	Balance

He continues, "A nickel content of approximately 3½ percent is preferred but I have found that nickel may be satisfactorily employed within the range of about 0.5–10 percent." He does not say why 3½ percent is preferred over say eight or nine percent. One could surmise that cost was a factor. He then discusses normalizing the rolled steel and preheating the parts near the welds. He successfully used welding rods of 25 percent chromium and 20 percent nickel. Having done this, he says, "I have been able to secure butt-welded joints in plates of the base material above specified having a Charpy impact value of about 18–20 ft. lbs. at a temperature of −260°F."[46] All these patents were filed after the Cleveland plant was in operation. It appears from the preceding testimony that they used the 3½ percent nickel-steel that Cooper had purchased, and they did so prior to any research on the material itself, although they did some testing on the welds after Pittsburgh–Des Moines came onboard. Nevertheless, either during or after the plant construction, the trace of his patent work seems to indicate he did more research on the material and welds and concluded that the 3½ percent nickel steel was optimum. One could argue that the research findings after the fact of using the steel could have been biased by the steel's existing use in the Cleveland tanks.

In summary, it appears that an extensive research program on the storage tank material was *not* done *prior* to choosing that alloy. Instead Cooper had chosen the material based on his review of materials available for low temperature uses, and his interpretation of an ASME code he thought could be applied to these low temperatures. He and Jackson then did low-temperature Charpy impact tests of the welded material to assure that the welds would hold. Although the material had been chosen before testing, Jackson implies he did do research later on tank materials that he tested and proposed in his patents. Although 18-8 stainless steel would work, he concluded that it was too expensive and found that low alloy steel with from 0.5 to 10 percent nickel would work and be more economical. Thus some ex post facto testing did seem to corroborate the choice of material already in place. All indications are that the pilot plant operated successfully over the months it was used, and the Cleveland plant operated successfully over the three-and-a-half years prior to the accident. Given the lack of code guidance, Cooper probably used the best material available at the time.

After the accident the composition of the steel in the tanks became a major focus of the failure investigation. One batch of 3½ percent nickel-steel was used in the three spherical tanks, and a different batch was used later in the fourth tank, the one that failed. The fourth tank was also of a different design, which may have been a contributing factor. Ironically, it also turns out that the range of nickel content Jackson found acceptable for use in the steel alloy includes the nine percent nickel-steel alloy that has since become the acceptable material for low temperature liquid storage.

Liquefaction Process

Cooper indicated in his testimony that liquefying natural gas was old hat; it had been done years before. He was correct, of course. He was aware of the Linde process and also of the Bureau of Mines work with extracting helium from natural gas starting during the First World War. However, there was still a choice to be made. By the end of the first decade of the twentieth century there were at least three processes that could be used to liquefy natural gas, mostly methane:

- the cascade system of cooling as used by Pictet
- the regenerative process of Linde using the Joule-Thomson effect
- the regenerative and expansion method of Claude[47]

The Hope research team, however, had seemed to narrow it down to two possibilities:

Finally after considerable laboratory work and research, the choice of a design for a liquefaction plant narrowed down to two methods. The first made use of an expansion engine, taking work out of high pressure gas and exhausting this gas at a very low temperature, which would be utilized as a cooling medium for the high-pressure gas to be condensed. The second employed the so-called cascade system of removing heat in steps through the medium of three or four circuits, each using a different gas which would liquefy at successively lower temperatures and by exchanging heat between the circuits. Both ideas were workable, but finally the cascade idea was adopted and all work was along that line.[48]

These two methods were, of course, the regenerative expansion method of Claude and the cascade method of Pictet. They chose the Pictet method. The reasons behind this engineering trade were not provided, and the original documentation no longer exists. The cascade method first used by Pictet, however, was probably seen as simpler if the right choice of liquid coolants was used. The reason for not using the straight Linde process was not given. However, it could have been the higher pressures involved, which would have meant a very robust construction for the equipment used. The most likely motivation for the choice of the system to be considered was the set of 1937 patents by Lee Twomey on a method of liquefying fuel gases. In fact, the patent issuance might have been the proximate cause of the pilot plant research. The patent was issued June 1, 1937, and Hope started the pilot plant research in August 1937. They were convinced of its ultimate success by the earlier work at Fort Worth and Amarillo, Texas, where natural gas had been liquefied to extract helium.[49]

Lee Twomey was certainly aware of the potential of storing natural gas on site as a liquid. In his patent titled "Method of Liquefying and Storing Fuel Gases," he discusses the idea of leveling the natural gas load on pipelines by continually moving the gas even during low demand periods.[50] The gas that is not used during these low demand times would then be liquefied and stored on site. He cites a 640-to-one ratio for storing liquid gas over storing it in the gaseous state. The gas is stored until needed and then regasified and put into the gas mains. The patent then goes on to describe a process that uses a cascade of cooling cycles, first with ammonia and then with ethylene, and finally an expansion into a tank containing liquid natural gas. This is the first time a system was described that would have as its main purpose the liquefaction, storage, and regasification of natural gas to achieve load leveling or "peak shaving." The patent spent almost no space discussing storage but mentioned it in context just for completeness.

Hope Natural Gas used the same coolant liquids proposed by Twomey, ammonia and ethylene, although both acknowledged other coolants could be used. In place of ammonia Twomey considered propylene, propane, allylene, methyl chloride, sulphur dioxide, and carbon dioxide. He considered ethane and nitrous oxide for ethylene in the second cooling stage. Hope had considered ammonia or isobutane for the first stage, and ethane or ethylene for the second stage. Isobutane and ethane were rejected because their temperatures didn't work out.[51] Once the ammonia and ethylene were chosen they were used for both the pilot plant and the Cleveland plant.

The choice of liquids is important because the boiling points of the liquids must be such that they can cool the gas in the next stage below its critical temperature, so it can be liquefied. The basic challenge is to remove the heat from the natural gas to get it down to its boiling point at atmospheric temperature, where it can be stored. For methane it first has to get below its critical temperature, which is −82°C (−116°F). Thus the second cooling stage, the one cooling the methane, has to get below this temperature. The boiling point of ethylene is −103°C (−153°F) so it works well as a second-stage coolant. Ethane has a boiling point of −88°C (−126°F), which makes it less efficient than ethylene. Similarly, the critical temperature of ethylene is 10°C (50°F), so the boiling point of ammonia at −33°C (−27°F) works well to liquefy ethylene. The gases in the cascade cooling cycles are used at their boiling points to take advantage of the large amount of heat needed to vaporize a gas at its boiling point, that is, the heat of vaporization (see Chapter 4).

Using the Twomey patent, including his choice of coolants, the flow diagram of the Cleveland plant is as shown in figure 5-2. It is essentially the flow diagram of the pilot plant also, because the pilot plant was used as the model for this plant. This design most likely incorporates the experience of the pilot plant, for example placing the carbon dioxide and water removal dryers up front rather than later in the process as the patent shows. This assures that neither frozen carbon dioxide (dry ice) nor ice can close the pipes as the temperatures get lower through the process.

Consider the liquefaction process shown in figure 5-2 in three stages: the ammonia circuit, the ethylene circuit, and the natural gas circuit. The temperature and pressure figures shown in the figure are approximate.[52]

The ammonia (NH_3) comes out of the ammonia evaporator as a gas at about three to four pounds per square inch gauge and 30°F. It is compressed to a higher pressure and therefore to a higher temperature because the compression adds heat. The ammonia is condensed in a water-cooled heat exchanger where the heat of compression is removed leaving the liquid ammonia at about 114 pounds per square inch gauge and 70°F. The liquid ammonia is cooled another 50°F by passing through two heat exchangers (1 and 4) cooled by very cold natural gas. It passes to the ammonia evaporator (ethylene condenser) through an expansion valve. The expansion through the valve is adiabatic (no heat transfer) and the liquid ammonia experiences a "flash evaporation" or "cracking" in which some of the liquid flashes into a vapor and some remains liquid but both drop significantly in temperature and pressure. Flash evaporation or cracking refers to the sudden expansion of the gas as it goes through the valve. This is the Joule-Thomson effect and therefore cools the liquid and drops the pressure. In this case the temperature is dropped to −20°F, low enough to condense ethylene, and the pressure drops to about three to four pounds per square inch gauge. As the ammonia absorbs heat from the ethylene it evaporates and the temperature rises to about 30°F where the cycle repeats itself. This completes the closed ammonia cooling cycle, which cools and condenses the ethylene.

The ethylene cycle is analogous to the ammonia cycle, except everything happens at a lower temperature. The ethylene enters the ethylene evaporator at about −145°F and five pounds per square inch gauge, where it condenses the natural gas. It is in turn compressed and then cooled in the ammonia evaporator as described previously. Similar to the ammonia, it is also cooled by two heat exchangers to −40°F before it is cracked through the valve into the ethylene evaporator, where it cools the natural gas.

The purpose of these multiple cooling stages—water, ammonia, and ethylene—is to eventually cool the natural gas, primarily methane, enough so it is liquefied.

Now consider the natural gas cycle. Again, referring to figure 5-2, the raw gas comes into the plant at about 30 pounds per square inch gauge and 30°F from the pipeline source. At this point its composition, as analyzed by East Ohio, is, typically methane, 86 percent; ethane, 8.4 percent; and propane, 3.6 percent.[53] It is first compressed by a large, 600-horsepower compressor to 600 pounds per square inch gauge. The 600 pounds per square inch gauge, or 614.7 pounds per square inch absolute gas, is below the critical pressure of methane, which is 673 pounds per square inch absolute. Therefore cooling the gas below

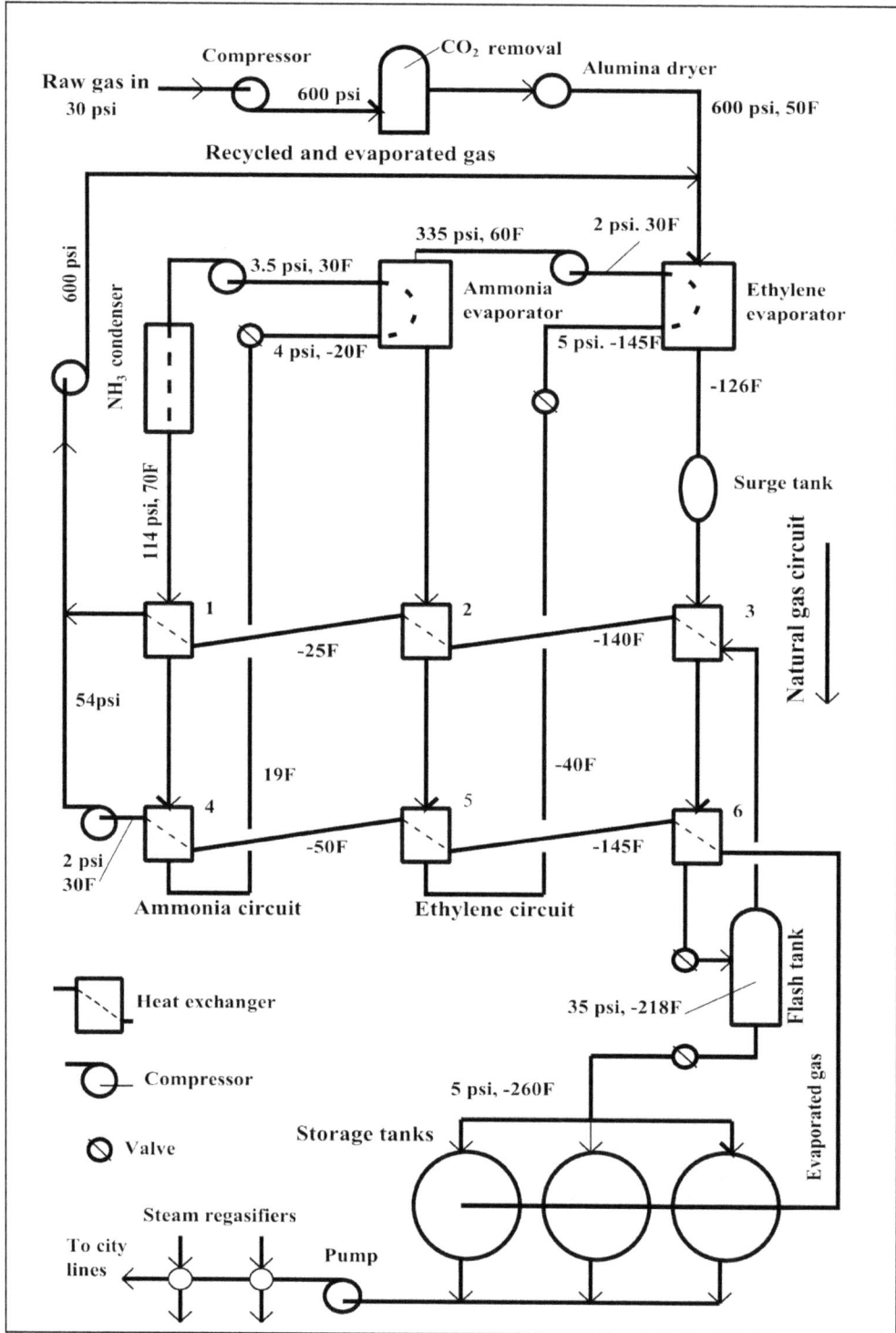

Figure 5-2. Flow diagram, East Ohio Gas Company liquid natural gas plant.

its critical temperature of −116°F will liquefy it. The pressure is raised so that later in the cycle the gas can be cooled by a series of cracking operations, that is, reducing the pressure through expansion valves to cool and liquefy it. The gas has been heated by the compression to about 50°F. Following the compressor, and following every compressor in the system, is an oil separator to remove any oil introduced by the compressor. These are not shown in figure 5-2. Prior to any cooling it is necessary to remove any contaminant that would freeze if it went through the cooling process and therefore close any pipes and/or valves. In this case contaminants include carbon dioxide and water vapor. The carbon dioxide is first scrubbed out using mono-ethanolamine and diethylene-glycol. Then the gas is passed through tanks of alumina (aluminum oxide) to dry it, that is, to remove the last traces of water. This was a lesson learned in the pilot plant when a frozen valve caused the operation to be shut down for a couple of days while the problem was fixed. This is one difference between this plant and the Twomey patents. Twomey did not have the carbon dioxide removal until the middle of the process.

The warm (50°F) gas is then passed through the ethylene evaporator, where the evaporating ethylene at −145°F absorbs heat from the gas, thus condensing it to a liquid at around −126°F, below the methane critical temperature of −116°F; the gas is now a liquid. The liquid goes into a surge tank. The surge tank is where the other gases such as nitrogen and oxygen that are not liquefied are rejected. The liquid gas is further chilled by heat exchangers 3 and 6 to about −139°F. Since the gas is now totally liquid, one might ask why this is not the end of the process. Although the gas is now a liquid, the pressure is still about 600 pounds per square inch gauge. This would require a very heavy, very strong container, which is not at all practical for large volumes of liquid gas.

The following steps maintain the liquid but reduce the pressure. The liquid gas is cracked or flash evaporated into the first flash tank, where both the pressure and temperature are reduced to 35 pounds per square inch gauge and −218°F respectively. In the flashing process about half the liquid flashes back to gas and half remains as liquid. This cold (−218°F) gas is recycled back through heat exchangers 3, 2, and 1 to cool the methane, ethylene, and ammonia and then recompressed and added to the original stream for reprocessing. The remaining liquid is cracked again through another expansion valve, reducing the pressure and temperature to about five pounds per square inch gauge and −260°F. This liquid gas ends up in the three storage tanks. Once again the liquid flashed into gas at this stage is recycled back through heat exchangers 6, 5, and 4, cooling the methane, ethylene, and ammonia, and then is recompressed and added to the original stream for reprocessing. The low pressure in the large storage tanks allows these to be constructed of steel of a thickness consistent with low stress. Of course the steel in contact with the −260°F liquid must be an alloy with appropriate toughness at low temperatures, as discussed previously. When it is time to regasify the liquid gas, it is brought up to pressure, and steam is used to supply the heat of vaporization to evaporate the liquid into gas, which is then sent to the city gas mains.

The plant had the capacity to convert four million cubic feet of gas per day into liquid. The regasification rate was three million cubic feet per hour. This process required a lot of power to compress the gases at various stages so they could eventually be expanded and therefore cooled. A total of 3,300 horsepower was used, divided into 600 horsepower for raw gas compression, 950 horsepower for recycling gas compression, 1,250 horsepower for ethylene compression and 500 horsepower for ammonia compression. Running these engines over a 24-hour period to liquefy four million cubic feet of gas took a lot of energy. The energy cost of converting the gas to a liquid was almost five percent of the amount of energy stored in the gas converted daily.[54] This would be at 100 percent efficiency. Considering other uses of power and engine inefficiency, the more likely cost would be closer to 10 percent or higher. It also took energy to convert the liquid to a gas again, that is, regasify it by adding the heat of vaporization. The actual estimate for that was about 20 BTU per cubic foot.[55] This would add another two percent to the energy used. The plant therefore used a lot of energy to liquefy and regasify the gas it stored. The payoff, however, was a supply of gas that could easily be returned to the city gas mains to maintain an adequate supply to all the users.

Storage Tanks

The material for the tanks had been chosen as the low-carbon, 3½ percent nickel-steel described previously. Of course to preclude a loss of heat, the tank holding the cold liquid gas (−260°F) had to be insulated. It appears that cork was chosen as the insulator without much, if any, consideration of other insulators; it was a good choice. For the tank in the pilot plant they had simply formed a two-foot-thick layer around the tank, glued it to the tank, and laid the combination in a wooden saddle for the experimental operations. The operational Cleveland plant had to have a more permanent and structurally sound container for the liquid gas. The plant was initially sized for peak-shaving to supply extra

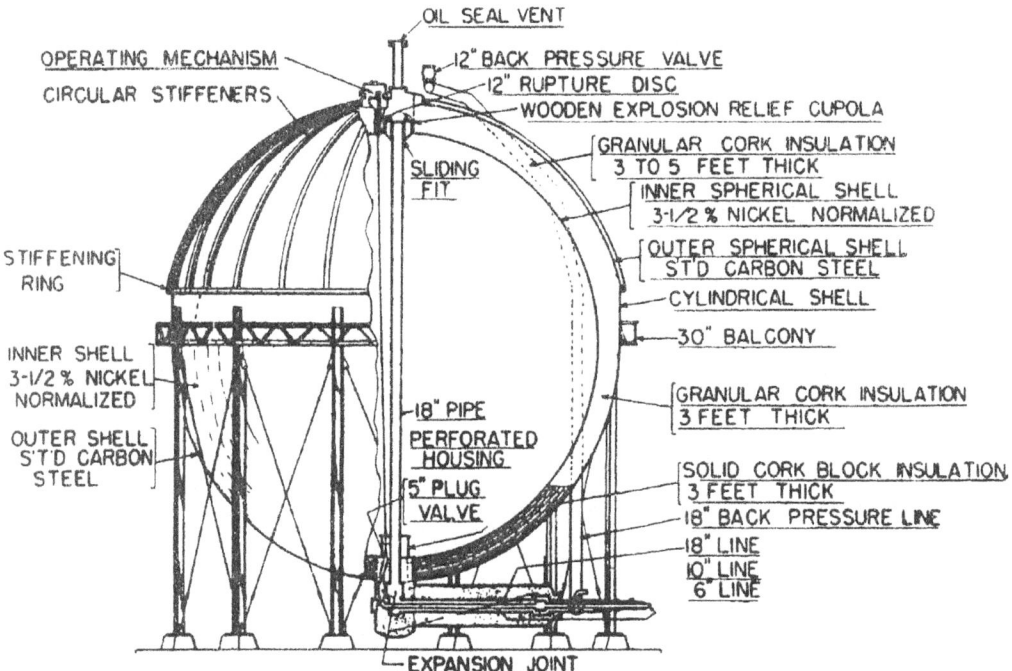

Figure 5-3. Liquid natural gas storage tank.

gas for a couple of cold days. The size decided on was 150,000,000 cubic feet. This was apportioned into three storage tanks of 50,000,000 cubic feet of gas each. When the gas was liquefied, the 600-to-one ratio of gas to liquid determined the inside diameter of the storage sphere to be 54 feet.

The storage tanks were designed as double-walled spheres with an insulating material between them. This is similar to the dual-wall design of a thermos bottle and for the same reason; that is, to keep the inside sphere cold and the outside sphere at ambient temperature. A spherical design was chosen not only to minimize the outside area for the volume enclosed but also because it was a smooth surface, easy to weld, and minimized the stresses. A sphere also has the least surface area for the volume contained. This was important to minimize heat loss. Figure 5-3 shows a drawing of the spherical storage tank.[56] The insulating cork around the inner tank was three feet thick around the entire sphere.

Formed, solid-cork blocks were used at the bottom of the tank for strength, and the inner tank was supported on the cork. This was necessary because there could be no thermal connection between the inner and outer tanks. No thermal connection meant there would be no metal-to-metal contact between the tanks, which would cause heat loss, thus evaporating the liquid gas in the tanks. The cork starting about halfway up the sphere was granulated. It was actually a better insulator because of the gas pockets in the granulated mixture. Granular cork could not be used on the bottom because it could not support the inner tank. A dry gas was circulated in the cork insulation to keep moisture out that would have frozen when exposed to the low temperatures. The outer tank, supported by the columns shown, was made of standard carbon steel. It carried all the structural loads.

All the piping, fittings, and valves around the plant were made of standard steel construction unless they encountered temperatures of $-50°F$ or lower. In these cases they were made of either pure copper or stainless steel. These materials either did not have a ductile-to-brittle transition or were tough enough to withstand the cold without brittle fracture.

One of the initial concerns was the loss due to evaporation because of heat leaks into the tanks. From the experimental work and the pilot plant they had calculated a heat transfer of about 0.25 BTU per cubic foot. Using this they calculated that about 500,000 cubic feet would evaporate per day for all three tanks. Early in the operation of the plant one tank stood nearly full for about three weeks, and they carefully metered the evaporation. It varied from 105,000 to 115,000 cubic feet per day. This caused them to conclude that the total loss per day for all three tanks would be less than 500,000 cubic feet per day, that is, less than originally expected.[57] This could have been due to the low molecular activity of the liquid they had observed in the pilot plant.

1939

The pilot plant was started in September 1939 and was in operation by January 1940. This plant was the prototype for the East Ohio Gas Company plant, which followed almost immediately after the successful operation of the pilot plant. The East Ohio plant was the world's first commercial liquid natural gas plant. It was used for peak-shaving, so 1939 could be considered the start of the liquid natural gas industry, that is, a transition point in the larger natural gas industry.

This year was also a transition year in many other respects, both domestically and internationally. The unemployment rate was high at 17 percent, but it finally started to fall for good. After a high in 1933 of 25 percent it had gradually reduced to 14 percent in 1937, when a recession hit and raised the rate back to 19 percent in 1938. As a result of this recession President Roosevelt went back to deficit spending in 1939 by raising federal spending 33 percent as a percentage of the Gross Domestic Product (GDP). Partly as a result of this, the Gross National Product (GNP) increased 7.9 percent in 1939. From here on the economy improved dramatically, heading into the war years.[58] Part of this borrowed money went to rebuilding the armed forces so that by 1941, U.S. manufacturing had shot up 50 percent.

Across the country some things continued as before and some things showed up for the first time. In April the Boston Bruins defeated the Toronto Maple Leafs for the Stanley Cup. On July 4, Lou Gehrig gave his "Luckiest Man" speech at Yankee Stadium when he bowed out of baseball, suffering with what has come to be known as Lou Gehrig's disease. At the end of the same season the New York Yankees swept the Cincinnati Reds in the World Series. The sports world experienced at least two new events. The Augusta National Invitation Tournament was officially renamed "The Masters." In March the first NCAA Men's Basketball Championship took place, in which Oregon defeated Ohio State. This, of course, led to our more recent "March Madness" and the "Final Four."

The movies, which were very popular, cheap, and plentiful during the Depression, had a banner year in 1939. There were the old standbys such as Andy Hardy and Charlie Chan; and Ronald Reagan appeared in no fewer than six films in 1939. Other notables included *Dark Victory*, *Goodbye Mr. Chips*, *Mr. Smith Goes to Washington*, and *Of Mice and Men*. The two blockbusters were, of course, *The Wizard of Oz* and *Gone with the Wind*, the latter taking the Best Picture Oscar over the former. New books included Steinbeck's *The Grapes of Wrath* and James Joyce's *Finnegan's Wake*. Agatha Christie continued her run of popular mysteries, publishing two that year.

Television made its debut that year and undoubtedly would have increased in popularity very rapidly had its development not been interrupted by the war. Franklin Roosevelt became the first president to appear on TV. In April, another big event of the year, the 1939 New York World's Fair, opened in Flushing Meadows, New York. Although broadcast to only to a handful of TV sets in the New York area, it was still a major event. Later that summer, Red Barber announced the first televised baseball game between the Cincinnati Reds and the Brooklyn Dodgers.

The defining event of 1939 was the September 1 invasion of Poland by German forces, which of course was the start of World War II. This event had been preceded by many others leading to this action. The Anschluss in Austria and the ceding of the Czech Sudetenland to Germany in October were preceding events in 1938. In the Anschluss, Germany marched into and annexed Austria. The infamous Munich Crisis was to guarantee "peace in our time" by allowing Germany access to that part of Czechoslovakia. In March of 1939 Hitler marched into the Czech part of Czechoslovakia to establish the Protectorate of Bohemia and Moravia. The territorial march continued. In short order the Spanish Civil War ended (to Hitler's benefit), Italy invaded Albania, and Hitler renounced the German-Polish Non-Aggression Pact, all in April 1939. The world was stunned on August 24 with the announcement of the non-aggression treaty between the two previously mortal enemies: the Third Reich and the Union of Soviet Socialist Republics (USSR). The reason became clear only days later when Hitler invaded Poland and the Third Reich, and the

USSR proceeded to carve up Poland. Great Britain and France had pledged to go to war to support Poland should she be invaded by Germany. They did shortly declare war but did nothing to support Poland in 1939, only getting into the war later when Germany invaded France. As a result, the German domination of Poland was complete within weeks.

With these events taking place on the world stage, it is probably not a coincidence that Hope decided to go ahead with the LNG pilot plant in September 1939. Although the U.S. was still in its isolationist phase, it was clear that manufacturing would pick up and more energy than ever would be needed to support it. The world's entry into the age of liquid natural gas was spurred on by the start of World War II.

Construction and Operation of the East Ohio Gas Company Liquefaction, Storage, and Regasification Plant

The Hope Natural Gas pilot plant was completed in January 1940. As things were heating up in the world they were cooling down in the eastern part of the U.S. In that same month a cold wave hit the eastern part of the country and all the natural gas plants were impacted; it was difficult to keep a sufficient supply of gas. Something had to be done, or shortages would mean that gas would continue to be cut off to some customers in a cold wave. The obvious solution was to lay in more lines to bring gas from the West Virginia fields. East Ohio had plans to extend a high-pressure line at a cost of approximately $2.5 million. Sometime during the operation of the pilot plant, East Ohio did a study and concluded that they could build an operating plant in Cleveland based on the Hope pilot plant for about $750,000.[59] (Later the estimate was raised to one million dollars and then to 1.25 million dollars.) The decision was apparently made in the spring, even before the pilot plant operation was complete, which was in May. The go-ahead was given to build the plant.

In the meantime the pilot plant continued to operate successfully at the Hope Cornwell Station in West Virginia. The Hope team arrived at the following conclusions on the operation of the pilot plant[60]:

1. The last possible traces of water and carbon dioxide must be removed, as failure to hold up the amine concentration at one time caused a 2-day shutdown due to plugging by CO_2 ice.

2. There is a continual increase in the percent of nitrogen, oxygen, or any other gas non-condensable at the low temperature and these must be continually removed. We found that a surge tank inserted in the gas line just after the ethylene condenser, where the gas is a liquid at 600 lb., with a bleeder to the engine fuel line solved this problem.

3. After going below −50°F, the pipe and tank steel becomes so brittle it is entirely unsafe. The metals that retain a safe Charpy impact-test value are, in the order of excellence, pure copper, bronze, monel metal, red brass, stainless steel, and steel plate with carbon content less than 0.09 percent and nickel over 3½ percent.

4. The best insulator we have found so far is cork, although something better may be discovered later. Formed cork was used on the pilot plant tank, but we found that loose granulated cork between the two walls gave still better results and was much cheaper. However, this must be kept perfectly dry to function properly. We have found a conservative coefficient of heat transfer in B.t.u. per square foot per inch of thickness per °F per hour to be 0.40.

5. The evaporated liquid has exactly the same analysis as the raw gas used as feed. However, the evaporation from the stored liquid is entirely methane and eventually if allowed to stand for long periods the liquid left will become increasingly higher in ethane-plus content. [In this early plant all the heavier hydrocarbons, for example ethane and butane, in the natural gas mix were liquefied. In later processes these were separated out and used separately so the resultant liquid is almost pure methane.]

6. At −250°F the molecular activity of the liquid is so low that it is an excellent insulator for itself, and to transfer heat into it the liquid must be broken up into very thin layers and its velocity must be kept very high and turbulent.

The lessons from these conclusions were all incorporated into the operational plant built by East Ohio. The pilot plant built by Hope Natural Gas, and the operational plant built by East Ohio Gas, once again showed the close cooperation between these two companies, which had been working together since they were incorporated in the same month in 1898 by Standard Oil.

On June 15, 1940, the City of Cleveland Department of Public Safety, Division of Building and Smoke, issued permit E 26310 to the East Ohio Gas Company to build "3 spheres to store Liquefied Natural Gas as an addition to the present gas storage." The latter were the traditional gasholders on the property. Some safety requirements were included: "Shortest distance to any building on the same lot: 80 feet.... Shortest distance to any building on adjacent lot: 70 feet." The spheres were to be 63 feet outside diameter, made of steel, and estimated to cost $260,000. (The actual sphere was closer to 60 feet on the outside with a 54 foot inner diameter, as stated previously.) The architect was listed as Pittsburgh–Des Moines Steel Co. Additional information was on a drawing by the Gas and Machinery Company, the prime contractor for the plant. (Gas and Machinery had the prime contract with East Ohio to build the plant. They had a contract with the patentee [Twomey] to be the exclusive licensee to operate under his two patents. Pittsburgh–Des Moines had a subcontract under Gas and Machinery to build the spheres.[61]) The location was east of East 61st street and north of the Pennsylvania Railroad spur. This described the location of the East Ohio Gas Company No. 2 Plant. The L. S. and R. plant was to be contained within the No. 2 plant. Besides the storage tanks, the plant included the cooling tower and the compressor building. The boiler plant, capable of producing 62,000 pounds of steam per hour for regasification, already existed at the No. 2 works.[62] It is seen outside the L. S. and R. fence in the upper right of figure 5-4, which was made after the fire. Storage tank 4 shown in the figure was added later; that is, it was not part of the original construction, which consisted of only tanks 1, 2, and 3. Because the plant was designed to liquefy four million cubic feet per day, it would require about 38 days to completely fill the tanks.

In figure 5-4 the three tanks are shown just north of the railroad spur (running east-west across the center of the map) and just east of East 61st street (lower left). The Lamson and Sessions Company (off the picture), where Ann Cimperman and John Penca worked, is due east of the plant across East 63rd Street, which is the street on the diagonal in the lower to middle right. Also off the picture to the north are the through-railroad tracks, running east-west, and a few hundred yards north of that is Lake Erie. Anthony Kasic's home was about 400 feet from tank 4, which was the one that ruptured. The closest home to a tank was at 990 East 61st Street, which was only about 100 feet from tank 1. Tanks 1 and 2 survived the fire. Item 65 (upper left) is the compressor building and item 9 (above

5. Liquid Storage 131

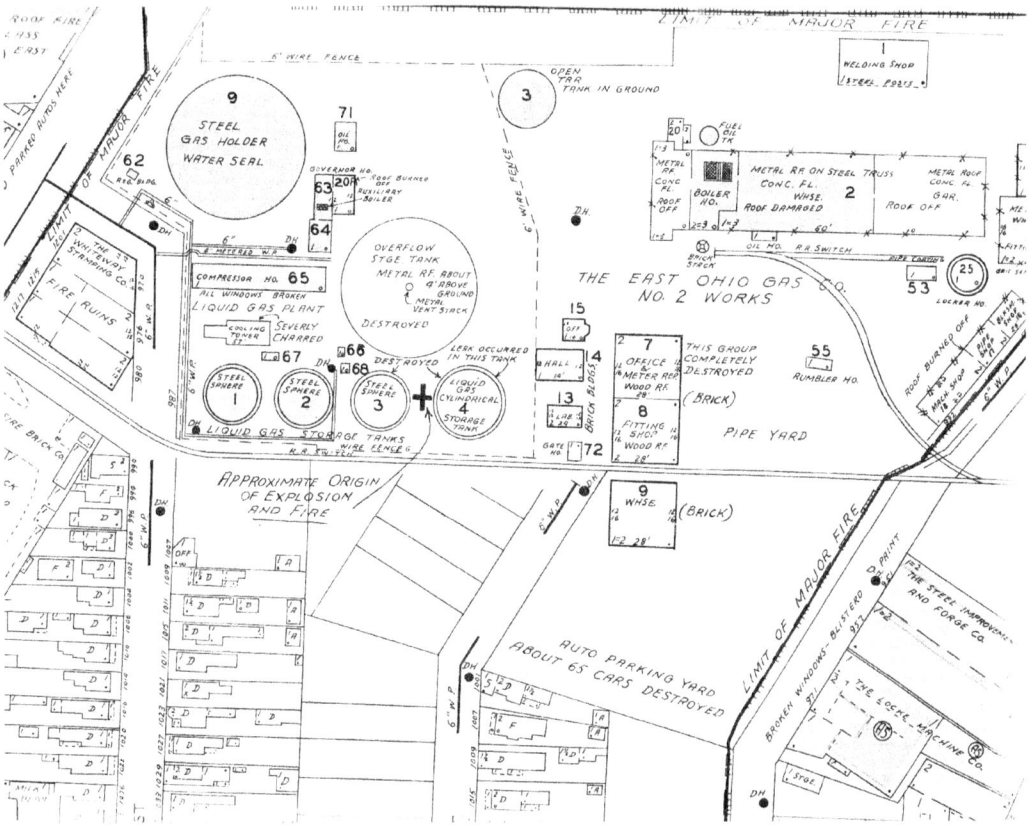

Figure 5-4. Layout of the L. S. & R. plant at the East Ohio Gas Company No. 2 works (courtesy American Insurance Association and Western Reserve Fire Museum at Cleveland, Inc.).

the compressor building) is a traditional water-seal gas holder on the site prior to the L. S. and R. plant. A six-foot wire fence is shown surrounding the L. S. and R. plant on the grounds of the No. 2 works. The note in the figure indicates the approximate origin of the rupture as being on the west side of tank 4. However, as will be covered, the testimony locates the origin as closer to the south or southeast part of tank 4. Figure 1–2 shows an aerial view during the construction of tank 3 and figure 1–3 shows the four tanks. Figure 5-5 shows the cooling tower, which was just behind tank 1.[63]

The plant was built in the fall of 1940 and was intended for completion that year so operation could start in late fall and the tanks would be filled by Christmas. As is common for projects of this size, some suppliers were late with equipment. Nevertheless, completion of a new plant of this size in only four or five months was a significant achievement. It was completed January 29, 1941, and the first production of liquid gas started on February 7, 1941. There were no significant cold waves in December and January. As John Clark, chief engineer of Hope, said,

> The first cold wave hit on February nineteenth, and at that time there was 16,000,000 cu. ft. of liquid gas in storage, and on February nineteenth 7,000,000 cu. ft. was regasified and put back into the lines and about 4,000,000 on February twentieth. On February 21 the weather moderated and it was possible to go back to liquefying again, and on March seventeenth,

Figure 5-5. LNG plant cooling tower (courtesy Youngstown Historical Center Dominion East Ohio Gas Company Collection).

when the most severe cold wave of the winter hit Cleveland, there was 50,000,000 cu. ft. in storage. During the two days of this cold spell, the plant fully justified its construction, as 16,000,000 cu. ft. was regasified and put back into the city plant on March seventeenth and 5,000,000 cu. ft. on March eighteenth. Due to the inability to foresee what was ahead in the way of weather, and the desire to conserve all liquid possible, only the minimum amount necessary to keep operating conditions normal was used. The result to the gas company of this plant was the ability to handle without curtailment an industrial load of over 40,000,000 cu. ft. per day, which most certainly would have been curtailed or shut off for at least two days, with the resultant loss of confidence on the part of the industrial users.[64]

So immediately after construction the plant proved its worth by maintaining gas flow to industrial customers when in the past it would have been curtailed. The plant had indeed justified its existence. Even though the U.S. was not yet in the war in early 1941, industrial output in the country was climbing rapidly because of it. So the ability of the plant to maintain normal industrial production during a cold wave must have been a great relief for the company and the city, especially since in previous years that had not been possible.

There was another advantage that accrued from the location of the plant in the city: "It also developed that the gas fed directly at the point of consumption was much more useful than if fed at any other point, as here it was all clear gain, with no added congestion in transmission lines loaded to capacity."[65] In other words, the stored gas was nearby, in the heart of the city. This is one of the advantages that manufactured gas once held, that it could be made close to the source of its need. This would later prove to be a problem when the fire erupted.

Expansion of the Storage Capacity

The East Ohio Gas L. S. and R. plant continued to work well. There were no gas shortages during the winters of 1940-41 and 1941-42. The U.S. entered the war in December 1941 after Pearl Harbor and after Hitler declared war on the U.S. a few days later. The first full year of the war for the U.S. was 1942, and as might be expected there was a major increase in armaments production in that year, which was sustained throughout the course of the war. Most historians agree it was the U.S. ability to supply arms not only for itself but for its allies, including the Soviet Union, that was the major U.S. contribution to victory in the war. Cleveland was a major part of the wartime manufacturing, so its energy needs skyrocketed at that time. Although the three LNG storage tanks had been working well for peacetime peak-shaving, the need for more storage became apparent. In March of 1942 East Ohio told Pittsburgh–Des Moines that they wanted to build an additional tank, but this time with a capacity of 100 million cubic feet, twice as much as any of the existing spheres, which had a capacity of 50 million cubic feet each.[66] As a result, on August 3, 1942, the East Ohio Gas Company applied for a building permit (no. G31615) for another storage tank. It was to be 76 feet in diameter and was to be located next to the other three tanks.

Originally they considered another spherical tank. However, that design was not practical, as Jackson discussed in his testimony:

> So we worked up a design of a spherical tank for that capacity, and the metal thickness increases quite a bit. The theory of the sphere is that the inner wall is supported throughout

about its lower third bearing on the cork board and that induces tension stresses and compression stresses, and as the size increases, these stresses get larger more rapidly than the capacity of the tank and in a very much larger sphere the thickness of the metal gets to be excessive.[67]

In other words, the weight of the inner tank on the outer tank increases such that the thickness of the steel in the outer tank would be excessive.

Theoretically, a sphere would be an ideal shape, because it has the least surface area that encloses the volume of interest. That would mean the least area for heat leakage. It is also the smoothest area; that is, it has no sharp corners and thus less concentrated stress. Later in the testimony Cooper acknowledged they could have built two more spheres identical to the first three, but there was not enough space (see figure 5-4). He also acknowledged that two more spheres would have required more steel, which was now harder to come by, and more costly. As East Ohio Vice President Hagan said,

> They [Pittsburgh–Des Moines] offered a design of the spherical tank for the one hundred million, ninety to hundred million if we wished to buy one, but they called our attention to the fact that it would take roughly about one hundred more tons of steel to build the spherical tank than it would to build the cylindrical tank, and when we ordered the cylindrical tank there was some question in the mind of all of us as to whether or not we were going to have the government give us the priority for the steel for this tank.[68]

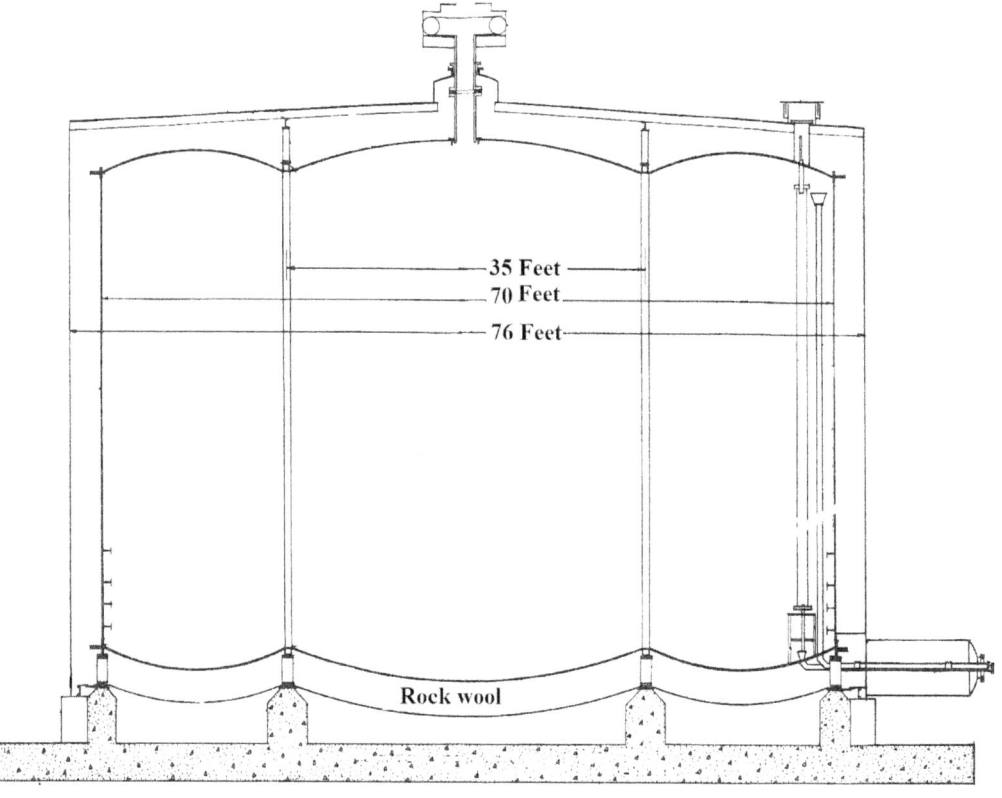

Figure 5-6. Cylindrical tank 4.

For all these reasons they decided to build a tank that was similar to a cylinder but resembled a cylinder within a torus.

Figure 5-6 shows the design of this tank.[69] It is nothing like the other three tanks, which are spheres. This tank was called "toro-segmental." There was no wall between the inner cylinder and the torus, only thirty steel columns supporting the inner tank. In other words, the inner cylinder and the torus were one volume.

The tank consisted of a concentric toro-cylinder (inner cylinder with a surrounding torus) and outside cylinder analogous to the concentric spheres of the original three tanks. The inner toro-cylinder, again analogous to the inner sphere, held the LNG. Its diameter was 70 feet. The outer cylinder surrounded the inner toro-cylinder with a space of three feet all around. Thus the outer cylinder was 76 feet in diameter. The space between the cylinders was filled with insulation. The inner toro-cylinder was formed of an inner-inner cylinder 35 feet in diameter and a surrounding torus with the outside diameter of 70 feet. The inner-inner cylinder was supported by a concrete wall, also 35 feet in diameter. The outer torus wall was also supported by a concrete wall 70 feet in diameter. These concrete walls sat on a concrete foundation slab. The outside tank was a pure cylinder. The height of the inner tank was 43 feet and the height of the outer tank was 51 feet. Both the torus and the inner-inner cylinder had spherical tops and bottoms, as did the bottom of the outer tank. There was three feet of insulation between the respective tank bottoms, as there was between the tank sides.

The choice of a "toro-segmental" design, that is the combination of the inner cylinder surrounded by the toroid shape, was probably used to limit the stresses on the inner tank and posts that would have resulted if a single set of supports at the outer perimeter of the inner tank had been used. In that case the cupped inner tank bottom would have been 70 feet in diameter and held in tension by the supporting wooden posts, which would have to have been much taller and stronger than they were to support the full weight of the inner tank. In one sense this design was like a suspension bridge, with the tank bottom suspended between the posts. In that sense it was nothing like a similar-appearing oil or gasoline storage tank, in which the bottom could be supported firmly by the underlying soil. In other words, the need for the insulation under the tank determined the tank design.

Just as it was necessary to prevent metal-to-metal contact between the inner and outer spheres of the original tank, it was also necessary to do the same for this tank. Wooden posts were used to support the inner tank to provide the thermal separation (insulation) between the two tanks. The inner-inner tank was supported by 30 twelve-inch by twelve-inch wooden posts on the 35-foot-diameter concrete base, which in turn supported 30 interior steel columns. The outer wall of the torus was supported on eight-inch by eight-inch wooden posts on the 70-foot-diameter concrete wall. To maintain thermal separation on the top of the inner tank, four-inch by four-inch wooden posts supported the roof rafters. There were a total of 110 wooden posts: 30 supporting the inner cylinder columns, 60 supporting the outer torus and 20 supporting the roof rafters.[70] Figures 5-7 and 5-8 show the wooden posts for the inner and outer tanks.[71] The steel base of the outer tank is in place during these construction photos. The concrete foundation (figure 5-7) can be seen on the outside rim of the tank.

The lower posts all had rocker plates on both sides so they could rock inward when the inner tank had the cold liquid and therefore shrank (contracted). This was the com-

Figure 5-7. Bottom of tank 4 (courtesy Youngstown Historical Center Dominion East Ohio Gas Company Collection).

Figure 5-8. Tank 4 wooden posts and lower circular box girder (courtesy Youngstown Historical Center Dominion East Ohio Gas Company Collection).

pensation for the temperature extremes encountered. The material for the inner tank was the same as it was for the spheres, that is, 3½ percent nickel-steel alloy. Although it was now wartime, and the material was undoubtedly hard to get, there was no early indication that the material was anything but the alloy as specified. That perception, however, would change after the accident investigation.

Wartime shortages did, however, affect the insulating material used. Cork was apparently not available, so rock wool was substituted. Although the design for tank 4 was different than that of the spheres, there is no reason cork could not have been used as the insulator; the design would allow it. However, the government wouldn't allow it because "there was a war on." Pittsburgh–Des Moines wanted to use cork, block and granular, for tank 4, so they submitted a request to the War Production Board for the cork. The request was denied. Hagan testified,

> The Pittsburgh–Des Moines Steel Company told us they could not get the cork, and it was our understanding that that was correct, that they could not get the cork. That there was a governmental regulation against the use of cork for this purpose or for that matter any purpose and they told us that they would experiment on other insulating materials, and it was at this time that they reported to us that they would use rock wool and that that would be a satisfactory substitute.[72]

The inability to obtain cork in 1942 seems to have been the conventional wisdom of the time and was not questioned by either failure review team. However, in a suit brought against the Pittsburgh–Des Moines Company that reached the Pennsylvania Supreme Court in 1949,

> the defendants testified that cork was not available but Exhibit 65, introduced by the plaintiff, showed that Central Insulation Company offered defendants cork for insulation on July 30, August 4 and August 10, 1942. The defendants ignored this offer and determined to use rock wool between the two shells of the No. 4 tank.[73]

Cooper acknowledged in later testimony that granular cork would have worked well if blown into the spaces between the tanks. East Ohio Vice President Hagan testified in the same case and said about the rock wool, "We never thought when we agreed with Pittsburgh–Des Moines to allow them to substitute rock wool for cork we were going to have to keep servicing it all the time."[74]

Which of these contradictory statements about the availability of cork is true is still open to question. However, it seems clear that Pittsburgh–Des Moines acted on the belief that they were prohibited from obtaining cork for the insulation. In any case, it was a significant design change to use rock wool instead of cork, and it could be argued that it contributed to the dire consequences.

Rock wool is also known as mineral wool or stone wool. It is an inorganic product made from minerals, typically basalt or slag or glass, which is melted and then spun into loose fibers that are intertwined. It is this fibrous material that provides good insulation by trapping air, not unlike fiberglass.[75] Although a good insulator, it must be kept dry and cannot support loads as cork does. If this was to be used all around the tank as an insulator, it would be necessary to support the tank bottom in some other way. This led to the wooden posts supporting the inner cylinder.

Besides the shape there was another difference between this tank and the three spheres. The spherical tanks, although more difficult to construct, had the advantage of a smooth, continuous surface, that is, no sharp angle discontinuities that could lead to stress concentrations. The design, which featured the "cradling" of the inner tank in the cork insulation supported by the outer tank, also had the advantage of insulating the inner tank from external perturbations because cork has vibration damping properties. In tank 4 the inner tank was only supported by the spherical bottom, which was held by the wooden posts; it did not rest on a cork base. It was like a suspension bridge being suspended between the two sets of wooden posts. That "suspension bridge" carried all of the weight of the liquid natural gas. All these design differences between the two tank designs became part of the discussion when tank 4 failed in 1944.

This new tank was completed in May 1943. At the end of May, Pittsburgh–Des Moines started to fill the tank to test it prior to turning it over to East Ohio. Normally they would not be generating LNG at this time of the year because it was not needed. The tanks would normally be filled in the fall. This fill was done just to check the tank before contractual handover from Pittsburgh–Des Moines to East Ohio. As they introduced the LNG the tank cracked. According to Hagan this was caused by the tank being improperly filled. The cold liquid was allowed to run into the "outer shell" or the "outer bottom" (see figure 5-7). This would be the bottom of the toroidal part of the tank. In other words it didn't cover the bottom of the tank evenly at first. This set up unanticipated stresses at the point where the liquid entered and the tank cracked. When asked why this was not a problem with the spherical tanks the answer was,

> Well, it was the difference in construction. You see, the liquid entered the bottom of the spherical tank so that the contraction occurred uniformly as the sphere filled, whereas the cylindrical tank has the toro-segmental bottom ... and the filling of the cylindrical tank allowed the liquid to gather first in this one portion of the bottom rather than uniformly distribute the liquid all over the bottom of the tank.[76]

The shape of the new tank now had caused problems because of the lack of symmetry in the design compared to the spherical tanks. The tank was repaired by welding. Steps were taken to prevent the crack from recurring, as discussed in the next chapter.

Summary

By early 1941 the problem of storing the energy of natural gas near the site where it was to be used appeared to have been solved. After it started liquefying gas and storing it in the three spherical tanks, the Cleveland L. S. and R. plant was used almost immediately, even before it was filled the first time. It was expected to be used to shave one or two peaks off the natural gas demand each winter. It did this the first time in early 1941 and successfully did it the next three years. The toro-segmental fourth tank was added in 1943, and it also contributed to keeping the supply flowing even in very cold weather. This last tank, number 4, increased the plant capacity by over 60 percent. This was important because the city energy needs increased significantly between 1943 and 1944 due to wartime production increases. As Matthew Braidech observed in the *Chemical and Engineering News* in March 1944,

> Just recently, on Feb. 14, when a cold snap was followed by a plunge of temperatures to sub-zero levels, acute gas emergencies drained the reserves of several Ohio companies to the point where it was necessary to cut off fuel services to 150 war plants and several thousand homes in some 350 counties, while Clevelanders passed the tension without discomfort.[77]

Howell Cooper recognized the feasibility of liquefying natural gas because of the work done twenty years earlier by the Bureau of Mines when they liquefied it to extract helium. He saw that the Twomey patents in the 1930s could lead to a practical commercial plant to do this. These observations came when there were natural gas shortages in Cleveland and other cities. Putting these things together, he started Hope Natural Gas on a research program in 1937 and by late 1939 was building a pilot plant in West Virginia to liquefy, store, and regasify natural gas. He correctly saw that the biggest challenge would be the storage tanks, which would have to hold the liquid gas for long periods at temperatures around −260°F. He knew, and demonstrated by experiment, that ordinary carbon steel becomes very brittle at these low temperatures and can be shattered by a simple hammer blow. Therefore, he sought a tougher material, one that had some nickel in it. For the pilot plant he used some two percent nickel-steel that was available from a supplier; he couldn't get a special run for the small amount they used. He alluded to some trouble he had had with the material but never said what that was.

The builders were breaking new ground here, using steels at very low temperatures. There was almost nothing in the design standards available that provided positive guidance on the materials. Given the paucity of information on low temperature metals, Cooper reviewed what was available and chose the material based on this review.

Once again he purchased some material that was left over from a previous job from another supplier. This time it was 3½ percent nickel-steel for the Cleveland plant. After the fact (after the purchase) Cooper and Jackson did some experiments on this material at low temperatures using liquid nitrogen (colder than liquid natural gas). They concluded a 3½ percent nickel-steel alloy would provide the impact resistance necessary to build a safe tank. Their tests included welding tests to convince them the welds also would hold.

So from early research in late 1937 to operation of the full-scale commercial plant in early 1941, the process took less than four years. Some of the conclusions reached during this very rapid development from pilot plant to operational plant would be questioned by the failure review teams during their investigations.

The future of storing, then using, natural gas this way appeared to be bright. Not only could it now be stored above ground for local use, it now became portable or moveable, if one considered the Cabot patents showing how to move these liquids by barge. Natural gas could now be moved around the world, not only by barge, but by ship. It would be possible to export energy to areas of the world that did not have their own resources. This is what probably waited in the future, that is, after the war.

This was all true until October 1944 when it all came apart ... literally.

6
Setback

The fires burned into the next day, which was Saturday, before they were totally extinguished. The search for victims started. This was very difficult because of the intensity of the flames, estimated to be as hot as 3,000° Fahrenheit. In some cases only fragments of bone were recovered and identified as well as could be done; there was no DNA testing at the time. There was a long time before the total number of dead was settled upon. The number bounced around for a while before most, but not all, agreed it was 130. In all, 109 were known to have been officially reported as missing. Of the 73 gas company employees missing, 54 were identified; of the 32 residents missing, 22 were identified; two nearby business employees were identified. Thus only 78 of those reported missing were identified. Reported missing, but unidentified, were 19 gas company employees, 10 residents of the area, and two roofing contractors, for a total of 31 missing but unidentified. In addition to the 109 officially missing, 21 others were "unofficially" missing, but they were part of the 130 bodies or parts of bodies that were found. They were neither reported missing nor identified. The 21 unidentified dead were buried in a common grave in Highland Park Cemetery in a service provided by many different denominations.[1]

The neighborhood between East 61st and East 63rd streets was flattened either by fire or by gas explosions. The Lake Court neighborhood north of the railroad tracks was also destroyed. The East Ohio Gas Company Number 2 Plant, which included the L. S. and R. plant, was almost totally destroyed. Amazingly, the two original tanks, numbers 1 and 2, survived the conflagration. Tank 3 was destroyed only because of its proximity to tank 4.

What remained was to start the recovery. The injured had to heal, and family life had to be restored. The neighborhood and the plant had to be cleaned and restored. Just as important, the cause had to be determined. This could mean the difference between the continuance of what appeared to be a promising industry and the demise of that industry, as the destruction of the *Hindenburg* marked the demise of the hydrogen dirigible era in aviation. There was a lot at stake.

Reactions

As might be expected the city was stunned. However, swift and positive action followed. Mayor Lausche quickly appointed a board of inquiry composed of prominent city leaders and technical experts. These included the Cleveland coroner, the directors of Law and Public Safety, city council members, and technical experts from the Case School of Applied Science. (This school became the Case Institute of Technology and later merged with Western Reserve University to form what is now Case Western Reserve University [CWRU].) This board held its first hearing October 24, at 10 a.m., less than four full days after the accident. This quick response obviously was done to gather information while memories were still fresh from the fire. Following these hearings two detailed technical studies were done to try to determine the root cause of the tragedy. The first report was delivered in July 1945; it was from the technical consultants on the mayor's board of inquiry.[2] The second report was by the U.S. Bureau of Mines. Their work was completed May 30, 1945, and the report was delivered in February 1946.[3]

The reaction to the disaster was rapid by the city, local citizens who helped rebuild, and the gas company, which quickly settled with many of the residents. Only a few cases went to court. These were suits against the builders of the tanks; they dragged on for a few years. In general the civic reaction was quite admirable.

What is a little surprising, especially looking back from an age that is used to protests, is the apparent lack of concern when the plant was built. There were numerous articles in the newspapers and in various technical journals about this new technology that would provide natural gas even during peak loads in very cold weather. However, there were no newspaper articles about any concerns from neighbors in the area about storing this amount of energy so close to a residential area. The original three tanks held the equivalent of 150 million cubic feet of natural gas. At about 1,050 BTU per cubic foot this was equivalent to about 159 billion BTU. This amount of energy would heat about 1,600 average homes for about one year. Or, to put it another way, if all this burned up within about two and one-half hours, the power generated would be about 25 million horsepower. This is approximately what happened, since tanks 3 and 4 together did contain about 150 million cubic feet of gas when they burst and spilled their contents over the neighborhood. Of course the fires they spawned burned much longer, even into the next day. As was pointed out, there was a house as close as 100 feet to tank 1, just over a fence and across East 61st Street. One would expect today that of course there would be ordinances against such a siting. However, even in the absence of such an ordinance there would be neighborhood protests that would clearly oppose that siting.

One could probably cite a few reasons the response to the siting of these tanks in a residential area was at best muted, if it existed at all. One was that there was much more confidence in, and deference to, local government and large corporations at the time. The assumption was that the city and the local gas company knew what they were doing, and what they were doing was in the best interest of the community. This was especially true of the immigrant community of that, and other, neighborhoods. Many of them were first or second generation Americans and they were interested in settling in and being accepted, not in making waves. It was also likely that many did not realize the significance of the construction. It was the gas company's property, and it could do what it wanted with it. On top of that, even though the houses were small and crowded together, they were glad to have them. There was a housing shortage during the war, so these people felt lucky to have homes. The attitude is different now; at least since the Viet Nam War government actions are looked on much more critically if not hostilely.

Similarly, large corporations are viewed with mistrust because of the history of some of their actions such as shipping jobs overseas, environmental disasters (the Gulf oil spill for example), and financial malfeasance, just to name a few. With more distrust of these institutions, that type of tank siting would probably not be tolerated by the populace now.

Another reason that the tanks' presence did not cause much concern was that the technology was new and did not seem threatening. The tanks were large, it is true, but they were filled with cold liquid, which probably didn't feel as threatening as, say, large tanks of gasoline. In fact there were ordinances on how one should store petroleum products, because these were known to be dangerous. It is likely that gasoline tanks sited at this location would have been prohibited. There were no ordinances on these types of storage tanks (LNG) so they were thought to be safe.

Despite all this reasoning, there was some concern expressed. It came after the war started, that is, after the plant had been in successful operation for some time. In July 1942 some residents expressed concern about what would happen if an enemy bomb hit the tanks. In a letter translated from the Slovenian newspaper *Ameriska Domovina* (American Home), an army lieutenant, Peter Kekic, assured the residents that the low temperature fluid could not ignite but would flow off into the lake. They would have to be careful that if it flowed around their feet they didn't get frost bite[4] (see figure 6-1).

The realization of the danger posed by the proximity of these tanks did finally start to take hold after the fire. A handwritten letter by an angry Cleveland dentist was received by the mayor on October 23 only three days after the fire:

> Dear Frank,
> I want to protest with all the vehemence at my command against the seeming negligence on somebody's part in allowing a *potential killer of more than one hundred persons,* some of our finest people, to remain within the limits of our community.
> You are not personally to blame as you are one of the finest citizens Cleveland has ever had but *can't we have more assurance that such menaces are not to be tolerated in our cities?*
> You have my sympathy & best wishes. Keep up your courage![5] [emphasis in the original].

Although this letter expressed confidence in the mayor, doubt and a conspiracy theory were also delivered in another handwritten letter, this one written November 2 from Bristow, Oklahoma.

> Dear Sir,
> I see by the papers you have started, a (10) ten man board, of inquiry, to investigate *disaster.* I don't know whether, this is the real thing, or a smoke screen.
> What ever you do don't allow thim to starte that Butane mixing plant in the city agane as it is to dangerous. You would [not?] think of letting thim build a gliserene plant neere the city, not to say inside, what has hapned can't be helped, but letting it happen agane can be helped. Pardon me for butting in. I would be pleased to here from you[6] [spelling and grammar are as in the original letter].

As different as the two letters are, they do express a common thought: This type of fuel storage should not be allowed in a city near a residential area. Needless to say these thoughts anticipated some of the board of inquiry questioning and later recommendations.

6. Setback

(C O P Y)

AMERICAN HOME PUBLISHING COMPANY
Publishers of

Tel. ENdicott 4088
Tel. HEnderson 0623

AMERISKA DOMOVINA

Slovenian DAILY Newspaper

Established 1898

6117 St. Clair Avenue
in our own modern printing
plant CLEVELAND, OHIO

TRANSLATION FROM AMERICAN HOME ISSUE OF JULY 28, 1942

GAS TANKS ARE SAFE IN CASE OF AN AIR RAID.

    Residents in the vicinity of E. 62nd St., have been concerned regarding explosions of gas tanks, if struck by a bomb. There is no need for alarm, because the tanks cannot explode.

    A visit was made to the Gas Company by Lieut. Peter Kekic, who is supervisor for all air raid defense work in the 2nd district, and his first assistant Mr. Nick Bohar.

    All facts were explained by Mr. George Binder and Chief Eng. C. F. Turner, and the following information was given us by Lieut. Kekic and Mr. Bohar for our readers:

    All the gas in these tanks is in frozen and liquid form. In case of a direct hit from a bomb, the gas being low in temperature, cannot ignite nor explode. The direct hit would only cause the gas to spill and flow off into the lake. Naturally, in that case, people in the vicinity would have to be careful not to step on the liquid which might cause frost bite.

    The conclusion is that resident in the vicinity of E. 62nd and E. 61st need not fear explosions or fire from these tanks.

    Lieut. Kekic requested us to appeal to more people to sign up for classes in First Aid and Air Raid Warden classes. This is for district No. 2, from E. 30th to E. 82nd, from the Lake to Euclid Avenue. Evening classes are Tuesday and Thursday 7:30 to 9:30 at Zele's Funeral Home, 6502 St. Clair Avenue.

    This district has a population of 95,800 which makes it necessary to have 1700 volunteer air raid wardens and assistants. At the present time there is only 500. Men and women are welcome. There is work for all. This district under Lieut. Kekic is one of the best organized in the city, and according to Lieut. Kekic, he has received much assistance from Councilmen Purcel and Kovacic.

    We appeal to our people to sign up either tonight or Thursday at Zele's Funeral Home or see Mr. Bohar.

    We must be serious about this and get ready for any emergency while there is still time.

— See Next Page —
For Clipping

Figure 6-1. Army letter of assurance (Youngstown Historical Center Dominion East Ohio Gas Company Collection).

Inquiry

Eyewitnesses

After the accident the most pressing question was what had happened. The whole thing came as a complete shock, and there was no idea of what had gone wrong. The mayor's board of inquiry continued to meet periodically for several weeks.[7] The chairman of the board of inquiry was Thomas Burke, director of law for Cleveland. Both Frank Lausche and Thomas Burke were involved in the election that took place within two weeks of the accident. Lausche was elected governor of Ohio and Burke was elected mayor of Cleveland, so their roles changed rather quickly after the accident. The three technical consultants on the board were on a technical subcommittee headed by Professor George Barnes. All three technical consultants were from the Case School of Applied Science in Cleveland.[8]

The questioning involved witnesses, plant operators, designers, and decision makers. The board sought to understand the events of the day so it could determine where to look for the cause. It sought to understand the plant operation, probing for possible failures that might have caused the accident. It questioned designers and decision makers for possible underlying design flaws.

Although John Roy Feightner was close to the tank that ruptured, he did not have a direct line of sight to the tank. He was on the north side of the compressor building and could not see the tanks directly (see figure 5-4). A number of people from the American Gas Association (AGA) testing laboratory on East 62nd Street did have direct view of the tanks from their offices. The only thing between the tanks and the AGA laboratory was the AGA parking lot (see figure 1–1). A number of them described what they saw in testimony to the board.[9] Hans Hense, Herbert Luoma, Franklin Wright, and Kendall Flint, all of the AGA lab, described similar scenes. Hense reported that around 2:45 p.m. he saw a leak develop in tank 4 and saw a stream shoot out from right of center about 10 feet above ground. He was looking north, so this would have been on the southeast side of tank 4. He observed for a few moments and noted that the first stream was to the left at 15 to 20 degrees angle from the horizontal, a second stream started to the right at a higher angle, and then a stream broke in the middle and started to go in all directions.[10] The tank seemed to give way. All this was accompanied by a lot of white vapor. This white vapor was the cold gas condensing the water vapor in the air.

At about the same time Herbert Luoma saw great quantities of white vapor spurting left and right out of tank 4. Within seconds the entire tank was obscured by white vapor, then the "whole thing seemed to open out.... It just sort of went 'swoosh.'" Franklin Wright's first impressions were exactly the same. At about 2:30 p.m. he felt a tremor like an earthquake. When he looked out the north window he saw white vapor with the appearance of steam coming from the number 4 tank at various points, approximately above the center of the holder. It was observed to be shooting out at various angles. The vapor became more voluminous and the tank appeared to be splitting apart; "it appeared as though it was bursting open." Kendall Flint observed it from his office on the north side of the building. He was dictating correspondence around 2:40 p.m. and saw vapor billowing from the tank between the bottom and one-third of the way up. He watched as the fissure increased in size.[11]

Other affidavits taken separately by the safety director had similar observations. John

Matter from the AGA laboratory looked out the north window and saw the left-hand side (southwest) of the cylindrical tank spewing streams of grayish-white smoke ("like burning funnels") from the top of the tank. E. J. Abbott at the same laboratory saw a thin white vapor and within seconds, "saw liquid jetting out in symmetrically spaced streams."[12]

It seems, from these early witnesses, that at least a couple of facts are clear. One is that it was tank 4 rather than any other tank; that was never in dispute. Secondly, even though there were later explosions and fires, the first instances of failure were clearly cracks or fissures in the tank from which these witnesses saw liquid and white vapor spew. The fact that they saw the liquid spewing from different locations and in different directions was probably an indication that the inner tank had failed, the space between tanks had filled with liquid natural gas, and the outer tank therefore failed in more than one location.

Visually all these witnesses had seen the early failure of the tank splitting open. Most of these and others also mentioned hearing a noise such as a rumble or tremor or concussion either just prior to or around the time of the fissures appearing. Russell Lake, for example, a superintendent at the Bishop-Babcock Company across East 55th Street (upper-left corner of figure 5-4), reported a dull concussion about 2:30 p.m. Franklin Wright felt a tremor resembling an earthquake, in which the building and desk seemed to shake, just prior to seeing the white vapor spewing from the tank.[13] John Roy Feightner had heard a noise like a "distant roll of thunder" before he stepped out the north door of the compressor building and saw the cloud of vapor rolling about 10 or 12 feet above the ground. John Matter heard a puff and an explosive noise that caused him to look out the window and see the grayish-white smoke. For F. E. Vandaveer at the AGA it was a low rumble that that caused him to swing his chair around to look out the north window to see the white vapor.[14]

The sequence of events was now becoming clearer. Some "concussion" or "tremor" or "rumble" occurred first. This caused a number of people who had direct visual access to tank 4 to observe the tank splitting and spewing liquid along with an accompanying white vapor. Although some described an early explosion, most described these early events as concussions or rumbles. The very earliest recollections were these sounds and sights. However, it wasn't long before these people and others started talking about flames.

The liquid natural gas would not ignite on its own as a liquid. However, some of it started to evaporate immediately. This was evidenced by the copious amounts of white vapor observed. The gas was colorless; the white vapor was the water vapor in the air being condensed by the cold liquid and gas. The white water vapor was harmless; the evaporated gas was not. The ignition range for natural gas in air is about 10 to 15 percent of gas concentration. When this concentration was reached, any ignition source could have set it off. No source was identified specifically, nor was that necessary. There were numerous sources of ignition on the property. Perhaps the failure of some electrical instrumentation on the tank caused a spark that ignited the gas. Whatever it was, the flames started almost immediately.

The white clouds that Hans Hense saw obscured the tank and traveled toward him in the AGA building on East 62nd Street. When they were about halfway across the north parking lot, between the building and the tanks, he felt a terrible blast of intense heat; the entire window was in red flames. Something had set off the gas approaching the building. The AGA laboratory was in a straight line south from tank 4, with nothing between the two locations except an AGA parking lot. The building was about 500 feet from the tank on East 62nd Street. As Franklin Wright was leaving the building he saw some flames that rose to the height of the building (25 to 30 feet). John Roy Feightner, who was closer to the rupture, saw the vapor, and before his eyes left the vapor it burst into flames. O. R. Pritchard, a sales and service engineer with the S. B. Martin Company, was visiting the Locke Machinery Company on East 63rd Street. He didn't even have time to shut off the car engine when he arrived. He saw the steam (vapor) rolling rapidly over the ground "like fingers" with a larger cloud coming behind it; then the outermost edges of the cloud burst into flames.[15] As Ann Cimperman described it, the rumble and fire seemed to come all at once.

The very early reports of rumbles or concussions and reports of seeing the liquid spew from the tank are fairly consistent. Later as the flames erupted, the story becomes more confused. The report of explosions is inconsistent. Some reported the first noises as explosions, whereas most reported these as rumbles or concussions. Later, however, there were reports of explosions. Russell Lake, for example, reported the first noise as a concussion (as did Feightner), and the second noise, which was quite pronounced, as an explosion. This was about twenty minutes after the first. Hans Hense ran out of the building up to St. Clair Avenue and East 62nd Street, where he watched for a while and also heard an explosion after twenty minutes. Franklin Wright thought he heard some kind of explosion as he was leaving the building. Later, also when he was at the corner of St. Clair and East 62nd Street, he heard two or three heavy explosions, one of which he concluded was tank number 3 going down. John Matter reported hearing an explosion several minutes after he left the building.[16] F. E. Vandaveer also ran to St. Clair and after about 30 minutes heard an explosion. There seems to be general agreement that some type of explosion occurred 20 to 30 minutes after the initial failure. It is certain that tank 3, the spherical tank closest to tank 4, did fail. This could have been the source of these reports. In a brief account John Novak, an East Ohio pipefitter, said that at about 2:30 p.m. he suddenly heard a loud explosion that was the first tank failing.[17] He then jumped a fence and watched the fire. He said he then saw the "ball tank" explode. He did not indicate how long afterwards this was. There were other reports of explosions happening later. These could have been various compressed gas tanks or any number of other objects, including some of the houses that exploded because of gas infiltration. The exact time of the failure of tank 3 had not been established.

The collection of this testimony, especially by people outside the gas company who had no knowledge of the plant operation, was important. It not only helped establish the timeline of the disaster but could help establish the reason for the failure. A tank ripping at the seams and spewing liquid gas that later catches fire would clearly indicate a different type of failure than a tank that exploded instantaneously. In this case it was clear (1) that the failure started in tank 4 rather than in any other tank or any other part of the liquefaction processing, and (2) that, although fire started soon after, the initial rupture was one of liquid pouring from the side of the tank.

Plant Conditions

The establishment of the chain of events by the eyewitnesses, especially outside the plant, was important for a basic understanding of what happened that day. There were two other areas that were important to understand. One of these was the design of the plant. For this the board questioned all those who had had an influence on the design or had been directly involved. This was important in order to determine if there was a fatal flaw in the plant design. However, prior to this the questioning was directed to the plant and its operation. Was the plant safe, and was it operating correctly? Were there any proximate problems that might have led to the catastrophe?

John Roy Feightner, assistant chief engineer of the liquefaction, storage, and regasification plant, was on-site and very familiar with the plant operation. (The chief engineer, Conrad Daiber, died in the fire.) It was Feightner's job to see that everything was in good order and operated correctly. In the course of his testimony Feightner went through the normal operation of the plant, describing general as well as specific operations.[18] He described to the board the process they used to liquefy the gas. The plant had been operating successfully for three years. They always kept some liquid in the tank, even over the summer, to keep the tanks cold and avoid radical temperature changes. So in the fall when they started filling the tanks for use during the winter, they started with about 60 to 70 million cubic feet less gas than they had had in the spring because of evaporation that occurred in the summer when the plant was not operating. They had started filling the tanks about two months prior to the accident. They were filled in the following order: tank 2, tank 3, tank 4, and tank 1. Tank 1 had just completed topping off at around 2:00 p.m. the day of the accident. Topping off for the spheres meant about 13 feet from the top; for the cylinder it was about one foot. There was much more room at the top of the cylinder than the spheres because of the shape. They didn't want the liquid too near the maximum level. The topped-off tanks would now be ready for use in the coming winter. After gas was used as needed during the winter, the liquefying process would be rerun until the tanks were again refilled. On this day they started the shutdown process because all the tanks were filled. This consisted mainly of removing the ammonia and ethylene refrigerants from the system.

Feightner had noticed nothing out of the ordinary that day, no outward signs of any trouble. Just prior to the accident at about 2:10 p.m. he had gone under tank 4 to retrieve a steam hose that had been left there from a previous operation. Again, there was nothing unusual about that tank at that time.

His testimony and that of others uncovered no unusual events during that day. However, four issues did come up that aroused the curiosity of the board and were the subject of much discussion not only with Feightner but also with others who testified later regarding the design of the tanks. The first was a crack in the bottom of tank 4 that had shown up when it was filled for the first time over a year earlier. The second had to do with frost spots that were periodically showing up on the bottom of tank 4. Third, the insulation in tank 4 had a tendency to settle over time. This meant more insulation had to be added. Was it possible this issue was related to the frost spots that showed up on tank 4? The fourth was the environmental vibration in the neighborhood from the railroads and the industrial processes. Did this contribute to the tank failure?

The Crack

As was covered in Chapter 5, the fourth tank, completed in May 1943, experienced a crack in the bottom while it was being filled the first time. Liquid gas leaked through the inner and then the outer tank. Pittsburgh–Des Moines (it was still their tank until it was turned over to East Ohio) led the analysis and repair effort, which took several weeks. The liquid had been introduced at the bottom of the toroidal portion of the tank. It did not flow evenly in the bottom, that is toward the center, but around the toroid. This uneven application of the cold liquid caused stresses that caused the tank to crack. The crack was on the bottom near the northeast part of the tank, near where the liquid was introduced. It was not at a weld but through a plate. This never happened in any of the spherical tanks. Because of the symmetry of the spherical tanks, the liquid was introduced in the center and the tank gradually cooled uniformly (contracted) as it was filled.[19] The repair for tank 4 was a plate that was welded over the crack.

Once the conclusion was reached that uneven cooling had been the cause of the crack, the fix was to provide for a more uniform cooling. This was done in two ways. First, copper pipes were added inside the tank to extend the introduction of the liquid to all parts of the tank simultaneously and thus reduce temperature gradients that would cause the stress. The second thing done was to introduce a cool vent gas to the entire tank to precool it prior to adding the liquid.[20] These changes worked, and there was no further trouble with that tank until the accident. After the accident they found the piece of the tank that had the welded repair. The weld, and therefore the repair, was intact, indicating that initial fix had worked and was not the cause of the subsequent failure.

This incident was another indicator of the new ground being broken in building this plant. The spherical tanks were symmetrical around all three axes. Thus the stresses were generally symmetrical; for example, the tanks cooled uniformly as they were filled. The cylindrical tank, number 4, was symmetrical around the vertical but not around any horizontal axis. This lack of symmetry led to a problem in filling the tank, so the filling process had to be changed. This problem had not been anticipated in the design of the tank; it probably should have been. The inner tank was not smooth. It had discontinuities such as where the saucer-shaped bottoms of the torus and inner cylinder met and where the cylindrical walls met the saucer-shaped bottom. Although the crack was not identified at either of these discontinuities, it should have been known that extreme temperature gradients would be set up when the liquid was introduced. This design anomaly may have contributed to the failure eventually and will be discussed later.

Frost Spots

Frost spots were periodically noticed at or near the bottom of tank 4. Once they were discovered the tank was checked daily for their existence. Feightner had been under tank 4 only 30 minutes prior to the accident, retrieving a hose and checking for frost spots. He and another person went in under the tank through a door in the concrete retaining wall. They were then able to get under the tank. This approach was necessary because tank 4 was lower to the ground than the other tanks. When asked about the purpose of the hose Feightner replied,

> We had noticed that due to poor circulation under there and the cold temperature, this tank was not as far off the ground as our spherical tanks, and it had collected quite a bit of moisture and had quite a little frost. The frost had done no damage, but we did not want it to freeze under there because eventually if it would go on the concrete walls, and with the temperature that we had there, there was no way of knowing just how the concrete was. So the concrete at the time was not frosted, the bottom of the tank was frosted some, which was

due to the dampness and the poor air circulation under there, and we just put a little heater in there to do away with the frosty condition and then circulated air under there to prevent that from happening again, and this hose was used in the operation ... and everything was okay at that time.[21]

Steam had not been applied directly but through a home-made heater under the tank. This incident with the heater took place months before the accident. They had been concerned about possible frost when they originally chose the spherical tanks. One reason they chose them was that they had the advantage that the bottom of the sphere was out in the air and would not get too cold.[22] After the frost was discovered, East Ohio asked Pittsburgh–Des Moines to look at it. After they (Pittsburgh–Des Moines) examined it in the summer of 1944 (consistent with the Feightner testimony that the frost had shown up about four months prior), East Ohio received a letter from them claiming there was nothing to worry about; there was no leak in the inner tank. This was undoubtedly true. Not only would a leak of the inner tank have continued to grow, but a simple heater as was used would not have gotten rid of a heavy frost caused by the liquid gas. A blower and heater system was installed at the suggestion of Pittsburgh–Des Moines. As William Hagan testified, "We put that there under their suggestion. We never would have thought of it ourselves. They suggested that."[23] Once the blower was installed the frost problem went away. The frost was caused by the moisture in the atmosphere as the air came into contact with the cold steel. The bottom of the outer tank steel would have been cold not only because the insulation between it and the inner tank wasn't perfect, but also because the tank was low to the ground and had poor ventilation; also it was surrounded by a great deal of the concrete base. This rather simple heater blower system was enough to keep the frost spots from forming and causing damage to either the outer tank or the concrete base. Although the blower system they used was effective, the term "frost" may have been somewhat of an understatement. In the letter from Jackson to Hagan he said, "The underneath side of the tank was examined and it was found that there was from ½" to two inches of ice on the underneath side of the outer shell bottom and around the upper portions of the concrete."[24] Nevertheless, this still did not indicate liquid gas leakage, which would have not been easily corrected with the blower. The letter went on to blame insulation settling for the problem and suggested more be blown in. They also indicated that no hydrocarbons had been detected under the tank. Methane, a hydrocarbon, would have been detected had the tank been leaking.

Once again, as with the crack that appeared during the initial filling, the geometry of tank 4 had caused a problem that had to be corrected. It was an easy fix but a needed one nonetheless. The spherical tanks, due to their height above the ground that allowed good air circulation, never had frost problems. The cork insulation in the spherical tanks also helped preclude the tanks from frosting up.

Insulation Settling

When Hope built the pilot plant in 1939 the company claimed experimentation was done on the insulation. It used cork insulation on a small experimental tank, instrumented it and measured heat loss through it. Hope scaled results to the larger tank in the pilot plant and applied a two-foot layer of cork around this tank. There was no steel outer layer around the cork. The experimentation addressed the thickness and heat loss, but apparently didn't address the material itself. Cork was chosen, and other materials were not considered seriously enough to be used in the experiments. Intuitively cork would seem to be a good choice, and it worked well in the pilot plant. When it came time to duplicate the pilot plant on a larger scale in Cleveland, cork was also the only insulator considered. Because of the extreme temperature gradient between the inner tank at around −260°F and the outer tank at normal outdoor temperatures, this insulation has to be considered a major design factor. It was fortuitous that cork worked so well.

The spheres were designed with a cork insulating layer three feet thick. The bottom of the tank had nine layers of four-inch thick blocks. They covered the bottom and went partway up the sides. The reason for the block geometry was that the cork also had to take the load of the filled inner tank. So the good properties that cork had in compression also served the tank design well. The remainder of the space between the inner and outer tanks was filled with granular cork. It was not only cheaper but lighter and had better insulating properties because of the dry gas kept between the inner and outer tanks. These three tanks with the cork insulation worked very well for four heating seasons, from early 1941 through most of 1944.

Things were different, though, when tank 4 was designed in late 1942. By this time the war was well underway and significant material restrictions were in place. Even prior to the U.S. entry into the war, the government grew concerned about national defense. It was also supplying the allies with war-making equipment. On January 7, 1941, the Office of Production Management was established to set policy and execute measures to plan for an adequate supply of raw materials and to set priorities for them. In July 1941, the president appointed the Economic Defense Board, and in August, the Supply Priorities and Allocation Board, to set priorities and allocate materials. After the U.S. entry into the war, on January 6, 1942, the Office of Production Management was abolished and the War Production Board established to set these priorities and allocations.[25] This latter date was about one year after the initial operation of the original LNG plant using the three spheres. As was discussed in Chapter 5, rock wool was chosen as the insulator for tank 4 instead of cork, because apparently Pittsburgh–Des Moines could not get approval from the War Production Board to use cork.

The method of placing the insulation was also different for tank 4 than it was for the spheres. When the outer sphere was built the cork blocks were laid down and the inner sphere was built in place on top of the cork. The inner sphere rested on the cork. This couldn't be done for tank 4; the rock wool insulation could not support the inner tank as the cork had done in the spheres. Instead the two tanks were constructed as described in Chapter 5, and the rock wool was blown in. As Feightner put it in an answer to a question,

    A. It was ground and blown in there
    Q. Blown in?
    A. Yes, sir, it was put in there as well as it could have been installed at the time.
    Q. Did you have to continually keep adding rock wool?
    A. We have added a couple of times there.[26]

So just as with any similar insulation blown into an area, such as an attic, it settled and had to be supplemented. When that was necessary, they added it through the top and pushed it down between the cylinders. Settling was caused by the weight of the rock wool;

it was much heavier than cork. The weight of the rock wool caused it to settle and displace some of the air or gas between the fibers. This left gaps in the insulation, which were clearly undesirable; they had to be refilled.

A gap of this type could also have been responsible for some of the frost spots. In his testimony Feightner acknowledged that in fact some frost spots on the outer tank were caused by this type of insulation gap. Because a frost spot on the outer tank could also be an indication of a leak in the inner tank, it was taken seriously:

> Q. Have you ever seen frost spots on the outer tank?
>
> A. Where the insulation—we have had several cases where the insulation is packed and there was a thin spot where the frost spots would come through, and by examination we found that it was due to the insulation not being proper at that point, and we remedied that, and when remedied that, the frost spots disappeared.
>
> Q. In other words, the previous occasions in the past you had spotted points of danger, which you remedied, is that right?
>
> A. That's right.
>
> Q. You had found the insulation had worn thin?
>
> A. That was not dangerous.[27]

Feightner went on to explain why he thought it was not dangerous. He said it just meant that more heat would get into the inner tank and boil off more liquid, which could be handled with the existing system. While this is correct, it is only partially correct. This is because a gap could allow a convective or radiative "heat link" between the inner and outer tanks, which would introduce not only excessive heat into the liquid, thus boiling more off, but also thermal gradients in both tanks that could stress the steel tanks. If this situation were allowed to exist for a long time it would damage both tanks. This does not seem to have been an issue, because they were very cautious about frost spots. They checked for them every day and either used the heater to remove the moist air from the bottom of the tank or added more insulation to eliminate frost spots caused by gaps in the insulation.

Once the rock wool was placed between the inner and outer tanks, the space between the tanks had to be filled with a gas along with the rock wool. Air could not be used because the normal moisture in the air would freeze on the inner tank. Instead, the natural gas that evaporated from the tanks was used. This gas was dry and because there was no air mixed in, it provided good insulation along with the rock wool and there was no danger of explosion or fire.

The inability to purchase cork for tank 4 had one other unintended consequence that may have been important. Apparently the original intention for tank 4 was to use cork in a similar manner as it was used for the spheres. Cork blocks would have been used under the inner tank to support it. The outer tank would have taken the load off the cork and inner tank, just as it did for the spheres. The absence of cork and the inability of rock wool to support the tank meant the bottom of the inner tank had to be suspended rather than just resting on the cork and outer tank. This meant that the stresses in this tank were different than they were in the spherical tank.

Vibration

The L. S. and R. plant, within the Number 2 Plant, was located in an area that was both residential and industrial. It also included through-tracks for the New York Central

Railroad. This environment therefore was subjected to a lot of ground vibration. Passenger and freight trains rumbling through at both high and low speeds caused vibration. Nearby industrial stamping plants used drop forges to form heated steel that also caused vibration. The compressors in the compressor building of the L. S. and R. plant, over 1,000 horsepower, caused vibration within the plant itself. This environment was questioned with respect to its effect on the structures at low temperature.

Although the rock wool would settle just because of its own weight, there was probably a component of the settling that was caused by the ambient vibration environment. Regardless of the cause, the settling insulation was observed and addressed on a regular basis.

When the board questioned the tank designer, James O. Jackson, chief engineer of Pittsburgh–Des Moines, about the effect of the vibration on the low temperature tank material, he said he was certain that had not been a problem. When asked if he had considered what vibration might do to the structure at low temperature he said, "No, I have taken that steel and cooled it down and worked it with a sledge hammer and it takes a lot more than what you ordinarily call ground vibrations to cause steel to break. Although we have no way to calculate what magnitudes of vibration it would take to make the tank break."[28] It is not clear what he meant by working it over with a sledge hammer. It was known that ordinary carbon steel when cooled to these low temperatures would break easily in brittle fracture, even with a small hammer. He probably was referring to the 3½ percent nickel steel, which they tested and found acceptable at Charpy impact values of 15 foot-pounds. But even this steel "worked with a sledge" under low temperatures might be expected to fracture. He was not questioned further about what he meant by this claim. He did acknowledge there were vibrations in the area and that even two of the compressors in the compressor room had to be fixed because they vibrated too much. Nevertheless, he said he never felt any vibrations at the tank locations, although he acknowledged that vibration probably did cause the insulation to settle.

Feightner was asked if he remembered any switching on the Pennsylvania Railroad track at about the time of the accident. He did not remember if there had been any or not. The Pennsylvania Railroad track he was referring is a spur shown in figure 5-4 that shows up as a double line just below the tanks, between the tanks and the neighborhood. These tracks were within only a few feet of the tanks, and any vibration on them would undoubtedly have been felt at the tanks.

The concern about vibration could take at least two forms. One is the concern that a pressure wave from something like that produced by a large drop-forge hammer could cause an increase pressure in the tank, which could lead to a rupture. A second is that a cyclic vibration could eventually cause metal fatigue that could lead to failure of the tank metal. This is like bending a paper clip back and forth until it breaks. This would require many cycles. These questions were brought up in the board hearing and will be discussed later in the chapter.

Summary on Plant Conditions

The plant conditions the day of the accident appeared to be totally normal, according to the workers on site that day. There was nothing to point to as a possible proximate cause of the accident. Other potential issues involving the plant and the environment were probed by the board of inquiry at the hearings. The initial crack in the bottom of tank 4 was determined to have been due to an improper filling procedure that, once corrected, was no longer a problem. Frost spots on the bottom of tank 4 (not the three spherical tanks) were recognized as danger indicators and were addressed immediately. The ones under the tank caused by poor circulation of air, and condensation of the moisture in the air, were corrected by a simple heater that warmed and circulated air under the tank. The ones caused by gaps in the rock wool insulation, because of settling of the insulation, were fixed by adding more insulation and packing it better. These fixes, which worked, would not have worked had there been an actual fluid leak in the inner tank. The tank was checked daily for the presence of these frost spots. Vibration causes settling also; it moves the particles around, reducing the space between them, much as one would shake a container to lower the level of granular particles in it. The vibration environment, because it was an industrial area, could therefore have caused settling also. However, some did not even notice vibration around the tanks. It was investigated later but was not seen as an issue at the initial hearing.

Investigation

East Ohio and their prime contractor, Gas and Machinery, did an extensive study of the fragments of tank 4, even to the extent of measuring them and reproducing then on a small-scale wooden model tank. They attempted to trace the nature and direction of failure using this model. No report on this activity survives if, in fact, a report was ever done. This information, however, was made available to the mayor's board of inquiry. The Pittsburgh–Des Moines Steel Company sent some representatives who were familiar with the plant design to help identify and classify the fragments. They did not write a separate report but assisted the mayor's board in its inquiry. The National Board of Fire Underwriters and the Ohio Inspection Bureau wrote a ten page report that discussed the accident mostly from the standpoint of damage and loss.[29]

Based on the eyewitness accounts and the questioning by the board on the plant operations and/or anomalies, there was clearly no obvious cause or smoking gun. More insight would be needed and more investigation was necessary to find out what happened. In one sense the future of the LNG industry would depend on the answer. The technical consultants on the mayor's board of inquiry did do more investigation; however, the investigation depended on getting more information on the design of the plant. A flaw in the design clearly had to be considered when everything else seemed to have been accounted for. During the hearings held by the board immediately after the accident, the board questioned a number of people who had made design decisions of one type or another. This information was then used to start the more detailed investigation.

The investigations covered a broad range of issues, but these can be roughly categorized into three areas. One is the choice of the tank material and the testing of that material for use in very low temperature conditions. Was the correct material chosen and used? Second, the tank design itself was questioned. It was dramatically different from the sphere design and from any previous cylindrical tanks. Third, the location of the plant and the containment system used for spills was questioned by the various investigation teams. The latter was looked at not as a cause of the accident but as a cause of the number of casualties.

Tank Material and Material Tests

Spherical Tanks

Chapter 5 covered the reasons for the choice of the tank material, the reasons Cooper gave for choosing 3½ percent nickel-steel. In their analysis of the failure the technical consultants of the mayor's board of inquiry looked into the testing of the material that was used for the tanks.

According to these consultants, in 1940 the Republic Steel Corporation carried out a series of standard acceptance tests on both plain carbon steel and 3½ percent nickel-steel. These included chemical analyses, tensile strength, and impact tests at both room temperature and at −320°F (liquid nitrogen). The unwelded steel plate showed an impact resistance of 55 foot-pounds at room temperature and 6.4 foot-pounds at the liquid nitrogen temperature. This agrees reasonably well with similar results measured by others (see Hurlich, for example).[30] Further tests on the plate were run by the Vanadium Corporation of Bridgeville, Pennsylvania, on July 3, 1940. (Because the consultants compared these results, they are presumably both from the nickel-steel rather than from the carbon steel.) These were run at −250°F, and the average impact value was 14.8 foot-pounds. The ASME code revision that came out in 1940 allowed for the use of low-temperature material if it had an impact strength of 15 foot-pounds Charpy; this probably would qualify. According to the technical consultants,

> There is no indication that the two sets of tests were made from the same heat [batch] of steel. This might account for the difference in impact strength or the second set of tests may have been carried out on more carefully prepared test specimens which might have considerable effect on test results.[31]

It is also known that impact resistance decreases with decreasing temperature, so the temperature difference (−320°F to −250°F) may have also contributed to the higher impact resistance of the Vanadium results compared to the Republic results. (It turns out that this temperature difference *does* have a significant effect in the ductile-to-brittle transition temperature of this material; see Chapter 7.) The Vanadium results would have been acceptable for the tank; the Republic results, although at a lower temperature, would not have been. There is also no proof that the Republic Steel tests were made on the same batch ("heat") as that used for the tanks. However, it does seem likely that both the Republic and Vanadium tests *were* run on the same heat of steel and that it was the same one used for the tanks. This is because the tests were run in the spring and summer of 1940 just after Cooper had Gas and Machinery purchase the steel from Republic. Thus the most likely difference in the test results is the test conditions mentioned by the consultants, or the different temperatures at which the tests were run. (The sensitivity of the brittle fracture transition of 3½ percent nickel-steel will be covered in Chapter 7.) It will be seen that it is difficult to get different batches of 3½ percent nickel-steel to consistently achieve 15 foot-pounds Charpy impact resistance at −260°F. This is near the ductile-to-brittle transition temperature (DBTT).

After the accident the U.S. Bureau of Mines sent in an investigation team also. They did not hold public hearings as did the mayor's board of inquiry but did talk to some people involved, including Jackson. Despite all the Charpy impact testing done on the 3½ percent nickel-steel, apparently Jackson still thought it was brittle:

In discussing the metal used in constructing the tank, Jackson stated that the nickel-alloy steel used was to all intents and purposes brittle at −260°F, despite a satisfactory Charpy impact value. He indicated that when a sheet of nickel-alloy steel was at a low temperature, a sledge might be driven through it. In his opinion, this should not obviate the use of this material for construction purposes, and he cited as examples the large number of brittle materials used in construction.[32]

This is a surprising statement, coming from a person who had done a lot of work for both his patents and design of these tanks on the suitability of 3½ percent nickel-steel for use at these temperatures. He had essentially set the standard for use of this material for these low temperatures. Regarding his comment on the successful use of brittle materials, he might have been thinking about the use of iron, which is brittle, in some structures such as bridges. At one time iron bridges had been common. However, there never had been a brittle material used at these low temperatures before. Although the inner tanks were protected by the outer ones, which were also used to hold the insulation, the possibility of causing the cold tank to fail by a simple impact as a sledge might deliver should have caused the designers to question the material.

So the three spherical tanks were constructed of 3½ percent nickel-steel using the best information available at the time. Despite Jackson's lack of concern about the possible brittleness of the steel in these three spherical tanks, they performed quite well for four seasons and two of them even survived the fire.

Cylindrical Tank

By the time of the construction of tank 4, things had changed. There was a war on and steel was scarce. Also the unfired pressure vessel code (1940) now no longer specified a lower temperature limit, but it did require that Charpy impact tests be done on materials to be used at low temperatures, and that the value of the test had to be at least 15 foot-pounds. This is higher than the 10 foot-pounds that Jackson had previously assumed was adequate.

Various tests were made on the tank 4 material after the accident. However, there were no low-temperature impact tests run on the tank 4 material prior to the construction of the tank. These post-accident tests showed some disturbing results regarding low impact values. *This means the material used for the actual build of the tank may not have met the standards required, that is, a Charpy impact resistance of 15 foot-pounds.* This issue will be discussed later.

When East Ohio decided in 1942 to build a fourth tank, they again turned to Pittsburgh–Des Moines to build the tank. There is no record that Howell Cooper and Gas and Machinery were involved at this time. It probably didn't seem necessary, since they were just adding one more tank to the existing system. Presumably Pittsburgh–Des Moines ordered the steel. This time it was from Carnegie–Illinois Steel Company.

As reported by the mayor's board technical consultants, in 1944 the Carnegie–Illinois Steel Company did some tests on various batches of the 3½ percent nickel-steel evidently used in the construction of the inner tank of tank 4.[33] (The reference indicates the 1944 date. However, considering the tank was completed in 1943, and used over the winter of 1943-44, it seems likely there is an error in the reference. The date seems more likely to have been 1943.) The testing was done to verify chemical analysis only. Carnegie-

Illinois explicitly said in the contract that they would *not* do Charpy tests down to the LNG temperatures; that that was the responsibility of the user, Pittsburgh–Des Moines. Carnegie-Illinois did some low temperature testing but only to −50°F because that was as low as they were equipped to test. Although the results at this temperature (−50°F) were similar to the results of Republic Steel tests at that temperature for the spherical tank's heat (in 1940), one cannot legitimately extrapolate the results to −250°F.[34] *There is no record that Pittsburgh–Des Moines did any Charpy impact test at low temperature for the steel used in tank 4 prior to construction of the tank.*

Jackson had previously tested the welds on the 3½ percent nickel-steel used in the spherical tanks to −260°F and showed Charpy impact results of over 15 foot-pounds. The technical consultants commented on the weld tests prior to the construction:

> A very extensive investigation was carried out prior to construction on the type of welding rod and welding procedure. The final selection of a 25 per cent chromium 20 per cent nickel rod showed that both the weld metal and the fusion zone had a higher Charpy value than the plate at minus 250°F.
>
> The average Charpy values were:
> Plate   14.75 ft-lbs
> Weld   21.50 ft-lbs
> Fusion Zone   15.50 ft-lbs[35]

This investigation was most likely the one that Jackson and Cooper had made during the early experiments on the welded material prior to the spherical tanks' construction, because this was the only time they did tests on the welds. So although the material of tank 4 *had not been specifically* tested prior to construction, there seems to have been general agreement that the Charpy impact value of around 15 foot-pounds at the liquid temperature of −250°F was acceptable and that the spherical tanks' material had this property. The question that remained open was whether or not the material for the cylindrical tank (tank 4) actually had that property; up to the point of construction it had not been tested.

After the accident many samples of tank 4 fragments were collected, categorized, examined, and analyzed. One observation was that many of the welds were of poor quality. However, despite this only a few of the breaks were in or around the welds; most were in the plate proper. This seems to be supported by the table above, which shows the weld to be stronger than the plate.

The Bureau of Mines investigative team did a minimal evaluation of the steel in the tanks. They took one small piece of the inner shell of tank 4 to their Metallurgy of Steel Section in Pittsburgh and analyzed the chemical composition of the piece. This compared well with the specifications for that steel. They did no tensile testing or Charpy impact testing on this steel, nor did they do any analysis or testing on segments from tanks 1, 2, or 3.

The technical consultants from the mayor's board of inquiry took 127 samples of the tank material, 121 from tank 4 and six from tank 3. They took a large number of samples, from various parts of tank 4, to have additional samples in the event some of the tested samples showed unusual conditions; they did not test all 127 samples. This team did their own analysis of a number of pieces including X-rays of welds, metallographic examination of grain size, tensile tests, and hardness tests. They sent seven of their samples to the U.S. Bureau of Mines laboratory in Salt Lake City, Utah, for metallographic examination, chemical, and mechanical properties testing. This was done independent of the Bureau of Mines investigation team. All of these samples were from tank 4. The chemical analysis did confirm the low carbon (0.04 to 0.12 percent), and the nickel (3.30 to 3.61 percent) content to be as expected. The Salt Lake Bureau of Mines lab found that the steel met all the specifications for chemical composition and tensile strength; however, it had very low Charpy values, two to 3.5 foot-pounds (see table 6-1).[36]

Table 6-1. Post-Accident Analysis

Specimen	Charpy Impact Room Temp. Foot-Pounds	Charpy Impact Liquid Air Foot-Pounds
1	18	2
2	41.5	2.5
3	41	2.5
4	33	2
5	37	3
6	22	2.5
7	15.5	3.5

Note: Specimens 2, 3, and 4 were the standard Charpy 10-mm-thick samples. The others were a non-standard 5 mm thick.

Liquid air is about the same temperature as liquid nitrogen (−320°F), so the Charpy values might be expected to be somewhat lower than any samples measured at LNG temperatures of −260°F. However, these values are *less than half* those measured by Republic Steel (see above) and Hurlich.[37]

Interestingly, other tests after the failure also showed very low Charpy impact values from samples taken from the tank 4 fragments. Although East Ohio settled quickly with most of the victims after the accident, there were a few who chose not to settle but to sue. Almost all claimed negligence because of the use of brittle material. One case reached the Pennsylvania Supreme Court. The plaintiff asked the Pittsburgh Testing Laboratories to do Charpy impact tests on 48 fragments of the inner tank of tank 4. The results were as follows:

> Of the 48 pieces, only one had a Charpy impact test of 10 ft. lbs.; 4 pieces had a Charpy impact test of 5 ft. lbs.; 15 pieces had a Charpy impact test of 4 ft. lbs.; 25 had a Charpy impact test of 3 ft. lbs.; and 3 had a Charpy impact test of only 2 ft. lbs.[38] [Note: These values were truncated to the unit value, not rounded to the next higher unit value.]

Many of these are similar to the results shown in table 6-1.

Although it had been well documented that higher Charpy values would have been necessary and expected, there are a couple of possible explanations for these low, post-accident, results.

One explanation is the test itself. The test requires a certain amount of care in its execution. This is especially true when parts are tested at very low temperatures, such as at the temperature of liquid air. It is required that the specimen be placed into the machine within five to 10 seconds after it is removed from the liquid air, and that the test then be executed quickly. Also, according to Dr. Thomas Siewert of the National Institute of Standards and Technology (NIST), "Charpy values tend to have large scatter, so I am not surprised by the range you mention."[39] (The range mentioned was that measured by the

Pittsburgh Testing Laboratories covered above.) A large scatter range can be seen in the room temperature Charpy tests shown in table 6-1. However, the low temperature results, whether by the Bureau of Mines or the Pittsburgh Testing Laboratories, were all consistently low, even if slightly scattered. When asked if Charpy values could change (decrease) over time if exposed to very low (−260°F) temperatures for long periods of time, Siewert responded that they tend to stay the same but could change if there was some metallurgical change (phase change in a metastable alloy), which would take a metallurgical analysis to determine. No metallurgical changes were mentioned in any of the testing laboratory results.

Another possible reason for the low impact resistance of the tank 4 fragments is that some or all of the material used for tank 4 did not have Charpy impact values any higher than a few foot-pounds *when the tank was originally constructed*. In other words, the original material was inappropriate. A chain of investigative events prompted by the court suits after the accident suggests this may have been the case.

On July 20, 1942, just after the new tank (number 4) was ordered, Carnegie–Illinois Steel had written a letter acknowledging receipt of orders from Pittsburgh–Des Moines for steel for a "structure to be exposed to a temperature of −260°F." The letter stated that Carnegie's responsibility was confined to the chemistry involved, and that Pittsburgh–Des Moines would be responsible for any impact tests to be conducted. Pittsburgh–Des Moines responded in three days, acknowledging, "Your letter is in accordance with our understanding."[40] As discussed previously, there was no record of Pittsburgh–Des Moines doing impact tests on the steel used for tank 4. However, J. O. Jackson, chief engineer of Pittsburgh–Des Moines, apparently used the services of two research engineers on the staff of the Mellon Institute in Pittsburgh for various analyses. Although they were on the Mellon Institute staff, he apparently paid them directly for their consulting work.[41] These two, Dr. J. B. Garner and R. M. Stuchell, were the two who had inspected tank 4 when it developed frost.[42]

The sequence of events was as follows: On February 15, 1943, when the tank was almost complete, an impact test was performed on at least one heat (batch) of the material being used for tank 4.[43] It is not clear who did the test or why it was done this late instead of prior to the tank's construction. This batch of material, which included material used for half the main girder supporting the tank, showed only one-fifth of the strength necessary, according to the attorney for the plaintiff. This would be about two foot-pounds, based on the minimum of 10 foot-pounds originally claimed by Jackson as necessary for these low temperatures, or three foot-pounds, based on the ASME 15 foot-pound requirement. Remember that the 1940 BPVC specified that a strength of 15 foot-pounds was necessary at low temperatures. At this point Jackson directed Stuchell and Garner to consult Carnegie-Illinois to find out what caused the low impact strength.[44] On February 26, 1943, a chemist at Carnegie-Illinois, A. W. MacLaren, talked to Stuchell and Garner about the test results. On March 10, 1943, he wrote a short report of that conversation[45] (see figure 6-2). In this report he referenced the heat number (29366), the test items, and the chemical specification of the material, 3½ percent nickel-steel. He clearly stated that the reference material was used in the tank along with other heats; that impact properties that were supposed to be on the order of 15 foot-pounds at −260°F were on the order of two foot-pounds; and that the grain size of the steel was on the order of three to four (McQuaid-Ehn), whereas satisfactory heats are on the order of seven- to eight-grain size.

(In general fine-grain steels [seven to eight] are generally tougher than coarse grain [three to four]. McQuaid-Ehn is one measure of grain size, that is, the internal structure of the steel. Some specific tests seem to show that "differences in grain size in the normalized steels appear to exert an influence on the impact toughness; the finer the McQuaid-Ehn or the normalized grain size, the lower is the temperature at which cold-brittleness is manifested."[46] However, the reference is for a particular steel at particular heat treatment conditions, unlike the steels used here. Thus, although there is some correlation to the Charpy test, it does not seem to be strong.)

MacLaren went on to say that further tests, implying impact tests at low temperatures, would be done on a cut from a plate (item 14) still at Pittsburgh–Des Moines. If these were low, then a coupon would be cut from the installation, the tank under construction, presumably from heat 29366, already part of the constructed tank. If the latter tests were low in impact value, he assumed all the plates from that heat would have to be cut out of the tank. He reiterated the fact that Carnegie-Illinois had based their quote only on the chemistry of the steel; Carnegie would not be responsible for low-temperature impact testing.

The plaintiff's attorney claimed that no other tests had been done and the work had been completed without replacing any material. Indeed, there is no record of additional tests. There is also no record of any material in tank 4 being replaced. This issue did not come up in any of the post-accident investigations, including the hearings of the mayor's board of inquiry, the U.S. Bureau of Mines investigation, or the report of the technical consultants of the mayor's board of inquiry.

This line of questioning, that is, whether the tank would have to be torn down if later impact tests confirmed the low impact value, was not allowed by the judge, whose position was upheld by the appeals court. Replacing the bad heat would have required the tank to be torn down, because the bad heat had been used in part of the main beam holding up the tank, that is, at the very bottom of the tank. Further data on whether or not additional tests were conducted is not available.

A definitive conclusion cannot be drawn on whether or not a heat of steel with low impact value was used in tank 4. It is possible that further tests on the heat did *not* confirm a low impact value so that all the tank material met the minimum impact resistance. Although "the absence of evidence is not the same as the evidence of absence," it is clear that the tank was *not* torn down and replaced. Therefore, either the steel was good or the bad heat was used. The latter case is entirely possible and, from the evidence, seems probable. The tank was almost complete. It had also been on a fast track since it was first ordered in 1942 because they wanted to have it available for the 1943-44 winter (which they did). Faced with tearing down the tank, they may have looked again at the test numbers and convinced themselves that the new tank would be fine; after all, the other three spheres had performed well over the first three years. The difference, of course, was that the first three tanks were constructed of 3½ percent nickel-steel from Republic Steel. That steel had been tested for impact resistance under low temperature prior to the construction of the spheres. In the case of tank 4, the steel was supplied by a different company, Carnegie–Illinois Steel. *They specifically disavowed doing any impact resistance tests. None were done until after the tank was almost complete, and those tests showed an unacceptably low Charpy impact resistance.* Taking a risk on a tank that was almost complete, and under time and cost pressure, the project manager may have talked himself into using the heat

R. W. Simon, Manager
ATTN: Mr. A. F. Sprankle

March 10, 1943

MELLON INSTITUTE
A/C Pittsburgh-Des Moines Steel Company
February 26, 1943

ABSTRACT: Report of low impact results at -260°F. on 3-1/2% Ni Steel plates investigated. Work at Mellon Institute had established that the heat yielding less than 15 foot-pounds was coarse grained. Samples to mill for investigation. Orders taken on basis of producing chemistry only, with no responsibility for impact properties.

REFERENCE: Cust. 435, June 8, 1942; Heat 29366 applied on Items 1, 5, 6, 14, 24, and 26; Specification C .08/.15; Mn .30/.60, P .045, S .045, Si .10/.20, Ni 3.25/3.75.

Interviewed Dr. J. B. Garner and Mr. R. M. Stuchell of the Mellon Institute staff. These men work on a project sponsored by Pittsburgh-Des Moines. Reference material, together with several other heats applied on the order, was applied in a storage tank for liquid methane. Operating temperatures of approximately -260°F. exist. Impact properties which are supposed to meet 15 foot-pounds at -260°F. were of the order of 2 foot-pounds. Mellon McQuaid-Ehn checks showed 3-4 grain size on the reference heat. Satisfactory heats were fine grained (7-8). Impact determinations were made on a modified Charpy specimen, which was normalized after machining.

Further tests will be cut from a plate (Item 14, 68" x 20.4" x 11') still held in plate form at Pittsburgh-Des Moines, Neville Island. Should these values be below the required minimum, a coupon will be cut from the installation. If these latter tests prove low, apparently all the plates from reference heat will have to be cut out of the tank.

It was pointed out to Messrs. Garner and Stuchell that a review of the inquiries covering this requirement had revealed that we had quoted on the basis of chemistry only, refusing to accept responsibility for low-temperature impact properties. It was pointed out that aluminum in the amount called for on the order; namely, .08% minimum had been added to the heat.

Two halves of impact specimens (the only samples Mellon would part with) were delivered to Homestead for grain size checks and aluminum analysis. Homestead was reported 4-5 McQuaid-Ehn grain size, with 7-8 actual ferrite grain size, and aluminum .004%.

This information has been referred to Mellon Institute and we await results of their further tests on the heat.

A. W. MacLaren

AWM:7
cc: Pittsburgh Sales (2)   Mr. E. L. Robinson
    Mr. John Mitchell   Homestead
    Mr. F. L. Gibbons, Chicago   Mr. C. H. Ow
    Mr. F. H. DeSante   File
    Mr. A. L. Kaye, Chicago (2)

Figure 6-2. Impact test report (courtesy Cleveland State University Library, Cleveland Press Collection).

as-is. It would not be the first or last time this type of decision would be made by a project manager on any project.

A different independent report also concluded that the tank 4 steel had inferior impact resistance at low temperatures. A consultant who worked directly for East Ohio did a detailed metallurgical analysis of some segments of the failed tank, number 4. When samples of tank 4 became available for analysis, the consultants for the mayor's board of inquiry took half the samples for their analysis and provided the other half to East Ohio. Presumably the East Ohio consultant did his metallurgical analysis on these samples and provided his results directly to East Ohio. This report did not survive.[47] However, in a 1953 symposium, a paper referring to this consultant's report stated that the consultant had done Charpy tests on the tank 4 segments at −248°F and found values of three to five foot-pounds. These results are consistent with the values shown in table 6-1 and seem to independently confirm them. He also reported that samples taken from sphere number 1, which had survived the fire but was dismantled later, also gave very low Charpy values of one to six foot-pounds. Although the findings on tank 4 are consistent with the investigative reports, these findings on tank 1 contradict the Charpy measurements made by the tank builders on the material heat used for the three spherical tanks. Those tests reported Charpy values of around 15 foot-pounds. This contradiction was unresolved and, without this consultant's report, will likely remain unresolved. His tests on the tank 4 fragments, however, confirm the other two independent tests of the tank material, which showed the tank 4 material had been below standard. *Thus three independent sets of tests confirmed that the material used in tank 4 had Charpy impact values of roughly two to four foot-pounds, well below the required 15 foot-pounds.*

For some reason, neither the mayor's board of inquiry nor the Bureau of Mines teams tested any samples from tank 3, even though the board took six samples from tank 3, so there is no way to compare their results with those of the East Ohio consultant who had tested samples from tank 1. The tank 3 samples should have had identical properties to those from tank 1 because they were originally from the same heat. Also surprising is that their two reports did not mention this consultant's report even though its issue date preceded the other two reports. It is likely these two teams did not see this consultant's report, because they would most likely have commented on it, even if they did not agree with all of it. The mayor's board of inquiry report lists other investigations that took place, but does not mention this consultant's study or report.

In summary, there is no definitive evidence, but there is strong evidence nonetheless, that a bad heat of material was used in tank 4, one that did not have the specified impact resistance at low temperatures and was too brittle.

Tank Design and Failure Analysis

Accident Scene

Following the recovery of the victims' remains, the accident scene was inspected thoroughly by the investigation teams. It was a difficult process because it was hampered by weather, snow and ice for several weeks (November 6–December 4), and by the rock (mineral) wool insulation from tank 4 that seemed to cover everything. The mineral wool was up to four feet deep in some places.[48] This hid some of the fragments, so it had to be

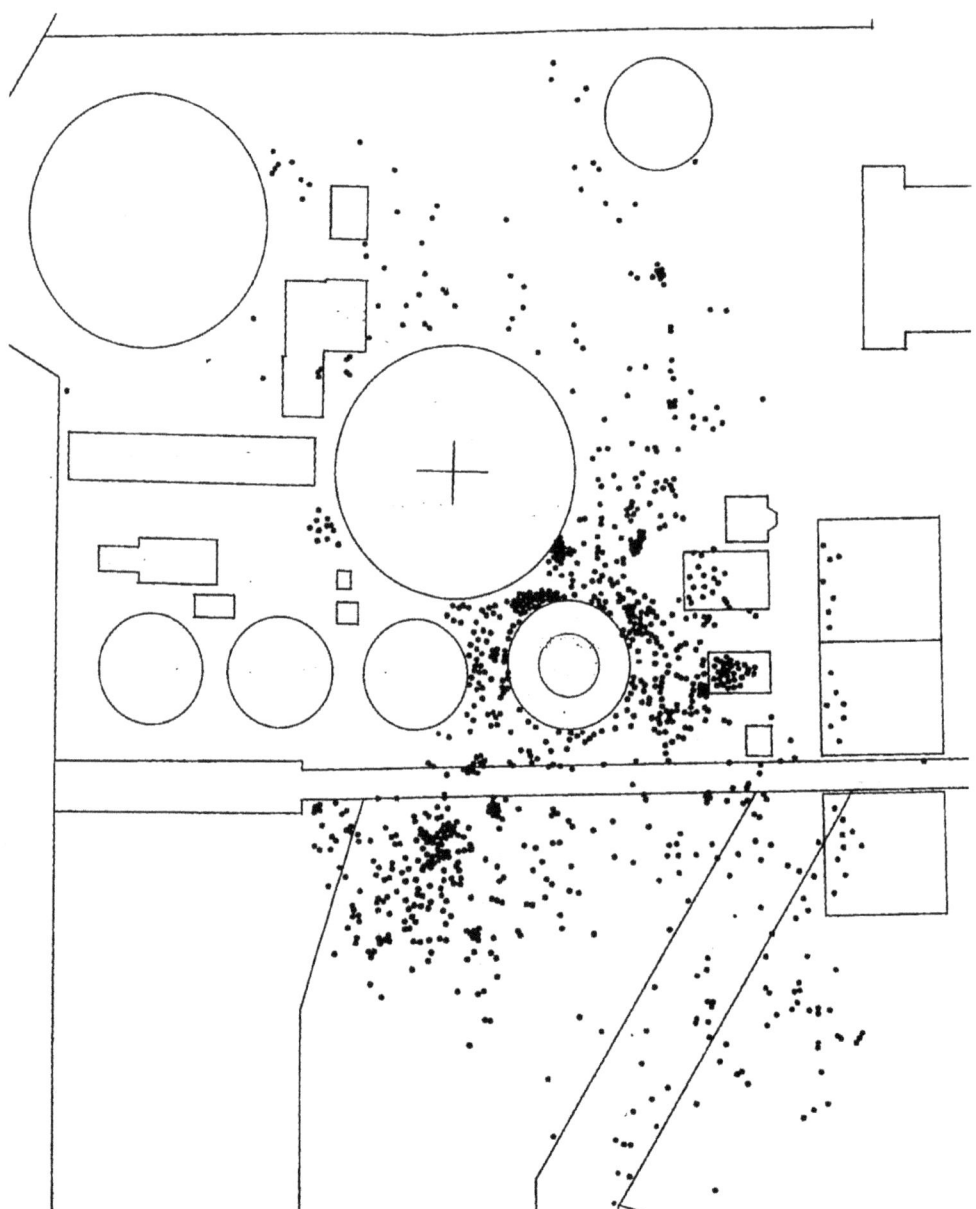

Figure 6-3. Distribution of fragments.

cleaned up before the investigation could start. The investigation was meticulous. All the fragments were numbered, their locations in the area noted and mapped. Figure 6-3 shows the map of the fragment locations.[49]

Over 2,000 fragments were numbered and identified as to their location in the tank. These were all examined for the type of fracture they had incurred. One interesting fragment was the outside of the outer tank. It was in one continuous piece as if someone had just cut it vertically and opened it up. It was lying flat with the outside up and oriented roughly north-south, with the top toward the east. It lay from the old gasholder in the north, between tanks 3 and 4 south to across the railroad spur south of the tanks. This seems to fix the location of the initial breakthrough at the east or southeast location of the tank.[50] This agrees well with the eyewitnesses from the AGA lab on East 62nd Street who were viewing it from that direction and who described the tank bursting in that location. The fact that the outside was up was an indication that the tank had burst, spilling its contents through the bottom.

Some of the fragments were as far as 200 to 300 feet from the original tank, and some of these were quite heavy.[51] The original thinking on this result, during the hearings, was that only an explosion could have moved these pieces that far. However, both teams came to the conclusion that in fact the surge of liquid from the failed tank provided enough force to move these pieces. There was little evidence of an explosion in the plant, so the failure was most likely the rupture of the tank and the spewing of its contents over a large area. Explosions were heard, but they could be explained by the resulting fires, which caused some other tanks, for example tanks of ammonia, to explode. Of course when the gas got into the sewers and then into the basements of many homes, a number of these exploded without being burned (see figure 1-6).

Tank Design

In addition to the materials used in the storage tanks, the investigation also looked into the tank design. The design of tank 4 was clearly unique, certainly different from the three spheres, and different from other cylindrical tanks. The latter difference was, of course, because of the need to maintain low temperatures and, therefore, to have insulation under the inner tank. This meant some kind of double tank had to be used, with insulation between the inner and outer tanks. So besides questioning the possible contribution of the materials to the disaster, the tank design also came under scrutiny. The key features that were examined were the wooden posts supporting the inner tank and the discontinuity in the shape of the tank near the bottom. The discontinuity is the angle between the side of the tank and the rounded bottom; the angle was 116°[52] (see figure 6-4). The three spheres had no such discontinuity; they were perfectly round.

The wooden posts, clearly seen in figures 5-7 and 5-8, were made of Douglas fir. They were used between

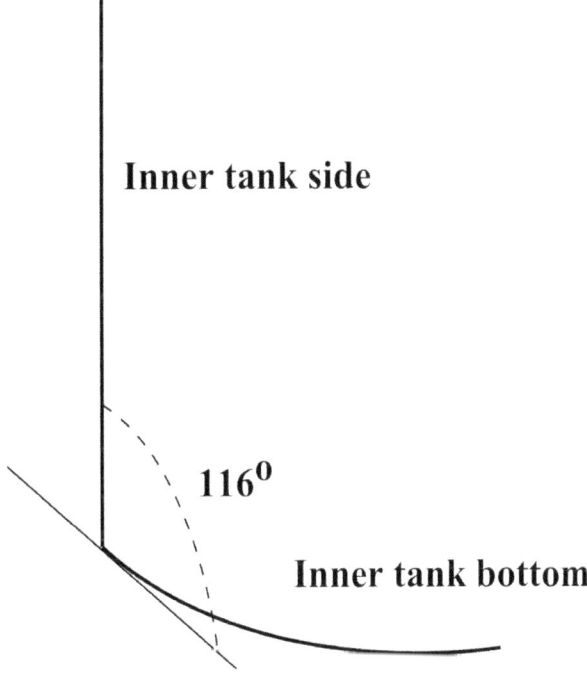

Figure 6-4. Discontinuity between tank side and bottom.

the inner and outer tanks to support the inner tank and to provide some thermal insulation between the two tanks (inner and outer). Wood is a much better insulator than steel or any metal, yet still is able to provide structural support for the tank. The strength tests on the wooden posts sponsored by Pittsburgh–Des Moines showed no deterioration of strength at liquid nitrogen temperatures.[53] Although the posts were between the inner and outer tanks, not immersed in the LNG, they were still in contact with the inner tank and, therefore, the tops got just as cold as the inner tank. Thus they were used to provide a high-resistance thermal path from the cold inner tank to the ambient-temperature outer tank. Measurements made (at the Mellon Institute) showed the thermal leakage through the posts to be about two to three times the leakage through the insulation, so they were still a source of heat transfer. One of the board members surmised that thermal leakage through the posts was probably the more important contributor to the frosting under the tank than gaps in the insulation; Jackson acknowledged that this could have been the case.[54]

The inner posts had slightly rounded rocker plates at both ends. These served two purposes. One was to allow a slight tilt to the steel columns above each post to account for the contraction of the inner tank as the cold fluid was introduced. In other words, the inner steel columns would move inward slightly when the inner tank contracted because of the cold fluid. The other advantage of the rocker plate was that it minimized the contact between the inner and outer tanks, thus reducing the thermal leakage. A circular box girder went around the inner posts between the posts and the steel support columns above each post (figure 5-8).[55] This design with the wooden posts presented some challenging stress computations. As Jackson had acknowledged, the company, Pittsburgh–Des Moines, had built many different large storage tanks for oil, water, and other liquids, but never one like this with these wooden posts.

Another feature that was a focus of attention in the tank design was the discontinuity between the inner tank wall and the "scooped" bottom of the tank. This angle of 116° was a sharp discontinuity, especially when compared with the spheres, which had no such discontinuities but only a continuously curving surface. The weight of the fluid on the inner cylindrical tank bottom had a tendency to "bend" the joint open, that is, to increase the 116° angle. This increased the stress in the joint. The inner tank, unlike the spheres, was also suspended from the wooden piers, so the whole weight of the liquid gas was supported by the steel bottom, which was in tension. In the spheres the weight of the inner tanks rested on the cork insulation; that is, they were not suspended but cradled in the cork. The outer tanks of the spheres carried the weight of the liquid gas and inner tank, but it was at ambient temperatures and also had no discontinuities, that is, it was just in tension. The discontinuity in the inner tank of tank 4 introduced high bending stresses that did not exist in the spheres, the steel plates of which were only in tension, not bending. This discontinuity was seen by one expert as the source of the initial flaw that caused the failure.

Failure Analysis

Analyses were conducted on various parts of the plant and on the design of the tank 4 structure to ascertain what actually failed and why. The investigation teams did a number of analyses and looked at many possible scenarios. One was the type of failure of the material. Was it a brittle or a ductile fracture? They looked in more detail at the issue of ambient vibration that was first brought up in the hearings. Could they have led to the failure? What about the base? Did the concrete base fail? Both teams did some stress analysis on the material of tank 4. These stresses were different from the ones on the three spheres, and they were higher. The chemical composition of the liquid gas was considered and whether or not this could lead to internal "superheating," which could cause stresses on the tank. Finally, they considered direct shocks on the tank itself that could have come from inspection equipment located on the top of the tank.

Fracture Type. The technical consultants of the mayor's board of inquiry (MBI) and Bureau of Mines (BOM) teams examined the fragments and came to similar conclusions. The primary mode of failure seemed to be brittle fracture. The BOM team concluded, "A detailed examination of the fragments from No. 4 tank disclosed that the fractures were characteristic of failure due to low-temperature embrittlement."[56] They went on to say that there was ample evidence of failures that occurred at a weld. The MBI team, however, did not find much evidence of weld failure; they found the welds to be generally intact. This team in general did a more thorough investigation, so their conclusions on the welds are probably more complete. They did, however, agree with the BOM team on the primary mode of failure:

> Owing to the fact that the metal of the inner shell was so very cold when it failed, and therefore very brittle, the herringbone pattern which appears so distinctly along the broken edges of metal which is torn or ripped under ordinary temperatures, was almost completely lacking in this instance. The fractures were largely smooth and even, like those of shattered glass.[57]

The MBI team found other fragments that were ripped rather than fractured by embrittlement. These were secondary failures, but they gave a good indication of the direction of travel of the rupture. Their conclusion was that the failure started at the top of the inner tank and propagated around to the bottom:

> In such violently shattered metal, there are bound to be primary failures and secondary failures, and some appearance of contradictory facts. Nevertheless, the consultants made a study of the assembled pieces to trace the direction of travel of the fractures and rips in the metal. This study disclosed sufficient *preponderance* of evidence to warrant the conclusion that the initial failure was at the top center of the inner shell; that the rupture took place radially outward from the center toward the upper ring girder; downward on the sidewalls to the lower ring girder; and radially inward on the bottom plates to the bottom center of the tank[58] [emphasis in the original].

This does not contradict other observations that the LNG spilled out of the bottom of the tank. The propagation of the crack would have been almost instantaneous, and the weight of the liquid would still have caused it to flood the outer tank, resulting in the bottom of that tank failing and releasing the contents.

This meticulous recreation of the sequence of events in the failure of tank 4 seems to answer many of the original questions concerning the failure but also leaves many questions unanswered. Some event initiated the rupture at the top center of the inner shell. The crack and/or rip propagated rapidly down the tank all the way to the center bottom. This ripping of metal was the probable source of the "concussion," "low rumbling," or "falling steel" sound described by many of the eyewitnesses and other people in the vicinity of the tanks. The cold fluid in the inner tank almost immediately burst into the outer tank. As the outer tank quickly filled up, it soon burst; it was never intended to hold this cold liquid. The outer tank wall burst along one vertical seam on the east or southeast side, as witnessed by many, and flew away, remaining in one piece. In a matter of seconds over one million gallons of liquid natural gas, previously contained in a vertical cylinder, were now free to flow in all directions away from the tank. This explained the white mist that the witnesses described, the water vapor in the air that was condensed by the cold liquid and gas.

Another indication that the tank ruptured, resulting in a sudden discharge of the fluid down and out of the tank, was the fact that the rupture disk on the top of the tank failed *inward*. A rupture disk is a safety device used to guard against a sudden increase of pressure inside the tank. It is a thin aluminum disk that is intended to burst outward if the tank pressure increases beyond a specified level. That fact that it burst inward indicates that the fluid contents of the tank rushed rapidly downward, creating a vacuum in the tank above the liquid and thus causing the outside air pressure to burst the disk in toward the tank. The sudden decrease in pressure in the tank was also recorded by the instrumentation on the tank. The MBI team acknowledged, however, that whether the disk failed inward because of low pressure or because of heat could not be conclusively determined.[59]

Vibration. The unusual tank design, in combination with the material used, was implicated by the two investigating committees in the tank failure. The Bureau of Mines report notes that there were reports of considerable vibration and seismic shock in the area caused by passing trains and a drop forge hammer nearby:

> It is well known that minor shocks can cause failure of brittle materials when these are stressed. It is also readily seen from the design of No. 4 tank that any ground shock would be transmitted directly to the inner and outer circular girders on the bottom of the tank. In this tank there was probably less cushioning of a ground shock than in the spherical tanks, because the circular girders were carried on wooden posts with steel end plates, which rested directly on the concrete foundation. In contrast the spherical tanks rested on a cork block 3 feet thick, which probably would damp-out any ground shocks. Thus, it appears more likely that No. 4 tank would have been more vulnerable to seismic shock than the spherical tanks.[60]

This implies they thought that vibration might have been the cause of the fracture, but they did not, in the end, conclude that it was.

It was noticeable that there were many ground tremors in the area. This was an industrial area and very near to the through-tracks of the New York Central Railroad. The nearby Bishop and Babcock plant had a drop-forge hammer, the impact of which could also be felt on the grounds of the L. S. and R. plant. There was speculation that these tremors may have led in some way to the failure of tank 4. Tank 4 would be more susceptible to any ground tremors just because of its construction. The outer tank was set on a concrete base. The inner tank was raised above this base and outer tank by the Douglas fir wooden posts described previously. In other words, the tank was solidly connected to the ground underneath and therefore would feel any ground tremors directly. The spherical tanks, on the other hand, had an inner shell that was supported by the cork insulation. This insulation not only separated the inner tank from the ground but also acted as a damper for any vibrations that might be transmitted to it.

Vibration may have affected the tank structure in any of three ways:

- By producing fatigue due to repeated cyclic loading. This is when a piece of metal is repeatedly bent back and forth until it "fatigues" and fails. This is normally demonstrated by bending a paper clip repeatedly until it breaks.
- By causing shock loading from a single impulse. Some single shock sends an impulse to the structure, which temporarily increases the g-load (gravity load) on the structure, causing it to fail. (Measuring the loads caused by vibration and shock are done relative to the local acceleration of gravity g, which is 32 feet per second squared at the Earth's surface.)
- By causing resonance failure due to vibration. This happens when two or more vibration sources operate at the same time near the resonance frequency of the structure and their peaks reinforce each other so that the total effect is magnified. This can lead to large forces on the structure.

A detailed survey of all the ground tremors on the plant grounds was commissioned by the technical consultants of the mayor's board. The survey showed that the acceleration caused by these tremors, the g-load, was very low, less than one percent g. These were deemed insignificant regarding failure that might be caused by fatigue or shock. There also was no indication that there were any resonance effects. These effects would also be damped by the large amount of fluid in the tank. Based on this analysis, ground tremors were ruled out as the root cause of the failure.[61] The mayor's board of inquiry acknowledged that there were tremors and vibrations of the railroads and stamping mills in the area. However, in this regard they concluded these were not of a magnitude that would cause failure in itself, although their effect may have added to other causes. They did note, though, that the spherical tanks with their cork insulation did provide superior isolation from tremors and vibration. The Bureau of Mines team also did not consider vibration in the area to be a cause of the failure.

Some thought was given to the base on which the tank rested. Did it crack, break, or in any way shift such that fracture stresses were set up in the tank, causing it to fail? A similar investigation was done on the base as was done with the vibration survey. Initial surveys of the site prior to design and construction showed that the soil at the location for tank 4 was not very good for a tank of this size. The soil under the three spheres had been acceptable for the design chosen. Years before, a stream had run under what had become the site for tank 4. It had since been covered and the water diverted. Also, the whole site had soil that had been fill-dirt from years of being used as an industrial site. As a result the original design proposed by Pittsburgh–Des Moines had been seen as infeasible. However, another company proposed a base design, a slab, that was acceptable. The slab was octagonal and made of concrete reinforced by four layers of steel reinforcing rods. The circumference was also reinforced. Following the accident, the stresses in the concrete base were checked and found to be within acceptable limits. (Ironically, the stresses were checked with the "Joint Committee Standards" as published by the American Society for Testing Materials. As was pointed out previously, Howell Cooper did not have the luxury of comparing the material he used for the tanks with any standard, because one did not exist at the time.) The concrete slab, although scarred by the fire, remained intact. A survey was done on the slab after the accident to compare its location after the fire to its location prior to the fire. Did it shift and cause the failure? Although minor differences were noted, there was no indication that the slab had moved in any way that could have caused the tank failure.[62]

Stress Analysis. Further analysis was done on the tank itself. The original designer had done an analysis that had assumed that all the stresses in the tank were either tensile or compressive stresses. He ignored bending or shear stresses. This was acceptable as long as the steel was not near a discontinuity such as the intersection of the vertical sidewall with the scooped top or bottom. This was where the bottom met the side at an angle of 116°. At these discontinuities there would have been bending and shearing stresses. The tensile and compressive stresses were kept reasonably low in the design, which helped compensate somewhat for the neglect of the other stresses. Nevertheless, these bending and shearing calculations were not done, but should have been done.

The MBI accident investigators did their own analysis of the stresses in the tank. They then compared them with the Pittsburgh–Des Moines calculations. In most case there was good agreement between the two. However, the post-accident analysis shows that the stresses near the lower belt ring were quite large: "Analysis of these secondary stresses by the consultants indicates some of them to be unduly high; as in the lower ring girder which supports the wall of the inner shell, where total stress may have been much higher than ordinarily allowed."[63] The lower ring girder, which supports the wall of the inner shell, was necessary for this uniquely designed tank. The lower belt ring is at the point of discontinuity between the inner tank sidewall and the scooped bottom of the tank. This can be seen in figure 5-6. There is a bending stress there well over four times any of the shear or compressive stresses in the tank. As the investigating team pointed out, this might not be a problem in a tank operating at normal temperatures because the plate would yield in the area and thus redistribute the stresses to a more favorable situation. As the MBI team noted,

> However, the existence of such effects at points of discontinuity makes it appear rather poor judgment to use the cylindrical form of tank under conditions where low-temperature brittleness may exist, when a spherical tank having no such discontinuities, and no solid connection with the foundation, could have been adopted.[64]

Thus, once again, the shape of the toro-segmental tank is compared unfavorably with the smooth, continuous surface of the spheres.

Despite the higher stresses at these discontinuities, the MBI investigating team did not locate the start of the rupture at this point but rather at the top of the inner tank, as quoted above. The large stresses at these discontinuities could have, however, facilitated the rapid rupture of the tank once it started. It is worth noting that one person did postulate that the initial rupture occurred at this lower discontinuity. The expert called on by the attorney pressing the suits for the plaintiffs who did decide to sue, examined the scene and the fragments of the tank. He testified that at that discontinuity there had been "a drawing out of the steel with a resulting 'ductile break' in the bottom of the inner shell and the consequent starting of a leak; this was followed, because of embrittlement of the metal, by a whole series of breaks around the attachment."[65] He postulated that the fluid then spilled into the outer tank, and the wooden post holding the inner tank fell inward, causing the inner tank bottom to collapse to the outer tank bottom. The bulged bottom of the outer tank, which was not bolted to the foundation, gave way and the cold fluid spilled out. The crashing of the inner tank to the bottom of the outer tank caused the multitude of steel fragments. Except for the initial location of the failure, at the lower discontinuity rather than at the top middle of the inner tank, his postulated scenario is very similar to that of the MBI investigating team. However, it is difficult to reconcile his statement about a "ductile break" when it was known after the fact that the material in the inner tank was brittle.

Chemical Composition. The chemical composition and very low temperature of the liquid gas may also have contributed to the failure, although there is no direct evidence that this happened. As noted in Chapter 2, natural gas is a mixture of gases such as methane, ethane, propane and butane. The post-accident analysis of the liquid gas from tank 1 showed it was about 71 percent methane, 27 percent ethane, and the rest oxygen and nitrogen.[66] The raw gas entering the system was from West Virginia and the Texas Panhandle. The constituents of the West Virginia gas were 85 percent methane, 10 percent ethane, three to four percent propane, and other gases such as butane and nitrogen. The Texas gas was 72 percent methane, 16 percent ethane, and about 12 percent nitrogen.[67] Thus the gas was enriched in the higher-boiling-point hydrocarbons (ethane) as a result of the distillation of the lower-boiling-point hydrocarbons (methane).[68] Being a mixture, these liquids act independently in their chemical properties. For example, they have different boiling points. Therefore if they sit as a mixture for a long time, they will evaporate at different rates. The atmospheric pressure boiling points are about −260°F for methane and −128°F for ethane. The evaporation process is like a fractionation or distillation process; that is, the lower-boiling-point methane tends to evaporate more rapidly than the higher-boiling-point ethane. The gas will evaporate especially quickly over the summer months, when it is hot and the tanks are not being refilled. According to Feightner's testimony, "During the summer months we had a certain amount of boil off every day for each million cubic feet of gas we had stored, and when we started up a couple of months ago, we had approximately sixty or seventy million cubic feet less of gas than we had in the spring."[69] As the lighter hydrocarbons (methane) evaporate, the specific gravity of the mixture will change and therefore the heating value will change. The heating value change is low, only around four to five percent (increase), and once gas is added the mixture goes back to its original state. This effect, although interesting, is not relevant to the failure.

However, a few of aspects of this chemical separation may be relevant. As the gas mixture sits undisturbed for long periods, because it is a mixture rather than a solution, the liquids will tend to stratify. This is because these liquids all have different specific gravities. The specific gravities of methane, ethane, and propane range from about 0.46 to 0.58 (water is 1.0). As noted by the MBI team,

> The relatively lower liquid temperature of methane would also tend to cause these higher hydrocarbons to become more viscous and promote the formation of a stagnant film layer on the liquid surface of the inner containers over and above that caused by the normal adsorption tendencies. This stagnation and stratification would no doubt cause a serious penetration lag of the conducting away of the heat from the walls and bottom of the container, and into the main body of the stored liquid.[70]

The stratification and stagnation would be enhanced by the fact the fluid was very pure. It had been through a process that removed impurities and thus was free of suspended solids that might promote mixing in the fluid. Also, heat transfer, which depends on molecular motion, is impeded by the low molecular activity of the fluid (−260°F); thus the fluid acts as a self-insulator. All these conditions combine to form a pure, quiescent, stratified, very cold fluid not likely to boil easily because it resists heat transfer from the walls of the container. This fluid is susceptible to superheating, a condition also referred to as ebullition lag, boiling retardation or boiling delay.[71] When heat is introduced the fluid resists boiling at its normal boiling point and becomes superheated. That is, it exists as a liquid in a non-boiling state above its normal boiling point.

When enough heat does enter, say from the heat path through the wooden posts, which transferred heat at a rate two to three times as fast as through the insulation, the fluid will finally boil, but now in a sudden, violent, almost explosive manner. This behavior is commonly called "bumping."[72] This bumping can cause a shock to the tank. A natural gas consulting engineer, P. E. Haynes, warned about this possibility as early as 1941:

> There should be a word of warning concerning the storage of large quantities of liquefied gases, especially over long periods. All gases that have been liquefied at low temperatures must have been purified beyond limits required for other purposes. They are almost free from suspended solids when they are liquefied. Due to the low specific gravity of liquid natural gas, solids do not remain long in suspension and the absence of suspended particles increases the tendency of the liquid to superheat. Unstirred masses of liquid methane may under some circumstances be dangerous.[73]

It is not likely that one bump from superheating would have caused a large enough shock to rupture the tank. Tank 4 had recently been filled, so it had been "stirred" such that one large bump probably was not an issue on October 20, 1944. However, this tank, along with the other three, had been dormant over the summer, so there was sufficient time for the superheating conditions to develop. This type of bumping could have occurred many times over these months. This is especially possible considering that summer sun heating the outer tank could send its skin temperature well over 100°F. With the inner tank fluid at −260°F there would have been an extreme temperature gradient across the wooden posts supporting the inner tank. It is not difficult to imagine superheating causing a series of minor shocks that acted on the brittle inner-tank material.

Other Tank Shocks. There was another factor that came into play with regard to shock at the top of the tank. There should be some consideration of the activity that took place at that location. A daily activity was the checking of the pressure relief valve at the top of the tanks. Testimony by a number of employees was given that said they would lift the valve off its seat to see if it "blew" or had a puff of pressure. This was to check if there was positive pressure in the insulation area, that is, the area between the tanks that was filled with dry gas to keep the insulation dry. They would then release the spring-loaded valve and it would reseat. There was a damper on the closure mechanism so it would not slam shut. The witnesses testified that it could, nevertheless, be closed with some shock. The MBI investigators also tried the undamaged valves (from the undamaged spheres) and were also convinced the closure of this valve could impart some shock to the top of the tank. In theory a small, repeated shock could have added to any small shocks caused by superheating bumping and could have eventually led to a fatigue crack at the top of the brittle tank that propagated through to rupture. The MBI team indicated,

> It may, therefore, be possible that superheating and periodic hammering of the cold metal by the bumping action resulted in localized cracking of the bottom and sidewalls of tank No. 4, and that perhaps the real trigger which caused the final collapse or disintegration of the tank was the jolt or shock (activating a more sudden form of "bumping") imposed on the tank by persons believed to be checking the pressure relief valves atop tank No. 4.[74]

The series of small shocks from the ebullient boiling caused by superheating, and the pressure relief valve, while not a smoking gun (there being no direct evidence), are certainly a plausible explanation for the initiation of a small crack in the brittle inner tank that finally propagated to tank rupture.

Location and Containment

The focus so far has been on an historical arc that covered the discovery and use of natural gas; the development of the industry, especially through East Ohio Gas and Hope Natural Gas; the natural gas shortage that developed; the liquefaction solution to the shortage problem; and the failure of the LNG storage tank.

Although the failure of the tank and the subsequent disaster did provide lessons that would eventually benefit the LNG industry, they also provided some more general lessons. The tank failed and so caused the industry to pause, take note, and decide how to proceed. The failure, however, caused more than just a pause in the industry's progress; it caused a lot of collateral damage: 130 people died. Had other risks been considered and mitigated it might have been possible to experience a tank failure with zero fatalities. In other words, there was more to the disaster than tank design.

One fact that is obvious now to anyone who looks at a map of the area, such as is shown in figure 5-4, is the proximity of the tanks to the residential neighborhood. One tank was separated from the closest house by only a chain-link fence and a railroad spur, a distance of approximately 100 feet. The four full tanks stored approximately 250 billion BTU of energy. As was pointed out, if the 150 billion BTU contained in the two destroyed tanks were dissipated in about two hours it would be equivalent to about 25 million horsepower. Today this would be seen for what it is, regardless of any tank design; storing that much energy, in the midst of a populous area, would be seen as too risky. At the time, however, that risk was not even considered; the plant was seen to be in an ideal location at the extreme end of the 140-mile pipeline, at the north side of the city about midway between the east and west boundaries of the area served, that is, right in the middle of all the customers. As we saw previously, no one questioned the plant's location at the time. That was how things were done. The company, which had its customers in mind, thought it was a positive move to help alleviate shortages that were rife at the time. The government approved it, which meant it must be ok.

The unexpected release of the fluid in the tanks was never considered. Cooper was asked about it in the hearings:

> Q: ... Did you feel in building these spherical containers, that there was absolutely no possibility of liquid leakage, major liquid leakage?
> A: Yes, I could see no way in which any considerable amount of liquid could ever get out of those tanks.[75]

This was a new, complex system, more complex than many other systems of the time, but the risk associated with it was not appreciated. There was no thought that this was a dangerous fluid, even though it was a condensed hydrocarbon (see the army's letter of assurance in figure 6-1). Since then, perhaps partially as a result of this accident, many complex risk management systems have been developed and are in use across many industries. Just one example is the Continuous Risk Management System used by NASA to assess and manage risks. A summary of that system can be used here to consider how this might have played out if risk had been considered.[76]

- *Identify the risk.* Identify scenarios that can have adverse consequences. In this case an obvious identifiable risk would be a tank rupturing and spilling its contents.
- *Analyze the risk.* Estimate the likelihood and consequences if the risk was realized. In this case the likelihood might have been rated low, but the consequences would have been rated very high: a fire in the neighborhood.
- *Control.* Given the risk identified and analyzed above, mitigate the risk. In this case once the danger of 250 billion BTU in the midst of the city was realized, the most likely mitigation would be to declare the location unsafe and move it farther away from this population. Granted, it would have been a bit more trouble if the plant were a few miles away, but the safety argument would have been persuasive.

This risk mitigation action alone, that is, moving the plant to an "LNG farm" away from a populated area, would have saved all the lives of the area residents even if the tank had failed.

This suggests another risk mitigation that was not taken seriously. Once it was determined that a tank could fail and that the consequences would be serious, then in addition to moving the system to a tank farm, how could the problem have been contained? One way would have been to build a dike around each tank such that if a tank failed and emptied all its contents, they would have been contained in the dike until emergency procedures could be implemented to handle the spill. Keeping ignition sources away from the dike would have been required, but even if it did catch fire, the fire would have been confined to the tank and dike and not impacted other buildings in the area. This risk mitigation would probably have saved the lives of the gas company workers in the area. (Moving the plant to a tank farm away from the city would have removed any danger to residents.)

There was what appears, in retrospect, to have been a feeble attempt to do this. However, it seemed to be feeble only because the premise was based on a small leak in a tank. No one considered that the tank would spill its entire contents. Near to the tanks, as shown in figure 5-4, is a circular figure labeled an overflow storage tank. This was once a standard gasholder similar to the one labeled 9 just to its northwest. (The number 9 tank was an active water-seal gasholder. This was the water that Feightner jumped into to save his life during the fire. He had noted that the heat from the fire had heated the gas in the gasholder, causing it to expand and raise the top of the holder while he was in the water seal.) There were pipes connecting the tanks to this overflow storage area. But, as stated, these were small and could handle only small tank leaks.

During the hearings, William Hagan, East Ohio vice president, was asked if he was familiar with the petroleum industry and the dike system they used. This was a dike around a storage tank that could contain the contents of the entire tank if it failed. He acknowledged that he was generally familiar with it but had no experience with it. He was questioned further:

> Q: Was it the intention of the East Ohio Gas Company in connecting with this abandoned gas holder pit and the connecting conduits and the dykes under the tank in No. 4 and so forth to provide for catching the spillage if it occurred?
> A: Yes.
> Q: Was the setup in your opinion adequate to catch the dumpage? Did you figure that was adequate to catch this dumpage if it occurred?

A: Yes I think so. Not to catch any such quantity of liquid that was thrown out there in an instant.

Q: At the petroleum plant it does catch it if it goes in an instant?

A: That is petroleum and this is gas. They are two different things. I don't know that it is practical to catch that much gas that is let out in an instant. I don't think it is and we would not have tried to do it, and if we thought or had the slightest intimation that much liquid was to be let out, as it was let out, we certainly never would have built that tank.[77]

The exchange went on for a while with Hagan insisting they wouldn't have built the tank if they had had to build the earthen dike around it. The exchange is interesting for a couple of reasons. One is the insistence again that they are dealing with something "different" ("That is petroleum and this is gas"), as though they were different kinds of material. In fact, they are both flammable hydrocarbons, although at different temperatures, so the lessons of the petroleum industry should have been relevant. Second is his insistence that they would never have built the tank if an earthen dike was necessary. The dike, which seems like a perfectly reasonable precaution, seemed inconceivable to Hagan. There seemed to be a mindset that they knew how to handle this esoteric material, and that outsiders didn't understand.

Another factor that contributed to the loss of life, although not to the tank failure, was the apparent lack of understanding of the city government in issuing a building permit for these tanks in this neighborhood. The city did have ordinances for handling flammable fluids such as gasoline or dry cleaning fluids. This was not one of those fluids, as far as they could tell. They had had no previous experience with this type of fluid, so they had no reference or ordinance to check. This again is reminiscent of Cooper's experience when building the tanks. He had no standard to look to for the steel specification. They went by the book, but there was no book. Apparently no one questioned it and the permit was issued within days, even though it clearly showed the proximity of the tanks to the neighborhood.

Although this was a new enterprise, that cannot be used as an excuse for the lack of foresight in the planning. As the mayor's technical consultants point out, "Because the development was new, precedent did not exist. Yet no project is wholly and completely unlike anything that had been built before, and there are in the L. S. and R. Plant many elements which can be appraised as to safety and adequacy, in the light of existing standards or usages."[78]

Many new, daring engineering projects had been built prior to this plant that have withstood the test of time. Perhaps the most recent example just prior to this plant was the completion, in 1937, of San Francisco's Golden Gate Bridge. A new enterprise does present new challenges but in turn requires an insight and oversight proportional to those challenges. In the early days of gas exploration there were many fires and explosions that took many lives. Eventually the industry figured out how to cope with these and operate safely. It appears that some either forgot the early lessons or thought that this new, cold fluid was so different and benign that it was not a danger. As Vice President Hagan expressed, this was a different beast; it didn't seem as though the rules of the petroleum industry applied.

Summary—What Happened and Why
The Incident

It is clear now what happened on that Friday afternoon in October 1944. Tank 4 ruptured and spilled its entire contents over the L. S. and R. plant and surrounding neighborhood. It did not explode, as some had speculated, but split open. A crack had started near the center top of the inner tank. It propagated radially to the side wall of the inner tank and then down the side. From there it continued radially toward the inside center of the inner tank. This caused the "rumbling" or "concussion" or "falling steel" sound that many heard. Several thousand gallons of liquid natural gas were dumped into the outer tank, which was never designed to hold that cold liquid. Very shortly after that, the outer tank split open at more than one place along the side. As it did so, the very cold liquid reacted with the moisture in the air to form a white mist, which was witnessed by many people who had a direct view from south of the tank. The initial failures took place on the south and southeast parts of the tank. The falling liquid of the inner tank caused the outer tank to come off its base, split open and be thrown off in one continuous piece away from the inner tank. The inner tank fragmented into over 2,000 pieces, which were carried off as much as 200 to 300 feet away by the liquid pouring out. Very soon after the tank split, and while the fragments were flowing away, the portion of gas that had already evaporated was ignited by one or more sources and a huge fireball engulfed the area just south of the tanks but including most of the plant and nearby neighborhoods. The subsequent events, which ended up tragically for many people, have been described.

The Prelude

When Howell Cooper experimented with low-temperature metals prior to building the pilot plant, he knew he had to use an alloy with some nickel in it to make it tough at low temperatures. He built the pilot plant tank out of two percent nickel-steel because that is all he could get at the time. One of the conclusions on the operation of the pilot plant was that one should use at least a 3½ percent nickel-steel for the storage tank. When he built the Cleveland plant, he again used an existing alloy to build the first three spheres, this time one available from Republic Steel. This was a 3½ percent nickel-steel alloy; it had more nickel and was therefore tougher than the material used for the pilot plant. He and J. O. Jackson did extensive tests on the material with welds and found it had a Charpy impact resistance at low temperatures of about 15 foot-pounds. The three spheres operated successfully for the life of the plant.

East Ohio decided in 1942 to add more capacity for storage, double that of one of the spherical tanks. There was not enough room for two more spherical tanks, and besides, two new tanks would take more steel than one larger one. Pittsburgh–Des Moines looked into the possible designs of a new, larger tank. They considered both a larger sphere and a cylindrical tank. The larger sphere could be built, but the walls would be rather thick and it would take more steel than the cylindrical tank. They proposed the cylindrical tank as being just as effective but less costly than the larger sphere; East Ohio chose the cylindrical tank. The cylindrical tank had a unique design to accommodate the insulation of the inner tank. The material they used for the cylinder was 3½ percent nickel-steel but this time from a different manufacturer. It turned out to be an inferior heat; the Charpy impact resistance was below what was required.

The Investigation

As usual, after this kind of disaster, the search for answers began. The cleanup began and a board of inquiry was established to find out what had happened. It started to get a lot of information in the hearings held immediately after the accident. A more detailed analysis by the technical consultants on the board uncovered even more detail on the plant operation, plant design, and possible causes of the accident. A rather detailed, but still incomplete, picture of the sequence of events was constructed. Some data, however, was not uncovered for years after the reports of the investigating teams. These data came out as a result of the court cases that followed and provided more detail on possible causes.

The investigators looked into the plant condition and operation for any clues in these areas that might have caused the problem. They found some anomalies but nothing that indicated that the root cause of the failure lay in that direction. The specific items that caught their attention were a crack that had appeared when the tank was first filled, frost spots that had appeared on the bottom of tank 4, insulation settling in tank 4, and the vibration environment in the area. These were easily eliminated as the cause of the failure.

Following the eyewitness accounts and the look into plant conditions and operations, the investigating teams got into more detail. This included looking into the tank material and any testing that went into its choice, the unique design of tank 4, and the location and containment system for the plant. The most likely causes for the failure of the tank came down to two things: one was an issue from the very start, the material used for the tank; the second was the very unusual design of tank 4. The most likely cause of all the casualties was the siting of the tanks, that is, the location of the plant and the lack of containment in case of failure.

The fragments of tank material were examined; a number of them were found to have suffered brittle fracture. How can that be when so much care was taken to identify and use a material that would resist brittle fracture? Right from the beginning it was known that ordinary steel would become brittle and fracture easily at these low temperatures (−260°F). They also knew that the addition of nickel to make a nickel-alloy steel would help make the steel tougher at low temperatures. They used a two percent nickel-steel alloy for the pilot plant because that was all that they could get at the time. It is significant, though, that the pilot plant operated only for a few months. It was started in late 1939, operated for a few months in early 1940, and was dismantled by mid–1940. There was never an explanation of why it was dismantled so quickly. Had it been allowed to operate longer, even as the East Ohio plant was being built, it might have been able to provide more long term data on the effect of low temperature on this two percent nickel-steel alloy. There was also the comment by Cooper, on which he never elaborated, that he had less than favorable experience with the two percent nickel-steel alloy in the pilot plant.

By the time the fourth tank was built things had changed; there was a war on. The steel, 3½ percent nickel-steel, was purchased from Carnegie-Illinois instead of from Republic. Carnegie-Illinois specifically eschewed any responsibility for doing any Charpy impact testing at low temperatures, claiming they were only responsible for the chemistry of the material. Analysis of the material after the accident confirmed the correct chemical make-up of the steel used. *However, there is no record that there was any Charpy impact testing on the material from Carnegie-Illinois prior to construction of the tank.* Finally in February 1943, when the tank construction was almost complete, some impact tests were run on the material. These tests showed low Charpy impact values, that is, values well below 15 foot-pounds. They also showed that the grain size in the material was relatively large, which is a bad sign indicating that the material might be brittle. At least one heat of the material being used for tank 4 was found to have had low impact values at low temperature. This prompted the comment that another test would be run from some of the material not yet used for the tank, and if that wasn't satisfactory the material from that heat would have to be removed from the tank under construction. There is no evidence that any material was removed from the almost completed tank. *It is probable, considering subsequent analysis, that the bad heat with low impact resistance remained in the tank.* The subsequent analysis was the examination of the fragments after the failure. Not only did many of them exhibit the glass-like fracture indicative of brittle failure, but many of them tested at Charpy impact values as low as two foot-pounds. *Thus for whatever reason, tank 4 seemed to have been constructed of at least some material that should have been rejected as too brittle to be used in those conditions.*

Besides the tank material, some of the unique design features of tank 4 were implicated in the failure. One was the discontinuity between the side walls of the inner tank and its scooped bottom. When stresses in this area were calculated, the bend and shear stresses were found to be high. In fact, one expert postulated that the leak had started at exactly this discontinuity. The spheres, on the other hand, had no such discontinuities, so the stresses were more uniform. The inner tank of tank 4 was supported by two concentric rings of wooden posts such that the bottom was hanging in suspension and not supported evenly. The spheres were built such that the inner tank was supported by the layer of cork between the inner and outer tanks. The cork was used for both insulation and support. Thus the inner spherical tank was cradled with much less stress than the inner cylindrical tank. Because of the war, cork was ostensibly unavailable for tank 4, so mineral wool was used as the insulation. It could not mechanically support the inner tank as cork did for the spheres; it did not have the compressive strength. Pittsburgh–Des Moines had built many cylindrical tanks for water and other fluids but had never built one of this type previously. The design of the tank was seen as weak, and although its features may not have led directly to the failure, it is likely they were a contributing factor.

The Codes

One topic the investigation teams did not look into was the set of codes and standards that Cooper and the Hope and Pittsburgh–Des Moines engineers had available, or did not have available, to them when they started to build the plant. It turns out that research in low-temperature metals was just starting around 1940 when the plant was built. There were no standards on low-temperature material use by either the ASME or ASTM. Cooper did try to use some information in a way he thought made sense, but it was not backed up by proven technology. They were clearly breaking new ground here in the use of 3½ percent nickel-steel. They did do some tests on the material used in the three spheres, and concluded that a nickel-steel alloy was the best material to use; these tests led him to conclude that the material would be adequate.

The Location

Finally, even with a tank failure the casualties could have been avoided had the tank location been different. The earliest letters to the mayor after the accident expressed anger about locating the plant so near so many people. The board of inquiry questioned this also. The failure to dike the tanks so that the entire contents of a ruptured tank would be contained was just another manifestation of the lack of appreciation of the risk involved. Where no concern about risk was evident before the construction, now all that was seen was the folly of locating such a dangerous element so near to so many people. That particular problem, siting this type of plant within city limits, has not happened again; a lesson was learned. It is still remarkable, though, that no risk analysis was done; that someone didn't envision a scenario that included the complete failure of one of the tanks. The lessons of the *Titanic*, barely 30 years previously, had not been learned. As will be discussed in Chapter 7, the *Titanic* also failed due to brittle fracture of the steel. It was easy to see the upside of storing the liquid gas so near the customers—one could alleviate peak shortages very easily; everyone would seem to benefit. The downside, a complete tank failure, was totally invisible. Even the designer of the whole system, Howell Cooper, testified that he could see no way for the LNG to get out of the tanks. Risk analysis has come a long way since then. It is likely that this siting risk would now be identified and mitigated.

The Conclusions

The root cause of a failure is usually identified as the event that starts the failure scenario. In this case that could be attributed to the possible "bumping." However, it seems reasonable to say that in this case that was almost incidental, that almost anything might have started the failure. It seems more appropriate to say the root cause of the failure of tank 4 was the inferior material used in the tank and the poor design of the tank. Once the tank had been set up for failure with material that was too brittle, there could have been a number of events that actually initiated the rupture, including the cold fluid "bumping" and valve "flapping" scenario.

The industry had to pause for a few years before moving ahead again with liquid natural gas. A suitable material and tank design had to be found and proven before confidence could be restored. A suitable material was found and better tank designs were developed in the following years so that the industry could recover. This story of recovery will be told in the following chapters.

7
Recovery

The recovery in Cleveland started almost immediately, as the *Cleveland Plain Dealer* reported the day after the fire:

> Even as the fire roared on, the City council prepared an investigation. Councilman Jack P. Russell announced he would introduce an ordinance covering the storage of liquid gas under pressure. "In no event shall any tank be located nearer than 2,000 feet of any inhabited dwelling nor within 1,500 feet of any public highway or within a like distance of the main track of any railroad, place of public gathering or store," the ordinance provides.[1]

That ordinance did not show up in the City Record. However, the City Record does show the City Council passing an ordinance on October 25 authorizing emergency funds for the area, another ordinance on November 15 rezoning the area to separate the residential and industrial areas, and a request by two councilmen to the director of public safety to report with recommendations as to

> whether or not tanks, vessels, or other containers used for the storage of gases or other products in any form, which, if normally or abnormally released, including release by explosion, fire, or other abnormal means would constitute the hazard to life and property within in any area in the 23rd Ward and necessarily related territory.[2]

These ordinances and the recovery and rebuild covered in Chapter 1 essentially ended the experiment with LNG in Cleveland, the city where it all started. The city continued to use the underground storage it went to right after the fire, and then suffered some shortages for a while until the gas from the Southwest could be delivered by pipeline. There was no attempt to go back to LNG for peak shaving. The LNG recovery, which did happen, took place elsewhere.

The recovery of the LNG industry took place over many years, in many different places, and with many different people and organizations. It included technology advances, as well as changes in codes and standards. That recovery is the story of this chapter. It is summarized in the timeline of table 7-2 at the end of the chapter.

The lessons learned from the catastrophe can be roughly categorized into three areas. One is the realization that the plant was in the wrong place, and that not enough attention was paid to safety issues. The tanks were not covered by their own (LNG) regulations, and regulations for storing flammable liquids were not applied. This realization started immediately after the fire and led to some immediate changes and some longer term changes. Second, even though there was no definitive cause found for the failure, the weakness in the material used for the tanks, and the weakness of the design of tank 4, clearly contributed to the failure. The root cause of the failure was probably the brittle material used in tank 4. These issues had to be addressed before a full recovery was possible. More research was done on materials and tank design, and the industry didn't really pick up again until these issues were considered closed. This took 15 to 20 years. Lastly, as odd as it might seem, there was a general consensus that this event did *not* preclude liquid natural gas processing from proceeding as long as safer practices were used. In other words, this was not a *Hindenburg* event. The strength of the concept was seen as sound and one that should be developed because of its advantages. As a result of this last observation, new materials and designs were developed and new plants located at safer sites were built.

Fire Codes

The dual nature of the LNG storage tanks, as both containers that must meet mechanical standards set by the ASME and as structures that must meet local building and fire codes, was introduced in Chapter 5. The guidance, or lack thereof, that Cooper had from ASME standards on materials was discussed in that chapter. Following is a brief discussion from the building or fire code aspect.

Humans have used the energy in fire for millennia. As useful as it is, it has always been a mixed blessing, sometimes causing great devastation. For most of history the dangers were accepted as the cost of using this energy. However, over the past 400 years as more people started moving into cities, and buildings used wooden construction, the problem of fire causing major loss of life and property became more acute.

In the latter half of the nineteenth century the issue of loss by fire was addressed almost simultaneously from two different directions. One was focused on recovering from the loss caused by the fire through fire insurance. The second was putting out fires before they could spread, mainly by using sprinkler systems. These two initiatives eventually came together by the end of the century and finally focused on *preventing* fires. Surprisingly, it took quite a while to go from the insurance and dousing concepts to the prevention concept.

The Great Fire of London in 1666 is credited with the start of fire insurance as a business. The fire destroyed about 80 percent of the city including 13,200 homes and 87 churches, and most of the City Authority buildings. The buildings were close together and a lot of combustible material was used. (Officially the fire killed only six people, but this number is in dispute because it is believed that many of the poor and middle class deaths were not recorded.) Even with this amount of damage, the city was rebuilt using the same type of building plans and spacing as before the fire.[3] The insurance at that time was confined to insuring buildings. It wasn't until 1707 that goods could be insured. Underwriting for ships' cargos started about this time in the early eighteenth century. The modern stock insurance company was originated in 1710 when two corporations were chartered for that purpose.[4]

Insurance came to the United States around 1728. The first American company, a mutual one, issued its first policy in 1752; one of its directors was Benjamin Franklin.[5] As the cities grew, sometimes in a haphazard way, Americans in general tended to be careless in managing fire risks. Fire seemed to be an uncontrollable hazard. The pioneer spirit seemed to encourage rebuilding after a fire either here or somewhere else, but moving on. In this atmosphere the insurance entrepreneurs saw opportunities. Many different companies were formed, and many rates applied. As rates were raised more companies got into the apparently lucrative business. More people in the business meant more competition. That competition encouraged rate cutting, which then made it harder to cover losses. Between 1849 and 1865 New York City produced more than 70 new companies. At the same time, fires were increasing and losses continued to grow. By this time the fire losses were getting out of hand. They had increased about 50 percent from 1864 to 1865 and by July 1866 they had exceeded the total losses of 1865.[6] The fire insurance industry was at a crisis point considering the fire losses, proliferation of companies, and radically variable rate structure.

National Board of Fire Underwriters (NBFU)

In July of 1866 a group of these companies came together to form a board for the U.S. fire insurance industry that would help stabilize the industry and bring some standardization. They formed what came to known as the National Board of Fire Underwriters (NBFU) primarily to support the fire underwriting industry. It was based on four principles: a practical and uniform rate structure, uniform compensation to agents, repression of arson (thought to be a common problem), and development of measures for the common interests of the industry. The National Board essentially became an organization for rate control. Note that there was nothing in these principles about fire prevention.[7] It took several more years before fire prevention came to be seen as an important principle. In his 1891 address the president of the NBFU called attention to the $140 million of fire waste in 1891 by saying,

> The people are beginning to realize that this enormous waste is becoming a national burden of serious import.... The press and the people seem to have arrived at the conviction that the destruction of property by fire is increasing far more rapidly than the growth of population.... The old theory ... that a risk should be written as found, and a rate adequate to the hazard be charged is fast becoming obsolete, and to-day *[sic]* all local and district associations, and all syndicates for writing great industries *are aiming to secure improvements in construction and greater care, and all favor the introduction of automatic and other appliances for the prevention and extinguishing of fires*[8] [emphasis in the original].

This last sentence was one of the first times reference was made to improving construction to help to prevent fires. This was 25 years after the founding of the NBFU. The automatic extinction of fires referred to the use of automatic sprinkler systems, which were starting to come into use (see the next section).

Fire prevention finally gained a new urgency. A letter was written to President Benjamin Harrison urging legislation on the investigation of fire causes and on the construction of buildings regarding fire hazards. The insurers were trying to make fire prevention a national matter. State legislation was introduced, not always successfully. In 1896 the NBFU voted to frame the National Board's Model Building Law.[9]

As fire losses climbed to $153 million in 1899 there was a realization that fire prevention had to be addressed more systematically: "Uniform rules in regard to devices and materials entering into fire hazard were necessary and precise knowledge must be substituted for guesswork."[10] The idea of putting engineering and science to work on fire prevention was taking hold. One step in this direction was by the NBFU, which assumed the expense of printing and distributing descriptions of the standards formulated by the National Fire Protection Association (NFPA) (see the next section).

In 1901, after the NBFU had grown to over 129 companies, it revised its principles. It pruned some of the more self-serving ones such as establishing a uniform system of rates and added an important fifth principle: "To influence the introduction of improved and safe methods of building construction, encourage the adoption of fire-protective measures, secure efficient organization and equipment of Fire Departments."[11] Fire prevention had become a major emphasis in reducing the loss of life and property caused by fire.

National Fire Protection Association (NFPA)

A few years after the NBFU started, in an effort to protect its insurance company members, another organization started looking at fire protection from a technical point of view. In this case it was the vision of controlling fires with sprinkler systems. Sprinkler systems can be traced back as far as 1806 in England, when John Carey first thought of dousing fires with water carried through pipes. In the United States James Bichon Francis is credited with installing the first sprinkler system in the Plant of the Proprietors of the Locks and Canals on the Merrimack River in Lowell, Massachusetts. In 1874 Henry Parmelee of New Haven, Connecticut, obtained a patent for a sprinkler head, and the first U.S. patent for a sprinkler system was issued to Phillip Pratt of Abington, Massachusetts, in 1872. Between 1878 and 1882 about 200,000 Parmelee sprinklers were installed in mills, mostly in New England. A group of insurers led by John Ripley Freeman of West Bridgton, Maine, an 1876 graduate of the Massachusetts of Technology who worked for the Factory Mutual Insurance Companies, started to meet to see how they could control this apparent fire epidemic.[12] In the meantime sprinkler systems continued to grow in popularity during the 1880s and 1890s.

By 1895 and 1896 various groups of insurers and sprinkler advocates were meeting to discuss standardization of sprinkler systems. They had been widely popular, but the non-standard systems resulted in plumbing nightmares. One of the groups released a set of sprinkler installation rules called "Report of the Committee of Automatic Sprinkler Protection." That same group met later in the year to form an organization that was known as the National Fire Protection Association (NFPA). The NFPA had a broader objective than just sprinkler systems; it started to address fire protection in general. The 1897 meeting of the NFPA outlined the principles still followed by the Technical Committees:

> To bring together the experience of the different sections and different bodies of underwriters to come to a mutual understanding, and if possible, an agreement on general principles governing fire protection. To harmonize and adjust our differences so that we may go before the public with uniform rules and conditions which may appeal to their judgment is the object of this Association.[13]

The NFPA expanded quickly and by 1904 included organizations beyond insurance underwriters. These included the National Electrical Contractors' Association, American Water Works Association, the American Society of Mechanical Engineers, and the American Institute of Architects. In 1911 the work of periodically revising the National Electrical Code was transferred to the NFPA Electrical Committee from the National Conference on Standard Electrical Rules.[14] The NFPA has continued to revise fire and safety codes. The NFPA's National Fire Codes are developed by technical committees staffed by thousands of volunteers. These National Fire Codes are adopted and enforced by various government organizations (for example, municipalities) throughout the world.

NBFU and NFPA Working Together

Late in the nineteenth century the underwriting and sprinkler industries started to see losses in an area that surprised them, an area where they thought they had reduced risk: areas associated with the more advanced buildings. They finally realized that the new and extensive use of electricity was causing fires that had not been possible prior to the use of electricity. It was recognized that electricity, as useful as it had become, was a potential fire hazard if not properly controlled. For example, "there were 65 installations of electric lighting in the mills insured by the Manufacturers Mutual Insurance Companies of New England which were followed by 23 fires in six months."[15] These issues now started to get addressed by the underwriters. In 1894 the Underwriters' Electric Bureau was established by William Merrill to test new electrical equipment for safety. Seven years later, in November 1901, this became the Underwriters Laboratories (UL). The UL became a fixture, and still is, for anyone buying an electrical appliance who wants to be assured it will not fail and cause a fire. Just as there was a proliferation of sprinkler systems, there was also a proliferation of electrical codes, not all of them consistent. By the end of 1895 there were five distinct electrical codes in the U.S.; consistency was needed.[16] In an attempt to achieve this, a group met in Boston in 1895. It included not only fire underwriters but also members of the fire sprinkler community.

So by 1895 there were various groups of insurers and sprinkler advocates who came together to address not only the persistent problem of lack of standardization in sprinkler systems, but also the new problem of electrical fires. It was these group meetings that provided the motivation to establish the NFPA, as discussed in the previous section.

These groups continued to meet throughout 1896 to cover both electrical codes and sprinkler installation codes. One electrical code, dubbed the "National Code," was approved. It was quickly adopted by the National Board of Fire Underwriters (NBFU) in lieu of its own code.[17] It was issued by the NBFU as the National Electrical Code (NEC). This was the code that was transferred to the NFPA as described above. A campaign was started to secure adoption of this code by cities and towns. By April 1901 it was being enforced by 125 municipal governments.[18]

It took a long time after the establishment of the NBFU in 1866 until the establishment of the NFPA in 1896. During that time progress was made in insuring against fire loss, but the idea of using science and engineering to *prevent* fires still seemed to elude the industry. However, by the turn of the century this problem was addressed, and by the early twentieth century there were enforceable codes in place, driven by the cooperation of the NBFU and NFPA, to assure safe building construction.

How to Address LNG Safety?

Although the NBFU and NFPA codes were updated when new information was available, they were not always current. In the early 1940s, for example, there were no codes for storing liquid natural gas. In this situation, in lieu of doing nothing at all, choices had to be made. The unspoken choice made for the liquid natural gas was to basically ignore any guidelines or rules for handling it because there appeared to be no guidelines or rules; it had never been produced or stored in such large volumes before.

It was different. For one thing, it was very cold, unlike any other liquid fuel. The low temperatures possibly gave the impression that the fluid was not dangerous. If it was so cold, how could it be flammable? The chemistry of LNG, of course, would not support this intuitive idea. Whatever the reason, the safety precautions used for handling other liquid fuels were not observed. Had the safety issue been pursued, what other model might have been used to safely contain this liquid fuel? The handling and storage of gasoline could have been used as a model. Another model that could have been used was the liquid petroleum gas model.

Gasoline, primarily produced from the fractional distillation of crude oil, is a mixture of many hydrocarbons. It can also be produced directly from "wet" or "casinghead" natural gas, which is often found where natural gas is found with oil. Natural gasoline can be condensed from this "wet" gas. Gasoline of course is flammable, more easily ignited than kerosene, which was addressed by the fire codes almost as soon as it came into existence. Following the standards on storage and use of kerosene in 1902, the NFPA initiated action in 1911 to consolidate these requirements into a suggested ordinance for all flammable liquids. In 1923 they saw the need to do a complete revision to consider large-scale storage. The popularity of the automobile undoubtedly contributed to the need to store gasoline on a large scale. The suggested ordinance for flammable liquids divided these liquids into three classes dependent on flash point: Class I (gasoline, naphtha, acetone and others), with a flash point below 25°F; Class II (alcohol and others), with a flash point above Class I and below 70°F; and Class III (kerosene, fuel oil, and others), with a flash point above Class II and below 200°F.[19] (Flash point is the lowest temperature at which a liquid can form an ignitable mixture in air near the surface of the liquid. The lower the flash point, the easier it is to ignite the material.)[20] Using these criteria, LNG with a very low flash point of −306°F should be classified along with gasoline in Class I.[21]

Chapter 3 of the NFPA suggested ordinance (1943 revision) on the storage tank capacity, location and other restrictions puts limits on storage tanks for flammable liquids. For above ground tanks, the minimum distance to adjoining property is very modest, only 25 feet minimum for tanks up to the maximum 50,000 gallons listed in the ordinance. However, the East Ohio tank 4 carried about one million gallons of LNG. There is a provision in the code (Chapter 3, section 47) that says,

> In particular installations these distances may be increased at the discretion of the authority having jurisdiction after consideration of the special features such as topographical conditions; nature of occupancy and proximity to buildings on adjoining property and height and character of construction of such buildings; capacity and construction of proposed tanks and character of liquids to be stored; degree of private fire protection to be provided, and facilities of the fire department to cope with oil fires. Consideration of these features shall also determine the distance for tanks of capacities of over 50,000 gallons.[22]

Had this code for flammable liquids been applied to the East Ohio LNG tanks, it appears the urban location chosen for the tanks would have violated all of its considerations.

Section 53 of the same chapter discusses the need for dikes around the tanks:

(c) All tanks containing crude oil or other liquids which have a tendency to boil over, and all tanks exceeding 50,000 gallons (1200 barrels) capacity shall be adequately and properly diked with a dike having capacity not less than equal in volume to that of the tank or tanks surrounded, minimum height of earth dikes to be 3 ft. and of masonry dikes 30 in.[23]

This is the containment system that mayor's board of inquiry was asking about at the hearings just after the fire. No dike had been provided for any of the tanks. For tank 4 there was a small conduit to the old gasholder adjacent to it (see figure 5-4). The idea expressed was that for a small leak in tank 4, the LNG would be would be conducted to the old gasholder pit where it would evaporate. The board questioned William Hagan, East Ohio vice president, about the adequacy of this design. They further pressed him on the lack of a dike, such as those used in the petroleum industry. There appeared to be a total lack of comprehension of the possible need for a dike because there was a lack of comprehension that the tank could ever fail so as to need a dike.[24]

The dialogue from the hearing quoted in Chapter 6 on this subject continued:

Q. You don't think it is necessary to provide for the catching of the sudden dumpage then?
A. Well, I would not know how to go about doing it. If I thought you had to do it, I wouldn't build a tank, and you would not have to catch it.
Q. If that tank were centered in an area which was surrounded by an earth dyke, as it is in the petroleum industry, if the dykes were high enough, the area is large enough, it could catch the dumpage?
A. Yes, you could catch the dumpage all right.
...
Q. So there is a way to do it?
A. Well, I don't think so. I don't think that anybody in the gas business would ever make such a design. At least I would not.

The dialogue goes on with Mr. Hagan insisting he would rather not build the tank if an earthen dike was required. Once again, a principal involved with designing and building the tanks could not comprehend a total failure that would dump the entire contents of a tank in a single incident. It appears they were convinced that the exotic material they were working with did not have to follow the same safety rules as other flammable liquids.

Although it seems that LNG should be classified as a Class I flammable material based on its flash point (like gasoline) and should therefore require a dike system, what if it were classified as a liquid petroleum gas (LPG) instead, gases that are very close in chemical composition to methane, which is the primary constituent of LNG?

Liquid petroleum gas (LPG) is a mixture of various hydrocarbons, but is mostly propane and butane. Propane (C_3H_8) and butane (C_4H_{10}) are substantial constituents of natural gas and are chemically close to the other major constituents, methane (CH_4) and ethane (C_2H_6). Although there were some bottled gas mixtures, mostly under pressure, coming from Europe in the 1903–1904 timeframe, the discovery of propane and butane are generally attributed to Walter O. Snelling in 1910, as discussed in Chapter 3.

The high critical temperatures of propane and butane allow these gases to be liquid at room temperature just by using pressure to liquefy them. In that sense they contrast with ethane and methane, which require pressure and low temperatures to liquefy; that is, ethane and methane have lower critical temperatures. Propane, for example, is stored under pressure as a liquid and becomes a gas when released from that pressure. This provides a convenient fuel for the professional and the homeowner. These liquid petroleum gases (LPG), although chemically similar to liquid methane, have very dissimilar properties, as covered above. (Nevertheless, LPG and LNG are sometimes confused and the terms incorrectly used interchangeably. Unfortunately, this has been propagated in various short historical articles on the Web that purport to discuss the early use of LNG in the 1912–1917 timeframe, when in fact they seemed to be referring to LPG.) One of the early users of LPG was Dr. J. B. Garner of the Hope Natural Gas Company. He used it to cut steel in the Pittsburgh area in 1916 when Hope started to produce LPG at their Hastings Station in West Virginia.[25]

If there is a similarity between LNG and LPG, could LPG safety standards been invoked when building the Cleveland plant? The NFPA initiated standards for LPG in 1924. Since then they have updated and consolidated them on a regular basis. The rules are similar to those for other flammable liquids but differ slightly in storage container requirements. Under the requirements for dikes, they say that because of the volatility of LPG, dikes are not normally necessary. In other words because they evaporate so fast into a gas at ambient conditions, a dike containment would be superfluous. However, the standard goes on to say,

> When, however, in the opinion of the inspection department having jurisdiction, owing to the slope of the ground or other local conditions, above ground containers are liable in the case of rupture or overflow to endanger adjacent property, each container shall be surrounded by a dike of such capacity as may be considered necessary to meet the needs of the situation under consideration by the aforesaid inspection department but in no case more than the capacity of the container.[26]

While this is weaker than the requirement for a dike for flammable liquids, such as gasoline, it still indicates that the inspector, if using this part of the code, could have and should have required a dike because of the "endanger adjacent property" provision.

Although there was no NFPA standard addressing the storage of LNG at the time (there is one now), there were NFPA fire codes that should have been seen as applicable. Of the two addressed above, the code for flammable liquids, classifying LNG as a Class I flammable liquid, appears to be the most appropriate one because of the liquid similarity of gasoline and LNG. This was the point that the mayor's board tried to make to the East Ohio vice president.

East Ohio Addresses LNG Safety

The lack of recognition that existing fire codes could have been used for the construction of the LNG tanks did not mean a lack of concern for safety by East Ohio; there was still a concern about the safety of the tanks. In 1940 the company contacted the Ohio Department of Industrial Relations, Division of Boiler Inspection, asking for advice on tank construction. This was confirmed by a December 1944 letter from that division to Dr. Samuel Gerber, Cleveland coroner and member of the mayor's board of inquiry. Dr. Gerber apparently had written to the division asking for this information. According to the letter from the chief of the division,

> Their company [EOG] ... showed that the vessels were only to be used as storage vessels and that the liquid was at a very low sub zero temperature.... After going over our Ohio Unfired

> Pressure Vessel Code, I could find nothing where the code had any provision for the construction of vessels which did not contain a pressure of 30 pounds or more; however, I took this matter up with the Board of Boiler Deputies of the Industrial Commission of Ohio and it was agreed that there was nothing to prevent the construction of these vessels.[27]

He went on to say that he and an assistant went to Cleveland on July 9, 1941, to look over the blueprints for the tanks. At that meeting Vice President Hagan stated that they wanted the "vessels built in the very safest condition and took this measure to satisfy themselves that there was nothing in the Ohio code to prevent their [the tanks'] construction."[28] So East Ohio did have a concern, but the lack of specific codes for LNG left them at a loss for how to address the safety issue. The use of the codes for storing gasoline apparently did not seem applicable.

Once again, the recognition that this was a very cold liquid seemed to mask the fact that it was also flammable. The low pressure in the tank meant there was nothing in the usual code that would prevent it from being constructed. There was simply no code that covered it. The good faith effort by East Ohio to check the code shows their concern about safety and their effort to make it as safe as possible. Clearly the codes at the time were inadequate. There was no specific state, municipal, or NFPA code that precluded the tanks' construction in that residential-industrial area, so the permits were issued and the tanks were constructed. No one seemed to question them until after the fact, when it suddenly became obvious that they shouldn't have been built there. One might say that despite good faith on the part of many people, there was a lack of imagination about what would happen if one of the tanks were to fail completely. Today this would be called a failure of risk analysis. That time was still an era of acceptance. The neighbors accepted the tanks; all the known codes accepted them. Similar to the acceptance of fires being inevitable early in the century, that was still the era of "accidents will happen."

New Standards for LNG

As one would expect, following the fire, a code was eventually developed to address the issues that led to the disaster, the catastrophic failure of an LNG storage tank. This took longer than one would expect. On the other hand, everyone was in shock and there was a lot going on. The war still had to be fought and won, as it would be within a year. The years immediately following would be taken up with many problems, including consumer goods supply, inflation, and the start of the Cold War. The immediate need for storing liquid natural gas for war production had eased by 1945.

The market for liquid natural gas did not pick up seriously for about 15 years, into the early 1960s. The potential for LNG was recognized and by 1962 some people were getting itchy about not having an accepted LNG standard in place to allow progress in the field. As H. H. Fitzgerald of Commonwealth Services Incorporated noted at a 1962 conference:

> There is a great economic need at this time for LNG storage for peak shaving. The Cleveland disaster dominates our history of the art, and, therefore, the recommendations resulting from this disaster still are our only recognized guide for the construction of new LNG storage plants. It is generally believed that these recommendations are ultraconservative.... We need a code that will modify the recommendations of 20 years ago and establish reasonable safe practices on the basis of the present status of the art.... It seems the time has come when

the industry must develop the necessary information, through research, to develop a sound and reasonable code for construction of storage plants that does not jeopardize public safety. Then gas companies in need of this form of peak shaving can progress with conservative plans for aboveground LNG storage plants.[29]

He was correct about the recommendations being ultraconservative. The first recommendation of the Bureau of Mines Report on the disaster recommended an LNG plant be no closer than one-half mile to the nearest property line. This would require a minimum one-square-mile site. It also suggested that a dike system be used as was used in the gasoline storage industry; this, though, was not an ultraconservative suggestion. As we have seen, the use of the standards for storing flammable liquids such as gasoline would have been a reasonable way to design an LNG plant. The first LNG plants of the early 1960s did adopt the safety concepts of the gasoline and LPG industries, including, for example, the NBFU "Pamphlet 59" on storing LPG at utility gas plants.[30]

These stirrings around this time showed up in actions taken by the American Gas Association among others. Around 1960, an American Gas Association committee began work on a standard for storing liquefied natural gas. A draft was submitted to the NFPA in 1964 with a request that it be considered as a standard.[31] The NFPA took the issue up in 1966. They established the Committee on Fuel Gases, and in 1967 that committee issued the first standard, NFPA 59A, "Standard for the Production, Storage, and Handling of Liquefied Natural Gas (LNG)." Things were moving rapidly in the field of LNG at the time, so by 1969 the first standard was out of date. Another committee was established, the Committee on Liquefied Natural Gas, and a revised standard came out in 1971, the first under this new committee.[32]

As these new LNG regulations were being considered, there was some public and vocal opposition to LNG fed by the Cleveland disaster and some new technical results about downwind vapor dispersion of potential LNG vapors. This resulted in some books and testimony against LNG at various hearings. This is in stark contrast to the lack of public awareness and apparent indifference when the first LNG plant was built in Cleveland. Public awareness of public policy issues, which was manifested in civil rights and anti-war protests in the 1960s, now started to show up in other public policy issues such as siting of LNG plants.[33]

As might be expected, many of the provisions of NFPA 59A reflect the lessons learned from the East Ohio disaster. Chapter 5 addresses siting of the storage containers:

> 5.3.1.1 Provisions shall be made to minimize the potential discharge of LNG at containers endangering adjoining property or important process equipment and structures or reaching waterways, in accordance with one of the following methods: (1) an impounding area surrounding the container(s) that is formed by a natural barrier, dike, impounding wall, or combination thereof.

The size of the impounding area or dike is specified:

> 5.3.2.1 Impounding areas serving one LNG container shall have a volumetric holding capacity, V, that is one of the following: (1) V = 110 percent of the maximum liquid capacity of the container.

The dike material is specified:

> 5.3.2.5 Dikes and impounding areas shall meet the following requirements: (1) Dikes and impounding walls shall be constructed of compacted earth, concrete, metal, or other materials.

The allowable radiant heat at property lines is limited to assure adjacent properties do not catch fire if there is a mishap. The radiant heat flux (Watts per square meter) is limited to 9,000 for

> the nearest point on the building or structure outside the owner's property line that is in existence at the time of plant siting and used for assembly, educational, health care, detention and correction, or residential occupancies for a fire in the impounding area.

The material used in LNG tanks is not really relevant to fire prevention per se, and the NFPA has no expertise in this. It does address it, however:

> 7.3.1.2 Those parts of LNG containers that are normally in contact with LNG and all materials used in contact with LNG or cold LNG vapor [vapor at a temperature below −20°F (−29°C)] shall be physically and chemically compatible with LNG and intended for service at −270°F (−168°C).[34]

Determining what material is physically and chemically compatible with LNG took the next several years after the accident. The materials are in the purview of the American Society of Mechanical Engineers (ASME) and will be covered in the next section.

Partly as a response to public protest and partly as a response to was what perceived as some inadequacy of the 1971 NFPA standards, Congress decided that the Department of Transportation should develop its own standards for LNG. Following the development of the NFPA 59A, the U.S. Department of Transportation (DOT) developed its own standard: "Liquefied Natural Gas Facilities: Federal Safety Standards."[35] The initial federal safety standards were developed as a requirement of the Pipeline Safety Act of 1979.[36] These standards have since been revised and are now closer in content to NFPA standards. The DOT standard also references NFPA 59A. The Ohio Administrative Code 1301:7-7-32 requires that the storage, use, and handling of liquefied natural gas shall comply with the NFPA 59A.

The LNG industry now had a fire safety standard. Although it was too late to prevent the 1944 accident, the lessons learned from that accident were incorporated in the standard. The industry has grown dramatically since the fire and, because of the standard developments, there have been no similar accidents.

The absence of specific standards for the storage of LNG at that time, however, does not automatically absolve the builders of new facilities from considering the safety aspects of that facility by thinking beyond the standards. The technical consultants of the mayor's board of inquiry stated it well in their report under conclusions:

> While it is admitted that it would be difficult if not impossible to cover all hazards by proper regulations, the attitude of intelligent skepticism and caution is something that can be exercised by those concerned by the application and enforcement of safety ordinances and codes....
>
> In general, practically all municipal ordinances and regulations are necessarily drawn up to cover the most frequently encountered situations with certain definite requirements. From the viewpoint of public safety this, in a way, is insufficient; the weakness in such ordinances lies in the fact that it is the extraordinary situation which may be the troublemaker. This deficiency in coverage is, in some degree, inevitable since only recurrent experience can be codified....
>
> It is therefore utterly inadequate to rely completely for protection on the mere enforcement of existing codes, though the usefulness of such codes is in no way disparaged. Protec-

tion in the long run must come from the careful review of proposed projects, and especially those beyond the bounds of well tested experience....

In short it may be stated that no set procedures, no set organization, and no set codes can guarantee safety. But it is advantageous to follow established practices wherever these can be made to apply with the probability of success.[37]

These comments remain relevant today, and not only regarding fire codes. Often when a tragedy happens, or any major problem occurs, the response is a change in the law or code or regulation that addresses the problem. This is admirable and often effective for addressing that problem, but there can be some pernicious effects of this approach if one is not careful. One is the relaxation after the fact caused by the feeling that "we have fixed the problem so there is nothing to worry about any more." The impact of this mindset is obvious; one's guard might be let down. The other is the one addressed above, that is, the thinking that every hazard can be controlled by adding another rule or regulation. For example, after the space shuttle *Challenger* accident, many changes were made to improve shuttle safety. These, however, did not preclude the space shuttle *Colombia* accident just a few years later. The remedy for both of these mindsets is what the authors call "the attitude of intelligent skepticism and caution."

Materials

The authors of the "Report of the Technical Consultants of the Mayor's Board of Inquiry" came to a number of other conclusions also. A couple of these probably would have occurred to those in the field, whether these consultants had come to these same conclusions or not. Their conclusions question the use of 3½ percent nickel-steel for use in the tanks:

> (12) the design of the works incorporated certain materials whose suitability for the service intended was not, in the opinion of the consultants, definitely established
> (13) the principal item in question is the use of the 3½ percent nickel steel for the inner shell and other structural elements in Tank No. 4 which is exposed to extreme low temperature under load. Tests by the U.S. Bureau of Mines on the particular nickel steel which was used in this tank show impact values which are much lower than those stated by the designer of the tank, to be satisfactory.[38]

Conclusion 12 questions whether the suitability of 3½ percent nickel-steel had been proven for use in these tanks, at those temperatures. Conclusion 13 specifically questions whether the nickel-steel in tank 4 had the correct Charpy impact values or were too low. The latter conclusion also questions the design of tank 4 ("under load"), which is the double cylinder supported by wooden posts and subject to shock and vibration not seen by the LNG in the spherical tanks. As covered in the previous chapter, the U.S. Bureau of Mines, at the request of the board of inquiry consultants, tested the fragments from tank 4 and found that the impact strength was very low compared to what had been set as the design standard (15 foot-pounds) for material in contact with LNG. The material used for tank 4 appeared to be a bad batch, not up to the impact strength of the material known to be used for the other three tanks (spheres). The consultant team, therefore, seemed to be steering clear of criticizing the use of 3½ percent nickel steel in general for this cryogenic use; it said the material's suitability was not established. It limited the explicit criticism to the specific material used in tank 4.

The U.S. Bureau of Mines report on the accident came to similar conclusions on the suitability of the material used for tank 4:

> It appears that the steel used in the three spherical tanks was suitable but may not have been suitable for the cylindrical tank. This point is raised because possible seismic shocks would have been cushioned to a greater extent by the cork insulation in the spherical tanks than by the wood columns in No. 4 tank....
>
> These considerations, along with the fact that most industries handling large quantities of liquid oxygen or air use stainless steel or suitable non-ferrous metal tanks suggest the possibility that the steel used in No. 4 tank may not have been suited to the particular design of this tank.[39]

The Bureau of Mines report went on to make a specific recommendation regarding the use of 3½ percent nickel-steel for this design:

> 4. The construction of a storage tank for liquids at low temperatures similar in design to No. 4 storage tank using low-carbon, 3½ percent, nickel steel, should not be undertaken unless the cause of the failure of No. 4 tank is definitely established and unless it can be proved beyond doubt that the properties of the steel were suitable for the particular design in question.[40]

Although the exact cause of the accident was never definitively identified, the doubt raised by these investigations was enough to cause mistrust on the use of 3½ percent nickel-steel for LNG storage tanks. Chapter 6 provides ample evidence that the brittle material (with low Charpy impact values at low temperature) used in tank 4 was the root cause of the failure. In the next few years the search for a reasonably priced alternative was the goal of those who still saw a future in this industry. But even as late as 1954 some, such as Robert Ormston of the Cincinnati Gas and Electric Company, were not optimistic about LNG tanks:

> The gas industry is ever striving to provide for the storage of B.t.u.'s in a form that can be quickly and economically delivered to the consumer during periods of maximum demand. Liquefaction installations have long been recognized to be particularly applicable in meeting these requirements. *Due to an unfortunate accident in its first application, interest in the process has apparently been abandoned*[41] [emphasis added].

Fortunately that was not the case, but the East Ohio fire did put a damper on the progress.

Brittleness of carbon steel under low temperatures was not well understood at the time. In fact that wouldn't happen until the 1950s, until the mechanics of brittle fracture of steel was researched and finally understood. Later into the 1990s, when other technology was available, a retrospective look at another disaster revealed some interesting analogies with the East Ohio disaster.

In August of 1996 researchers brought back a piece of steel from the hull of the *Titanic*. The chemical composition analysis first revealed that the steel had a high sulfur content, which was one indication that it was brittle. High sulfur content increases the brittleness of steel by interrupting the grain structure. Electron micrographs of the specimen also showed a large grain size in the steel. Tougher steels have a finer grain structure. Charpy impact tests, the most common test used to test steel toughness, especially for low temperature use, were conducted on the specimen. These results showed the impact energy at around zero degrees Celsius, the temperature of the water the *Titanic* was in, to be around four foot-pounds. (The change in temperature scale name, from Centigrade to Celsius, took place in 1948.) This is very low and suggests that the impact of the iceberg, while bad under any circumstance, was much worse than it should have been because the steel cracked open as if it was a piece of glass hit with a hammer; it appeared to have failed by brittle fracture. The high oxygen content of the steel had contributed to a high ductile-to-brittle transition temperature (DBTT) of 25°C to 35°C. This meant that at about 0°C the metal was in the brittle range.

The crack propagated past the seams with other plates because the rivets holding the plates together were also subject to the same impact properties and failed the same way. The collision damaged almost 300 feet of the ship's hull, which contributed to the rapid sinking. Thus post-accident analysis about 80 years after the *Titanic* sank indicated it probably sank because of the use of an improper material, one that was susceptible to brittle fracture at North Atlantic water temperatures. The *Titanic* had failed from the same brittle fracture that caused the failure of the East Ohio LNG tanks.[42] An interesting observation made after the *Titanic* results were available precisely summarizes the case for the East Ohio disaster: "In the case of the Titanic disaster, the causes for the sinking indicate that shipbuilding technology was far more advanced than the understanding which engineers had of the materials they were using to build the ships."[43]

New Alloys

Peer-reviewed research on materials for low temperature use was starting in the early 1940s at the International Nickel Company, just when the first tanks were built in Cleveland. Previous to this the only research on steel for low temperature was apparently the work done by Cooper and Jackson for the tanks at East Ohio. There are numerous papers and articles on the East Ohio tanks, before and after the building of the East Ohio plant, referring to research done on the materials for the tanks, but no specifics are provided on what materials were tested; only that 3½ percent nickel-steel was chosen. In other words, no peer-reviewed research was published so the results could be checked.

The need for a high-strength material that would withstand very low temperatures to be able to store and transport liquid industrial gases such as oxygen, nitrogen, and argon was not ended with the East Ohio tank development; in fact it was just beginning. Avoiding brittleness at these low temperatures was a primary goal of this research. The liquid temperature of these gases was even lower than that of methane, for which storage tanks were being built. Clearly one of the motivations for this research was the defense industry, which was gearing up for war, whether or not the U.S. was to join the war that was in progress at the time.

Low Temperature Metal Research

In 1939 the International Nickel Company was doing most of the research on low temperature metals. Their peer-reviewed research was still looking for a nickel-alloy steel that would be satisfactory down to −200°F. Up to this point, when these low temperatures were encountered the material of choice was stainless steel or a high-nickel alloy, which were very expensive. T. N. Armstrong and A. P. Gagnebin of International Nickel were looking for less expensive alternatives. They acknowledged that previous work (also at International Nickel) had shown that a tough, low-carbon steel containing a minimum of two percent nickel would give Charpy values in excess of 15 foot-pounds down to as low as −75°F. This is approximately the sublimation temperature of carbon dioxide; not very low for liquid gases. Their intention was to go much lower, down to −200°F, with nickel-steels that would be more cost effective. They experimented with wrought steels and found they could achieve Charpy values of around 22 foot-pounds with 3.6 percent nickel-steel at −200°F and around 35 foot-pounds if about 0.08 percent aluminum was added. They also confirmed the inadequacy of two percent nickel-steel, which at this low temperature had a Charpy value of only about three foot-pounds.[44]

So by 1940, the year the East Ohio tanks were built, the peer-reviewed research showed that 3½ percent nickel-steel was good down to around −200°F. The internal research of Cooper and Jackson had convinced them that they could achieve 15 foot-pounds Charpy down to −260°F. This was the basis for using that steel for the spherical tanks. In his 1942 patent application, Jackson never claimed the addition of the small amount of aluminum, but he also claimed that 10 foot-pounds Charpy at −260°F was satisfactory.

Armstrong, G. R. Brophy, and A. J. Miller of International Nickel continued that low-temperature work through the middle 1940s. Undoubtedly their work was strongly influenced by the search for better materials to support the wartime manufacturing, but it probably also was done with the East Ohio tragedy in mind. Armstrong and Brophy started with 3½ percent and five percent nickel-steel and found

> that with carefully controlled conditions applied in the laboratory, a value of 15 ft. lbs. Charpy can be met with low carbon 3½ percent nickel and with 5 percent nickel- steels at temperatures down to −265°F. However, tests made on specimens from a number of plates from *different commercial heats of low carbon 3½ percent nickel steel indicated that a specification value of 15 ft. lbs. Charpy could not be met consistently at temperatures much below −150°F*[45] [emphasis added].

This result alone shows that it may have been luck that resulted in having a good heat from Republic Steel for the spherical tanks built in 1940, because it was not possible to get consistent commercial heats that would provide 15 foot-pounds Charpy down to −260°F.

In a patent for these low-temperature steels, applied for in 1946 and issued in 1948, Brophy and Miller presented some interesting results that showed a dramatic reversal point at about −220°F, below which the Charpy impact values for lower alloy nickel-steels (3.77 to 7.01 percent) drop dramatically with temperature compared to the higher alloy nickel-steels (8.5 to 12.92 percent). Above the reversal temperature of −220°F, the lower alloy nickel-steels actually have a higher Charpy impact resistance. This is shown in figure 7-1.[46] As they say, "this reversal is very pronounced at temperatures below −260°F."[47] The figures also show that both two percent and 3½ percent nickel-steel are well below five foot-pounds Charpy impact values at −320°F.

Of course, −260°F is the temperature of LNG. As Brophy and Miller point out, the metals used for low temperatures up to this time ("prior art") had been 3½ percent nickel-steel, the alloy used in the three spherical tanks at East Ohio. (They reference the Jackson patent [2,337,049] as the prior art in this field.) They further point out that these steels "are characterized by a very substantial sharp drop in impact resistance on entering the

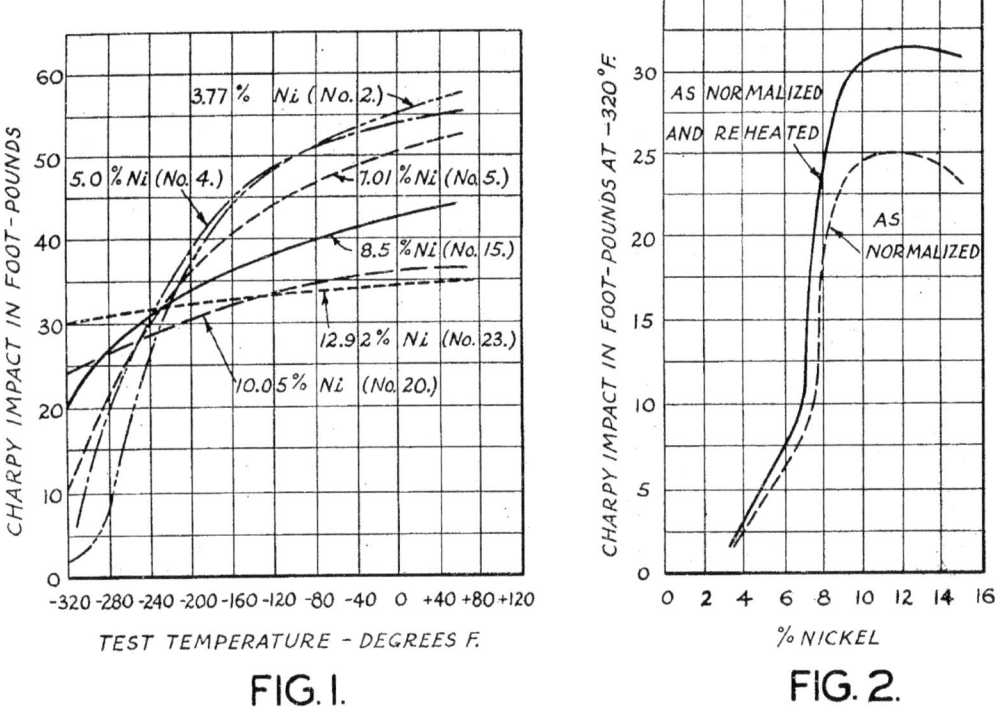

Figure 7-1. Nickel-alloy steels at low temperatures.

extreme lower range of frigid temperatures of from below about minus 240°F to minus 310°F and lower, particularly below minus 260°F."[48] By singling out these particular temperatures, it appears that they had the East Ohio tanks in mind. The chart in figure 7-1 does demonstrate the rapid falloff of the Charpy impact resistance at low temperatures for the low alloy nickel-steels. Comparing this chart to the ductile-to-brittle (DBTT) chart of figure 5-1 shows that transition range for 3.77 percent nickel-steel is approximately between −260°F and −180°F, and that at −260°F it would be considered brittle even though the Charpy value is approximately 15 foot-pounds. Small variances could easily change the Charpy value several foot-pounds either way, thus confirming the previous conclusion that Charpy impact values could not be consistently met below −150°F. So by 1946 we had rigorous laboratory tests and peer-reviewed results that showed 3½ percent nickel-steel was not adequate for LNG temperatures.

The chart on the right of figure 7-1, figure 2 from Brophy and Miller, shows the steep rise in toughness, even at a very low temperature, as the nickel content of the alloy is increased to between eight and nine percent. This increased toughness shows that Charpy values well above the 15 foot-pounds minimum required by the ASME Boiler Code could be met by these alloys. Their search for a tough alloy that could be used at low temperatures and produced at reasonable cost seems to have paid off. This material, nine percent nickel-steel, eventually came to be the material of choice for storage tanks for liquid gases at −260°F and below. However, it still had to go through more testing and examination before it became the standard. This would take a few years.

Recognizing that Charpy tests alone had limitations with respect to real-use situations, a series of tests were run in 1948 on small nickel-steel pressure vessels filled with liquid nitrogen. Tanks 42 inches by 12 inches were constructed with both 8½ percent nickel-steel and 18-8 stainless steel (18 percent chromium and eight percent nickel). They were filled with liquid nitrogen and a 293-pound weight was dropped from five feet (1,465 ft.-lb.). Although there was some deformation, neither the 8½ percent nickel-steel nor the stainless steel tanks suffered brittle fracture. The tests were repeated with the tanks under pressure and the impact increased to 3,000 foot-pounds with similar results. When only 925 foot-pounds of energy was similarly applied to a carbon steel vessel, it shattered badly on the first blow. The effectiveness of this nickel-steel alloy was proven again, this time under field-like conditions.[49]

Field Testing

Based on all the successful testing done in the early to late 1940s with nine percent nickel-steel, the ASTM came up with a specification for it, and the ASME approved its use for double normalized and tempered, shop-fabricated and *stress relieved* cryogenic vessels in 1952.[50] (Many operations on a steel alloy, especially welding, can cause internal stresses in that alloy. These stresses can be relieved by certain heat treatments after the welding.) Note that this acceptance required stress relieving after welding. This meant that the vessel had to be stress-relieved *after* construction. This is why the acceptance was for shop-fabricated vessels only; they had to be able to fit into a chamber for stress relieving after they were welded. Nevertheless, this was an important step and, as a result, hundreds of cryogenic tanks were built using nine percent nickel-steel by the early 1950s. However, the large field-built tanks necessary to store LNG were still not possible because they could not be stress-relieved after welding. Because of the catastrophic consequences of the brittle fracture of the East Ohio tank, and because of the fear of similar consequences of brittle fracture of a new tank, work continued to look for a material that would allow a field-built tank, one that would leak before failure.

In the meantime the promise of LNG kept things moving. Other materials were considered for use at cryogenic temperatures. (A distinction is made between low-temperature steels and cryogenic steels. Low-temperature steels are those used down to −150°F. They can be used for propane, carbon dioxide, and ethane, for example. Cryogenic steels can be used as low as −459°F for such liquid gases as methane, LNG, oxygen, nitrogen, and helium.[51]) As early as June 1945, a month before the report of the mayor's board of inquiry came out, there were comparisons of different materials that could be used for very low temperature applications. As Paul Petty of Hydrocarbon Research noted, "Deoxidized steels of 3½ percent and five percent nickel fall short of the −300 mark, but they may be considered for service at −150 and −260."[52] It was noted, though, that aluminum was good for low temperatures, with the Charpy values actually increasing as the temperatures dropped from −200°F to −300°F. Austenitic 18-8 stainless steel was quite acceptable at low temperatures and had been successfully used for liquid oxygen for many years. Its Charpy values were above 50 foot-pounds down to −300°F.[53] The cost of very large stainless steel storage containers, however, was prohibitive and the material is difficult to weld. Although commonly used in the cryogenic industry for many components, it never became practical for these large containers. Aluminum, although more expensive than nickel steel, was used in LNG storage tanks in the 1950s and 1960s; the price differential was not prohibitive.

Updating the Code

The increasing interest in cryogenics in the 1950s led to a series of tests by a collaboration of three companies, U.S. Steel, Chicago Bridge and Iron, and the International Nickel Company. Based on International Nickel research, U.S. Steel fabricated the nine percent nickel-steel, and Chicago Bridge and Iron fabricated the test vessels. The object was to see if they could prove the toughness of the metal and welds without the need for stress relieving. This would allow field-built tanks much larger than factory-built tanks. They built a total of six cylindrical tanks and three rectangular tanks. (The rectangular tanks were in recognition of the growing industry of shipping LNG overseas. Rectangular tanks were more practical for ship designs at the time.) They used various combinations of heat treatment on the steel: quenched and tempered, and double-normalized and tempered. Some of the tanks were stress relieved and some were used as welded. In October 1960 these tanks were filled with liquid nitrogen and, before a group of industry representatives, were tested to destruction. The burst stresses for all the vessels were from four to six times higher than the allowable stress specified in the ASME codes. In some cases the as-welded vessels were stronger than the stress-relieved vessels.[54] This was the test that made the difference and proved the capability of these alloys for field-erected LNG tanks. As L. P. Zick, et al., noted in *Mechanical Engineering* in 1963,

> In March 1962, after a review of data from this test program as well as supporting data from laboratory tests, the ASME Boiler and Pressure Vessel committee accepted 9 percent nickel steel in either the quenched and tempered condition or the double-normalized and tempered condition for use in welded pressure vessels at temperatures down to −320F and in thicknesses up to and including 1¼ in. without stress relieving (Case 1308), later increased to 1½ in [Case 1308-3].[55]

In 1962, about 17 years after the investigating teams found fault with the steel in the East Ohio tanks, and about 22 years after the low-temperature material research had started, the industry had developed a tough steel that could be used safely at temperatures as low as −310°F and was economical to produce. Although the resurgence of LNG had already started with some experiments in the 1950s, this alloy steel now provided a basis for a new boom in LNG activity that was about to start in the 1960s.

INSULATION

A number of commentators on this catastrophe blame the tank failure on the inability to get the proper material for the tank because of wartime shortages. They usually mean the contractor couldn't get the appropriate steel alloy. As we have seen this is not the story. Cooper and Jackson did have the 3½ percent nickel-steel that they had determined was proper for the tanks; they had the steel they thought was appropriate. However, they did not have the results of the Armstrong, Gagnebin, Brophy, and Miller research, which showed that achieving proper ductility in the steel alloy with only 3½ percent nickel was very difficult. The steel heat used for tank 4 proved this point; it did not meet the specifications for impact resistance.

These commentators might have been right in another sense, though. The inability to get cork during the war required East Ohio to use a different material for the insulation: rock wool. Although rock wool might have good insulating properties, it could not be used to support the inner tank as was done with cork in the three spheres. The tank bottom had to be suspended on wooden blocks to preclude its sitting on top of the insulation. It is easy to imagine that if the cork blocks used for the spheres had been available, the tank 4 design would have been totally different. The cork could have supported the floor of a conventionally designed cylindrical tank. There would have been no need for the highly stressed lower ring girder and the wooden posts. This would have reduced stresses and "softened the ride" for the inner tank, just as it did in the spheres. So wartime shortages *did* change the tank design, which might in turn have contributed to its failure.

When the LNG industry started to come back after a few years, one of the most notable changes was the design of the storage tanks. These changes included both the steel alloy and the insulating material.

First Steps Back

East Ohio's decision to immediately empty the remaining two tanks and cease operation of the L. S. and R. plant and, in fact, the whole No. 2 Plant, was clearly made for a couple of reasons. One, of course, was to restore the confidence of the community in the company. They still had to supply natural gas to many thousands in the area, so rebuilding that confidence was essential. The other was the realization that the several million BTU stored in those tanks still represented a danger to the community, a realization that was missing prior to the fire.

The dismantling of the plant and switching to nearby underground storage, however, did not solve the shortage problem, which was the reason for the plant in the first place. Gas shortages continued for a few years, until a more regular flow of gas could come from the more distant fields of Texas and Louisiana. The Public Utilities Commission of Ohio prohibited East Ohio, and other companies, from installing new heating installations or additional equipment from September 16, 1947, to April 1, 1948. They were concerned that gas supplies would be insufficient over the 1947-1948 winter season.[56] The 1946-1947 season had been a rough one, and this one would be about the same. But the East Ohio president, J. French Robinson, assured customers, "All the companies problems will be behind us the following winter, 1948-49." The company laid 50 miles of 20-inch pipeline from Canton to get gas from underground storage more quickly. They also drilled 25 additional wells in the storage area to get the gas to market more quickly. Gas wells in the Canton area were being depleted, so new gas was not becoming available. Major quantities from the Texas fields had not yet started to flow but were expected in 1948.[57]

Some progress was made by 1949. East Ohio was given permission to add 25,000 new gas heating customers, 95 percent of them for residential heating. Residents were now rapidly converting from coal to gas because of its advantages. The new installations would be about half, and half would be conversions from coal.[58] That didn't quite do it. The city was still growing; it hit its population peak in 1950, both residentially and industrially, and more energy was needed. In March of 1950 the *Cleveland Press* reported:

> Near-zero blasts due in Cleveland tonight brought a shutdown order on gas for industrial production purposes today in Cleveland and five northern Ohio counties.
>
> Only enough gas was furnished to industries to prevent damage to equipment, according to East Ohio Gas Co. officials. The full service reduction was to become effective at 6 p.m.

Layoffs certain to mount in the 700 plants affected by the system-wide fuel curtailment began almost immediately.[59]

Here was the reason the plant was originally built: to preclude these types of shortages during cold snaps.

The gas shortage in the Cleveland area eventually ended. The city growth slowed (and even reversed), and more plentiful supplies were made available from the Southwest fields. But as we have seen, this was an ongoing problem for quite a while after the L. S. and R. plant ceased LNG peak-shaving operations. It is possible the strong growth in energy needs would have outpaced the peak-shaving capability of the L. S. and R. plant yet again, as it had in 1943 when they built tank 4 to meet expanding needs. Presumably, though, had there not been an accident, an additional tank, number 5, might have been added.

As might be expected, Cleveland was not the only city experiencing peak gas shortages. Chicago was also having peak supply problems. Because of this, Chicago companies planned a similar LNG liquefaction-storage plant to be built in 1949. The liquefaction process was to be a cascade process similar to the process that had been successful in Cleveland, but this time using propane and ethylene instead of ammonia and ethylene as coolants. The location and design of the LNG storage tanks, however, was to be completely different from the East Ohio plant; they had learned the lessons from that plant. The site was a rural one, 586 acres of farmland rezoned for industrial use. The nearest inhabited dwelling was only very slightly less than one-half mile away. The high tension electrical lines and railroad were two and one-half miles away. The 83-foot-diameter cylindrical tanks were spaced at 180-foot centers. The tanks were to be made of a cupro-nickel alloy surrounded by block insulation and with outside tanks of steel. The tank base was to be a concrete slab topped with block insulation. The lessons from Cleveland had clearly been learned. The Federal Power Commission concluded:

> Applicant has specifically considered each finding and recommendation made by the official committees appointed for the study and investigation of causes of the failure in one of the liquefied natural gas storage tanks at the Cleveland plant of East Ohio Gas Co., and presented evidence that the proposed plant meets the applicable requirements of those recommendations. In addition, an official of the U.S. Bureau of Mines testified that the design of natural gas liquefaction and storage facilities and location of the plant proposed by the applicant conform to the intention of the recommendations of the U.S. Bureau of Mines Report on the Investigation of the Fire at the Liquefaction, Storage, and Regasification Plant of The East Ohio Gas Co.[60]

This plant was never built, ostensibly because a nearby underground storage had proven more cost effective. However, it is not hard to imagine that building the first plant after the Cleveland fire might have been a factor also.

The only other known plant around this time was one built in Russia near Moscow in 1947 by Dresser Industries Limited of Dallas for about six million dollars. The liquefaction rate was about the same as that of the East Ohio plant, 4.5 million cubic feet per day. The storage capacity was 162 million cubic feet. This was at the height of the Cold War, so little is known about the plant. Apparently, though, it worked successfully and eventually was used to supply vehicle fuel.[61]

For obvious reasons, the interest was still there to store natural gas to be used especially for peak-shaving. In 1950 a method was developed to store the gas by absorbing it into a granular material and storing it in this material. The gas would be liquefied and poured over this unspecified mineral, trademarked Methanite, which would absorb it and store it. In the final stage it would be stored in the granules at the normal temperature of −260°F, the same temperature as LNG. There would be no free liquid natural gas, only granules. At its best capacity it could store 300 cubic feet of gas in one cubic foot of granules; about half that of natural gas as a pure liquid. It would be regasified by running warm gas through the granules. If this material is spilled it takes a while for the gas to desorb from the granules, and therefore any fire that might result is very low level and easily contained and extinguished compared to an LNG spill. This was clearly marketed for the safety aspects of storing liquid methane and was demonstrated with a small pilot plant.[62] Although appealing at first, the method was never commercially useful. There were difficulties in desorbing the gas quickly enough for use.

Cryogenics

After the East Ohio fire there were no large tanks built for LNG storage or any low-temperature fluids for many years. The awkward design of tank 4, driven by the need to use a loose, non-load-bearing insulation such as rock wool, because of wartime shortages of cork, was abandoned. Partly because of the fire there was little interest in LNG. This started to change after the war when new interest was shown in very low temperature fluids, and the focus changed from pure research to engineering use of these fluids. The science of cryogenics was to change toward the engineering of cryogenics.

Cryogenics is defined as the branch of science that deals with very low temperatures. The word comes from the Greek words *kryos* meaning "frost" and *genic* meaning "to produce." Under such a definition the term could be used to include all temperatures below the freezing point of water. However, Kammerlingh Onnes, the first one to liquefy helium, first used the word in 1894 to refer to much lower temperatures.[63] The definition of low temperature has changed in a relative sense over hundreds of years. Prior to the nineteenth century, when gases were first liquefied, very low temperatures meant ice. Ice was found to be a useful commodity for preserving foods, and it was collected and stored for that purpose. The liquefaction of the so-called permanent gases, methane, oxygen, hydrogen, and helium, changed the idea of what very low temperature meant. Table 7-1 shows the low temperatures of some liquid gases. Over the years the term *cryogenics* has generally been used for temperatures below −150°C (−238°F) or in the Kelvin scale below 120 K (−153°C).[64] More recently cryogenics has meant working with very low temperatures, near to absolute zero, 0 K or −273°C.

Table 7-1. Boiling Point of Liquid Gases

Cryogen	Boiling Point at 1 Atmosphere	
	°F	°C
Helium	−452	−269
Hydrogen	−423	−253
Methane	−258	−161
Nitrogen	−320	−196
Oxygen	−297	−183

Since 1895, when Carl von Linde started to liquefy air in quantity, cryogenic liquids have been used for scientific research. This was enabled by the invention of the Dewar flask (1892), which allowed the transport of cryogenic liquids to various laboratories for experimentation. There were some expectations of practical use of liquid air very early. The *New York Times* commented on an 1897 demonstration on liquid air in New York and speculated:

> "But how does this concern me?" asks the practical man. It might concern him very intimately if he would. When the heat of this coming Summer reaches 95 degrees in the shade and even sitting becomes a torture, let him think how cooling it would be to have a fluid some 315 degrees below zero at his side. If it is possible to keep dead animals frozen for weeks during the heat of Summer, why should not living people be given a comfortable atmosphere in their homes and business?[65]

Over the next 50 years much advancement was made in cooling and refrigeration. The applications included mechanical ice making, quick freezing foods, and air conditioning. These, however, used conventional equipment and temperatures well above the cryogenic gas temperatures shown in table 7-1. However, in the 1940s, the emphasis in the field of cryogenics changed from science to engineering, and this stimulated great improvements in system performance. This was probably another example of the stimulation of innovation by the war effort. As noted in a NIST (National Institute of Standards and Technology) publication on cryogenics, "Some of the engineering applications that evolved over the next decades included storage and shipment of gases such as oxygen, nitrogen, hydrogen, helium, and natural gas in liquid form; production of oxygen for making steel; rocket and aircraft fuels; energy transport and storage; electronics; and facilities for high energy physics."[66] The use of cryogens in the mid–1940s helped research on the understanding of the ductile-brittle transformation of materials discussed in a previous chapter. This in turn led to the development of materials such as the nine percent nickel-steel that could be used to make larger cryogen storage tanks.[67]

Use of larger quantities of cryogens made possible industrial applications such as the quick freezing of food with liquid nitrogen, and steel making with oxygen. Liquid oxygen (LOX) was first used by Dr. Robert Goddard in 1926 as an oxidizer for a rocket fuel. This was a small experimental use. However, in the 1950s experiments were done with liquid hydrogen as an aircraft fuel by the predecessor agency to NASA.[68] Later liquid hydrogen and oxygen became very common fuels for many rockets. These cryogens were used in many other fields, such as medicine, for everything from freezing tissue to cooling magnets in magnetic resonance imaging (MRI) machines.

The widespread use of these cryogens meant larger production needs and therefore the need for larger storage tanks. So though the LNG industry had not yet recovered from the Cleveland fire, there were other users in need of storage tanks for cryogenic liquids. These needs helped drive the design for new cryogenic storage tanks. This in turn enabled the design for new LNG storage tanks when the liquefaction of natural gas finally did return in 1959.

New Tanks

The investigating teams had called into question the suitability of 3½ percent nickel-steel for these low temperatures. Although subsequent research (Armstrong and Brophy) has shown that this nickel-alloy steel is indeed questionable for use at these temperatures, which is in the DBTT range for 3½ nickel-steel, it is possible to achieve an appropriate toughness, and use the material successfully, if the batch used has the correct properties. When the three spherical tanks were built, Charpy tests were done at low temperature and the material from the batch used was found to have a Charpy value of 15 foot-pounds. It appears that tank 4, although specified to use the same composition steel, in fact had an inferior batch with a Charpy value well below the specified 15 foot-pounds. The brittle steel used thus made it more susceptible to failure than the other three tanks.

Although the Chicago plant was not built, the tank design they proposed presaged the cryogenic tanks that were starting to be built in the early 1950s: flat-bottomed cylindrical tanks. Spherical tanks are more efficient for storing very cold liquids because the surface of a sphere provides the minimum surface area for the volume contained and therefore minimizes the heat loss. However, there is a practical limit to the size of the sphere that can be built. They discovered this in Cleveland when they did a design comparison between a sphere and a cylinder for the fourth tank, which was to hold twice the volume of the original spheres. The amount and thickness of the steel was very high compared to that of the chosen toro-segmental cylinder design eventually chosen. Spherical tanks are also more complex to build, especially as they get larger. Spheres are still used when the temperatures are very low and heat loss has to be minimized such as for liquid hydrogen or helium, but these are usually not as large as the original East Ohio spheres.

Flat-bottomed cylindrical tanks, as used in the oil and gas industry, were going to be much easier to construct and hold greater volumes of LNG if two problems could be solved. One was the development of an economical metal for the inner tank that could withstand cryogenic temperatures; that is, it had to remain tough and not become brittle at these temperatures. This research was going on in the 1940s and 1950s. The story of the nine percent nickel-steel alloy that met this need was discussed above. After 1962 this became the material of choice for cryogenic fluids down to the temperature of liquid nitrogen (−320°F). Stainless steel had always been used for very low cryogenic temperatures, but it was very expensive and was not the answer for large tanks.

The second problem that had to be addressed was the insulation material to be used. Cork is one of the oldest insulators in the refrigeration industry. It was used very successfully, in both the solid block form and granular form, in the three spheres at East Ohio. It had not only good insulating properties, but good mechanical properties as well; it could be used to support the full inner tank, the one holding the LNG. The problem with cork, however, showed up almost immediately: it was in scarce supply. It was not available in 1943 when the new tank was designed for East Ohio because the limited supply was controlled by the government for the war effort. There was no reason to believe the supply would increase after the war, either. Cork is a natural organic product produced from slow growing trees, mostly from Portugal. It could not support a fast growing cryogenic tank industry.

The insulating materials of choice in the reviving LNG industry and growing cryogenic industry were perlite and Foamglas.

Perlite is a naturally occurring siliceous volcanic rock. In its crude form, before processing, it looks like ordinary volcanic rock. The crude perlite is first crushed into smaller granules. The key part of the process is the next step, in which it is quickly heated to 1,600°F. At this point, because of the presence of two to six percent water, the crude perlite pops like popcorn, creating countless tiny glassy bubbles as the water vaporizes. It is these tiny glassy bubbles that give perlite its thermal insulation properties. This expanded perlite is a white powdery mineral, perhaps accounting for its name; it came to be known as perlite in 1822. It wasn't until about a century later, in the 1930s, that research was done for uses of perlite. In 1938 L. Lee Boyer applied for a patent for a process to expand perlite as described above and convert it to an insulating material. The war stopped any progress in this area, but it was picked up again in the 1940s and 1950s in the U.S. and Holland.[69] The Bureau of Mines minerals yearbook did not even pick it up until 1952. In that edition it showed expanded perlite production had grown from only 18,600 tons in 1948 to over 154,000 tons in 1952. It did not even list cryogenic insulation among the uses it did mention, which were loose fill insulation, exterior cement stucco work, refractory brick, and roofing tile, among others.[70] Expanded perlite production rose rapidly worldwide in these years because its value as an insulator was recognized, no more so than in the industries using cryogenic fluids, such as LNG.

The other insulator that became common at about the same time was Foamglas, from the Pittsburgh Corning Corporation. Whereas perlite is formed from volcanic rock, the trade-named Foamglas is made from sand and recycled glass. Molten glass is extruded in a hollow tube then ground into fine powder and mixed with carbon. It is then put into a stainless steel mold and put into an oven that is heated to produce a cellular glass block with millions of hermetically sealed glass cells; the powder expands to fill the mold. There is no external binder; the glass cells are sealed to themselves. This provides not only good insulation properties because of the gas filled bubbles, but also an impermeable barrier to moisture. Thus, when it is used for low-temperature insulation, moisture cannot penetrate and then freeze. Once out of the annealing oven the foam glass blocks are removed from the mold and shaped for use.[71] The Pittsburgh Corning Corporation started to experiment with what eventually became Foamglas in 1941. They first started manufacturing it for industry in 1947.[72] This was about the same time perlite was becoming popular as an insulator.

Thus by the late 1940s, less than a decade after the East Ohio LNG plant was built, there were two good insulating materials available that had not existed when the plant was built. Once again the plant was built in advance of the availability of another critical technology. This time it was the insulation rather than the steel.

With acceptable, strong, and easy-to-work-with insulation now available and a cryogenically acceptable material for the inner tank (aluminum or stainless steel), flat-bottomed cryogenic storage tanks became available in the early 1950s. The tanks used either perlite or Foamglas for the base. This could be in various forms, such as concrete blocks made with a perlite aggregate, or perhaps Foamglas blocks as described above. These materials could withstand the weight of the cryogenic liquid. The space between the inner tank and the outer tank would be filled with loose perlite for insulation. It is not clear who made the first tank of this general design, but one of the earliest adopters was Chicago Bridge and Iron (CB&I), a company that had built steel storage tanks for over half a century. In 1953/1954 they constructed a liquid oxygen tank in Ashtabula, Ohio.[73] A sketch of their tank design is shown in figure 7-2.[74] The inner tank was made of 304 stainless steel and was 56 feet in diameter and 36 feet high. The outer tank was 64 feet in diameter and 45 feet high. The four-foot space between the tanks was filled with loose perlite and the base was made of Foamglas blocks. Over the next four years they built six more of these tanks meant to operate at −300°F. (Liquid oxygen is stored at −297°F.) In 1957/1958 CB&I built their eighth tank of this type; this time for LNG. The tank was built for Constock

Methane to fill the *Methane Pioneer* for its transatlantic voyage to Canvey Island near London. It was the first flat-bottomed tank ever built for the export of LNG.

The tank was built at the Lake Charles, Louisiana, export terminal, which was expressly set up to export the plentiful natural gas of the Gulf Coast area to England. The inner tank was 67 feet in diameter and 56 feet high; it was made from aluminum. The outer tank was 73 feet in diameter and 61.5 feet high; it was made from carbon steel. The three-foot annulus between tanks had a fiberglass blanket and perlite insulation, as did the roof. The bottom insulation was Foamglas block. CB&I built their first nine percent nickel-steel tank in 1963. For several years, some tanks were constructed from aluminum and some from nine percent nickel-steel. Gradually, nine percent nickel-steel replaced aluminum as the industry standard.[75]

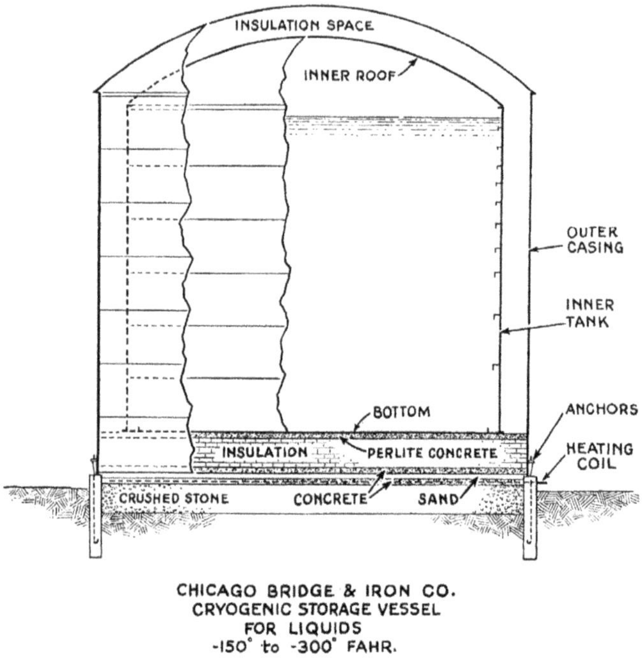

So by the mid–1950s all the factors that had led to the failure of the storage tanks at the East Ohio plant had been addressed and, one way or another, solved. It took until the 1960s before the NFPA took up the formal process of revising the codes, but the poor location for the plant had been recognized early and it was clear that that kind of siting would not be chosen again. Research on metals for low temperature use was going on through the 1940s, and by the mid–1950s many nine percent nickel-steel tanks were being produced in the smaller sizes so they could be stress-relieved after welding. In 1960, through Operation Cryogenics, it was shown that properly heat-treated nine percent nickel-steel could be used for large tanks built on-site without the need to be stress-relieved. Aluminum had long been known to be good at these low temperatures and was available, but nine percent nickel-steel turned out to be more economical in the long run. New insulation materials that had become available after the war could also now be used to build safer, more conventional flat-bottomed tanks.

Thus the pieces were in place to resume production and use of LNG. It didn't happen immediately, mostly because of the concern about the Cleveland fire. This skepticism was present in the 1950s and even into the 1960s. It would take some bold move to get the process moving again. That move did happen, but in an area one might not expect. It happened because some people saw the need to move the energy contained in natural gas from one location to another. One need was a domestic one, the desire to move natural

Figure 7-2. CB&I cryogenic storage tank (courtesy CB&I and Linda Hall Library of Science, Engineering and Technology).

gas from the Gulf coast to the Chicago stockyards in a cost effective manner so as to bypass rising gas prices in Chicago. The other need was the need for more energy in England, a country that had no existing natural gas sources, a need seen by the Gas Council in that country. These needs combined to reinvigorate the LNG industry by producing LNG and moving it to where it was needed. The result of these early efforts was the *Methane Pioneer*.

Methane Pioneer—*The Next Step*

One of the signs of the reviving LNG industry was aptly named the *Methane Pioneer*. The story starts in the early 1950s. C. M. Sliepcevich told this story well in a 1962 Sigma Xi lecture. He started with the observation that the gas industry recognized a lot of potential in the growth of the LNG industry. This was balanced by hesitancy, most likely because of the East Ohio fire:

> It was left to a relatively small power company, which was generating power for the Chicago Stock Yards, and its dynamic chief executive, William Wood Prince, to break the ice and take the bold plunge. Armed only with his self-imposed motto of awareness: "Remember Cleveland," he rolled-up his sleeves and went to work on LNG in 1951.[76]

A 1951 decision by a Chicago gas company to raise rates didn't sit well with Prince; this led him to want to control his own gas supply. He and a consultant had an idea to liquefy natural gas along the Gulf Coast and barge it up the Mississippi and on to Chicago to use at his facilities. They would build a barge-mounted liquefaction plant, go to nearly depleted gas wells in the Gulf Coast area, liquefy the gas, put it on another barge and ship it up the river. He might have gotten the barge-shipping idea from the 1915 patent by Godfrey Cabot for a liquid gas barge transport system. As a byproduct, he planned to use the refrigeration capabilities of the LNG to preserve products from his stockyards. He researched and developed the barge at the Ingall's Ship Yards in Pascagoula, Mississippi, around 1954. At about the same time he thought it would be a good idea to have a close working association with someone in the gas processing industry. He found E. F. Battson, a willing vice president of Continental Oil Company. A task force under Battson's technical advisor made a detailed study of the Chicago Stock Yards Research Division barge idea, but also did an independent study of the idea. They concluded that the Mississippi barge idea was not economical but also concluded that ocean transportation from gas-surplus countries to gas-deficient countries was an attractive idea. How they went from barges on the Mississippi to ocean transport is not clear, but they did. In 1955 a joint venture was formed by Continental Oil Company and the Union Stock Yards and Transit Company, called Constock International Methane Ltd.

In 1947 in a speech at the Oil Industries Club in London, H. S. Gibson of the Iraq Petroleum Company expressed concern that the expected rise in petroleum production in the Middle East would also give rise to that byproduct, natural gas, which would have to be disposed of or used somehow. Even at this late date natural gas was still seen as a nuisance byproduct of oil production, as it had been in both Appalachia and Texas. He went on to say,

> It does appear that we should be able to liquefy, ship, and deliver this product at a cost of the order of 6d. or 8d. per gallon—100 cu. ft. of gas, say one therm.... There would be many diffi-

culties but I do not think that any of them would be insurmountable[77] [d. is one penny in the old currency system (pre–1971), which counted 240 pennies to the pound. One therm is 100,000 BTU].

Around that time in 1947, authorities active in the oil trade were estimating that by 1957–1962, Middle East oil production would reach 100 million tons per year. In fact, by 1956 it had hit 170 million metric tons. Gibson's remarks reflected a growing realization that energy needs would be increasing rapidly. These same authorities observed that in the U.S. the percentage of energy use from natural gas had risen from 12 percent in 1937 to 25 percent in 1955. The North Thames Gas Board continued to be interested in liquefied natural gas as a solution to peak loading ever since it was first proposed by Professor Egerton of the Imperial College of Science, London, in 1937.[78] They were well aware of the U.S. efforts, including the Cleveland plant and the accident, but were still optimistic that a repeat could be avoided.

In a House of Commons debate on the National Coal Board's report for the year 1953–54, the House was told of a gas industry technical mission to the United States to discuss a "revolutionary" method being considered to enable liquefied natural gas to be transported by ship. No action was taken immediately, and in 1956 there was still skepticism about that prospect. J. W. Pratt of Shell Petroleum answered a question at the Institute of Petroleum in London:

> In regard to the question of natural gas and its transportation, no one has yet been bold enough to build a ship that will carry the liquid gas from places where it is available to places where it could be consumed, much as the British government would, I think, like to see that happen. I do not know of anybody, although many are working on it to some extent, who has taken the step of risking the building of a special ship, or the adaptation of an existing ship. It would cost at least £2 million and, when it was built, one could not be sure that any port in the world would allow it to enter and risk the accidents that might conceivably happen, if things go wrong, or that the crew could be persuaded to go on board when collisions or other stresses might release forces that might annihilate them.[79]

Things were starting to change, though. Charles Kelly mentioned in a 1958 article that the U.K. Gas Council was considering some action:

> The GAS COUNCIL has expressed its intention of importing liquefied natural gas. This intention has been described in Parliament as a "bold experiment," not a project.... Engineers of the North Thames Gas Board have made several visits to the United States and have assisted in trials there to obtain data for the design of a ship to carry refrigerated methane. At the end of the year (March 31, 1957) the stage had been reached where the *possibility* of importing a trial cargo of liquefied methane into the country *could* be considered[80] [emphasis in the original].

That was the start of the joint venture between the Gas Council and the Constock Liquid Methane Corporation. (Constock Liquid Methane Corporation was a subsidiary of Constock International Methane Ltd.) The joint venture was to develop LNG facilities on both sides of the Atlantic to produce, store, load, ship, and unload LNG for shipment across the Atlantic from Lake Charles, Louisiana, to Canvey Island near London. Although producing and storing LNG had been done before, the facilities for the loading and unloading and the ship itself had to be developed.[81]

Barging LNG up the Mississippi to Chicago was abandoned, but barges were built to act as pilot plants for the LNG facilities development. They were completed in 1955 and moved to Bayou, Louisiana, in 1956 for testing. By 1957 the design and specifications were complete. Also by this time other countries (France, Italy, Sweden and Japan) showed an interest in importing LNG. Britain, too, was interested: "By the fall of 1957, the British Gas Council made a declaration of intent to import LNG at a rate equivalent to 100 million cubic feet of gas per day, which amounted to about 10 percent of their total gas consumption."[82] The actual contract was delayed until trial runs were made from the U.S. to Great Britain. The Lake Charles facility was completed in 1958. It was mounted on one of the barges so it used the Claude cycle, which although not as efficient as a cascade process has the advantage of being lighter and more compact than the other process. The storage tank at Lake Charles was described in the previous section.

The ship, the *Methane Pioneer,* was a converted dry cargo ship, a World War II Liberty ship. Figure 7–3 is a U.S. Maritime Commission photo of a Liberty ship, circa 1945.[83] It had a large double bottom and ballast tanks on the sides. Ballast would be important because the low density of the liquid methane, about 40 percent of the density of water, might cause the ship to ride too high in the water in rough seas. The five aluminum tanks were essentially square in cross section to maximize the load capability. The main problem in the development was the insulation. The insulation not only had to withstand the normal thermal gradients between the bottom and top of the tank when it was only partially filled and the thermal gradient separating the cold inner tank from the hull, but also had to withstand mechanical stress from the pitching and rolling of the ship. Being on a ship, it had to maintain structural integrity for up to four hours in case of a fire on the ship. Loose fill insulation was not an option. The only solution they found at the time was balsa wood, which was used on the sides and bottoms of the tanks.

Figure 7–3. World War II Liberty ship (courtesy American Merchant Marine at War).

The Methane Pioneer took on its first load of LNG, equivalent to 115 million cubic feet of gas, and departed from Lake Charles on its historic voyage, January 28, 1959. It arrived at Canvey Island on February 20, 1959, and discharged its cargo into 2 insulated, land storage tanks, each having a capacity of 670,000 gal (equivalent to 55 million cubic feet of gas).[84]

This was a historic voyage for more than one reason. First, it validated the 1951 idea of William Wood Prince to get the natural gas industry back into liquid natural gas. Basically, he rolled up his sleeves and said, "Yes, we understand what happened in Cleveland, but let's get moving again with LNG." He started this work to solve a problem, a gas rate hike of which he disapproved. This is often the result when an innovator faces a problem; he or she tries a new approach. While others were still wringing hands about the implications of the Cleveland disaster, he did something about it. This makes him one the early pioneers in the recovery of the LNG industry.

The second historic aspect of the voyage was that it was the first step for a whole *new* industry, the shipment of energy in the form of LNG from places where there is a surplus of this energy (natural gas) to places where there is a shortage. Ever since natural gas had been used as an energy source, about 80 years prior to this, it had been limited by the means available to move it, mostly pipelines. It could not be moved as easily as coal or oil even though it had many advantages over these other fuels. That is why so much had been flared off in Appalachia and in the Southwest before it was captured and moved via pipelines. It was still being flared off where oil was produced in the Middle East, on the order of 600 million cubic feet per day.[85] This waste was recognized by far-sighted people in Great Britain who wondered why this couldn't be captured, liquefied, and sent to them. The British Isles had little or no natural gas; they were still depending on manufactured gas made from coal. So in another case of "necessity is the mother of invention," the Gas Council in Great Britain and Constock Liquid Methane in the U.S. teamed up to develop a system to move the LNG across the ocean, thus starting a new industry.

Risk, Risk Management, and Black Swans

In Renaissance Europe all the swans anyone had ever seen were white. The observation was apparently so universal that the conclusion was reached that *all* swans were white, and the expression "black swan" became a phrase to indicate something that was impossible. Then about three centuries ago, when non-native Australians first saw a black swan in Australia, everything about the term changed. The unexpected sighting caused some to wonder if anything should be unexpected or considered impossible. More recently, Nassim Nicholas Taleb used the terminology to characterize events of low probability that could have large impacts. He defined the term Black Swan event as one having three attributes. First, it is an outlier; that is, it is totally unexpected. Second, it has a major impact, and third, despite its outlier aspects, it makes us concoct explanations for its existence, after the fact.[86] These attributes are seen in such events as the original black swan sighting, the *Challenger* accident, 9/11, and the financial meltdown of 2008. (Nate Silver argues that the 2008 financial meltdown was not really a Black Swan event because too many people in the industry were aware of the problem and trying to warn others, unsuccessfully as it turned out. This may have been true for some insiders, but for most outsiders this could clearly be seen as a Black Swan event.)[87] The East Ohio fire catastrophe clearly falls into the category of a Black Swan event; it was totally unexpected, it had a major impact and, as we have seen, in retrospect it should have been predictable. If the last attribute of a Black Swan event causes us to make it explainable and predictable, how does that then differ from much more recent perceptions of risk and risk management? If it is explainable in hindsight, why can't it be predictable in foresight?

Part of the answer to these questions is the fact that as intuitive as risk and risk management seem today, the evolution of the perception of risk was slow. It has only been in recent decades that it has been examined seriously and attempts at managing risk have been more systematic.

Fate has been man's lot for millennia. The dictionary defines fate as that which unavoidably befalls you. Things happen because they are ordained to happen. If they are good things you are lucky; if they are bad you are unlucky. The sun comes up in the morning, providing light and warmth. Lightning strikes a tree and starts a fire. A hunting companion is attacked and eaten by a saber-toothed tiger. You eventually make adjustments and, when possible, avoid the areas where the tiger hunts. So the man who does well in this gets to pass his genes on to others who learn to cope in other situations. You also look for ways to protect yourself by appealing to a higher power, for example, the sun or an animal spirit. Even though you survive and adapt you attribute the success or failure to the gods or fate.

As time passes man adjusts and realizes that not everything is inevitable; some things can be anticipated and controlled. Although lightning striking a tree and starting a fire cannot be controlled (we still can't control this), it is possible to control a fire and use it for cooking and warmth. As civilization progressed, man learned to adapt to both his environment and to his neighbors, the latter adaptation either positive (trade) or negative (war). The adaptation required an implicit assessment of the risk of an activity either with the environment, the saber-toothed tiger for example, or with one's neighbors.

Risk is defined as the exposure to the chance of injury or loss. You willingly expose yourself to the possibility of injury or loss only if there is a positive opportunity to achieve something better. Thus if a man was building a home, he might weigh the risk of building it near the river where a flood might take it away or on a grassland where it might be subject to destruction by fire. A home near the water would provide an opportunity to be near that needed resource; one in the grassland the opportunity to be near game for food. In all cases, though, for most of human history, he saw himself in the hands of fate; there was nothing he could do about ensuing events once he made the choice. If a flood or fire hit he would lose everything and start over. On the other hand, he could not continue to live or make progress if he did not take a risk for the opportunity. As Peter Bernstein notes, "The word 'risk' derives from the early Italian *risicare,* which means 'to dare.' In this sense risk is a choice rather than a fate."[88]

Around the middle of the seventeenth century, about the same time as the Great Fire, various mathematicians, including the Chevalier de Mere (1607–1684), Blaise Pascal (1623–1662), and Pierre Fermat (1601–1665), were working on the early phases of the mathematics of probability theory. The fascination started with games of chance, for example how often the roll of a die would come up to a certain number. The excitement came from the fact that this was the first time numbers could be used to describe seemingly random events. As Bernstein notes,

In 1654 ... the Chevalier de Mere, a French nobleman with a taste for both gambling and mathematics, challenged the famed French mathematician Blaise Pascal to solve a puzzle. The question was how to divide the stakes of an unfinished game of chance between two players when one of them is ahead.... The 1654 correspondence between Pascal and Fermat on this subject signaled an epochal event in the history of mathematics and the theory of probability.... They constructed a systematic method for analyzing future outcomes. When more things can happen than will happen, Pascal and Fermat give us a procedure for determining the likelihood of each of the possible results—assuming always that outcomes can be measured mathematically.[89]

As the years passed, mathematicians transformed probability theory and tools from toys about games into useful methods to handle information: "By 1725, mathematicians were competing with one another in devising tables of life expectancies, and the English government was financing itself through the sale of life annuities. By the middle of the century, marine insurance had emerged as a flourishing, sophisticated business in London."[90]

These results have been paying dividends in modern insurance and risk management over the past two hundred years. However, even as risk was becoming better understood and ideas on mitigating it improved, there were still some areas that in hindsight seemed to come late. For example, it wasn't until June 1952 that a graduate student in economics at the University of Chicago, Harry Markowitz, wrote a paper in the *Journal of Finance* that first suggested that stocks in a portfolio should be selected including risk as a factor. In other words, diversifying your selection of stocks in a portfolio was a way of mitigating risk. Up to this point the objective was always to maximize returns. Diversification of a stock portfolio, which seems intuitively obvious now, is a fairly recent strategy: "Diversification is both observed and sensible; a rule of behavior which does not imply the superiority of diversification must be rejected as both a hypothesis and as a maxim."[91] So even in 1952, twelve years after the construction of the East Ohio LNG plant, there were areas where understanding of risk and risk management were evolving.

As sophisticated as the financial system risk analyses became, the judgment of the participants was, and still is, a critical component for success. If a risk is not judged appropriately or ignored completely, sophisticated financial tools will not correct a problem. This is what happened in the financial crisis of 2008, which almost caused a collapse of the world financial system. The risk associated with the U.S. mortgage market, especially the subprime market, was not recognized by many in the business. The assumption was that home prices would always go up because that was the history up to that time. There was a failure to acknowledge that there was a risk that they could go down. Therefore, when the housing market stalled, many financial derivatives based on the faulty assumption failed, causing a crisis that was averted only by government action worldwide. An appropriate assessment of risk is required for effective risk mitigation. This was another classic Black Swan event. It was totally unexpected, the impact was serious, and after looking for explanations, reasons were found for why it could have been predicted. Thus in some respects risk management is still as much art as science. It should also be noted that the probabilities and statistics of the insurance and financial worlds do not inform a designer of a physical system how to build a safe system; something more is needed.

In the past risk management had been predicated on reacting to existing events, that is, reducing the impact of a loss, and then taking steps to prevent the loss from recurring.

An example of this is fire insurance. After the Great Fire of London insurance companies were established to help people cope with fire loss. Despite the loss protection, fires still occurred until someone decided that just compensating people after a loss was not good enough; means had to be found to prevent fires in the first place. This led to fire codes and building codes that indeed did reduce the risk from fire. Of course fires still do occur for many reasons including risky behavior by some, accidents, and natural causes such as lightning, but the overall fire risk for society is lower now because of fire risk management.

However, there are always new risks of which we are not aware until they are exposed, as perhaps by a Black Swan event. Examples of these might include the 9/11 attack, and the use of improvised explosive devices (IED) against the U.S. troops in Iraq. Once these became extant, measures were put in place to mitigate the risk in the first place and to minimize the consequence. Thus a whole new agency was established, the Transportation Security Administration (TSA), and placed under a new Department of Homeland Security (DHS), to protect against another terrorist attack. New vehicles were designed to minimize the impact of an IED attack. Casualties at home and abroad had spurred the development of mitigation for these risks. The LNG tank failure at East Ohio had a similar response. Once the risks were exposed it became obvious in hindsight what had to be done to dramatically reduce these risks. Locating the plant away from populated areas, using a diking system to catch any tank contents, using better materials and tank design were all quickly identified as risk reducers and ways to make an LNG plant safer.

Human nature and the natural world are such that risk and loss due to risk will never disappear totally; neither will Black Swan events disappear. Despite the advances in risk management over the years, we have not achieved a loss-free world, let alone a risk-free one. After all, even if risks are mitigated not all losses will be avoided. Risk is the exposure to the *chance* of loss, and that chance is still there. Nevertheless, keeping the attributes of a Black Swan in mind, the unexpected, the major impact, and especially the knowledge after the fact that it seems predictable, can provide a template for considering future system designs. In one way this is what happened after the war was over.

During the war, risk analysis and assessment were essentially moot subjects. At the risk of oversimplifying to a level of absurdity, war is a risky enterprise. Many risky things were done for the sole purpose of achieving victory. After the war, though, things were different, and it is no exaggeration to say that the atomic bomb had changed everything. Some risks now were not just different in degree but in kind; some of the threats were now existential, especially ones from the Cold War. The Cold War, the nuclear power industry, and later NASA all had an impact on how risk would be viewed in the future. The common denominator regarding risk for these activities was that one no longer had the luxury of *reacting* to problems once they arose; the consequences of reacting rather than anticipating were unacceptable. Many of the possible scenarios for nuclear war posed existential risk. These scenarios were considered using risk-based analyses based on game theory originally developed by John von Neumann (1903–1957). Von Neumann was a Hungarian-born physicist and mathematician who developed game theory in the late 1920s and later applied it by consulting with the RAND Corporation on war games during the early Cold War years.[97] Nuclear war scenarios were "unthinkable" and clearly could not be tested or played out in practice; risk analysis was based on mathematical models.

Similarly, the nuclear power industry and NASA, both nascent operations in the

1950s, could not depend on ex post facto risk analysis. Nuclear accidents could not be allowed to happen and then be analyzed for risk mitigation. The scenarios had to be postulated, then analyzed, based on probabilities and consequences. The NASA experience was not quite as catastrophic as a nuclear accident; the public was not endangered; but the experience was more a consequence of the mission of the agency. Once launched, a spacecraft could not be called back, for repair so in order to assure mission success one had to think of everything ahead of time. Of course in the early days of NASA there were many failures but, surprisingly, also many successes. This author, a system design practitioner at NASA in the early decades of the agency, spent a great deal of time imagining various ways a mission could fail and then devising ways to preclude that happening. The mathematical underpinnings were not available at first, but clearly the importance of anticipating all types of failure was recognized.

Things have changed and now NASA uses probabilistic risk assessment (PRA), a mathematical model-based system, to inform the risk management process. By its own acknowledgment, however, the agency was late to the table in the sophisticated area of risk management:

> Over the years, NASA has been a leader in most of the technologies it has employed in its programs. One would think that PRA should be no exception. In fact, it would be natural for NASA to be a leader in PRA because, as a technology pioneer, NASA uses risk assessment and management implicitly or explicitly on a daily basis.... Methods to perform risk and reliability assessment in the early 1960s originated in the U.S. aerospace and missile programs.... It would have been a reasonable extrapolation to expect that NASA would also become the world leader in the application of PRA. That was, however, not to happen.... Early in the Apollo program, estimates of the probability for a successful roundtrip human mission to the moon yielded disappointingly low (and suspect) values and NASA became discouraged from further performing quantitative risk analyses until some two decades later when the methods were more refined, rigorous, and repeatable.[93]

In other words, the original risk analyses on Apollo were so disappointing that had they been rigorously applied, we might never have made it to the moon. So, clearly, the Apollo engineers had to use a lot of manual "what if" scenarios. Risk analysis and risk management were, and still are, evolving. What eventually happened is that the first comprehensive PRA was done in the mid-1970s in the nuclear power arena. Its purpose was to quantify risks to the public from nuclear power plant operations.[94]

Despite the complex mathematical models that can be used in risk analysis, most risk can be addressed simply and basically by using the triplet that NASA uses as the starting point or basis for the risk management process.[95] It amounts to answering the following questions:

1. What can go wrong?
2. How likely is it?
3. What are the associated consequences?

In one sense these are the questions engineers and architects have asked for millennia when building new systems, from the pyramids to the Gothic cathedrals of the twelfth century to the Apollo missions. (Note that the terms *engineer* and *architect* are used, not *scientist*. The noted aerodynamicist Theodore von Karman observed, "Scientists discover the world as it exists; engineers create the world that never was.") They would look at their design, do a stress analysis, add safety factors, and come up with a final design. Sometimes it would work and sometimes it would fail. There were many engineering failures throughout the years, but collectively we learned from experience. We don't know how many would-be cathedrals collapsed before they built the magnificent ones we see still standing today.

In the progression of knowledge, it took until after World War II for designers and analysts of complex systems to ask the first question, "What can go wrong?" in depth and pursue it to all possible outcomes. It is rather puzzling that something that seems so simple in retrospect was not asked earlier. In the case being discussed here, the potential failure of an LNG tank containing about 100 billion BTU (and a plant containing about 250 billion BTU), should have prompted the question, "What can go wrong?" We know from the testimony after the accident that neither the managers nor the engineers in charge of building the plant ever considered that question in depth. In fact, one person explicitly stated that he saw no way the LNG could ever get out of the tank. Had the question been considered properly, the possibility of total and instantaneous tank failure then would certainly have suggested dire consequences and the misplacement of the plant, no matter how low the likelihood of failure. If the plant was to be proposed today the location alone would spell the end of the project or at least its move to a different location.

Although risk and loss will be with us forever, a lot of progress has been made in understanding how to address it. Had some of these approaches been available in 1940, the East Ohio fire might have been avoided. This will become even more important in the future as our systems become even more complex. What will be the risk analysis done for a human mission to Mars?

Coda

As mentioned in the introduction to this chapter, there were roughly three lessons learned from the disaster. One had to do with the location of the plant and the fire codes that did or did not apply to its construction. Another had to do with the materials used for the tanks and the design of tank 4 which was influenced by those materials. Last, despite the mistakes made in the construction of the plant, the consensus was that such a plant was not inherently unsafe and that once the first two problems were corrected, a safe plant could be built. This latter observation did open the door to the eventual recovery of the LNG industry.

Location

Immediately after the fire it was realized almost instantaneously that locating these tanks, containing about 250 billion BTU of energy, in the heart of the city was a bad idea. Why wasn't this realized earlier? Weren't there codes that would have precluded this design in this location? The short answer is yes, but no one apparently recognized the applicability of the existing codes, and rigorous identification of risks and possible mitigations had not yet become a required design practice.

The main stumbling block seemed to be the nature of this new fluid. It was like nothing they had worked with previously. It was very, very cold. It did not seem particularly hazardous; how could anything so cold be a fire hazard? It could not easily be pigeonholed into one of the existing codes as they saw it. It wasn't that East Ohio was unconcerned about safety; they were. They even made a special trip to Columbus to check about the applicability of state codes for this material. The officials there agreed it wasn't covered by any existing state code. Not having any reason to reject construction on that site, the city quickly approved the building permit. There seemed to be a collective lack of imagination by both builders and regulators in failing to see this fluid as a flammable hydrocarbon like any other hydrocarbon. Considering that the whole purpose of storing it as a liquid was to regasify it later and use it as a fuel, this is surprising.

With some consideration it seems the recommended ordinance of the NFPA for storing petroleum products such as gasoline should have been followed. This set minimum distances from tanks to occupied buildings and required a dike that would contain the contents of an entire tank should it fail. Gasoline, a very flammable liquid hydrocarbon because of its low flash point, a Class I material, could have been used as the model. LNG is also a low flash point hydrocarbon and should have been classified as Class I material and handled in a manner similar to the way gasoline is handled. Yet even after the accident, during the testimony, a company official still could not see the similarity in properties, saying, "That is petroleum and this is gas. They are two different things."

The investigating groups made some conservative siting recommendations for future tanks. These hampered, to some extent, the redeployment of LNG tanks in the near term. However, as people in the industry were getting itchy about getting back into the business, because of the potential for LNG, action was taken to come up with codes specific to LNG. As in the past, fire code development was a slow process. Finally in the late 1960s the work started and by 1971 the NFPA had a standard, 59A, on storing and handling LNG.

Materials and Design

It was repeatedly stated, both prior to and after construction of the tanks, that the material used had been tested under low temperatures and found to be satisfactory for use with LNG. They tested the heat of the 3½ percent nickel-steel used to construct the three spherical tanks and found a Charpy impact resistance of 15 foot-pounds, which exceeded the lower limit of 10 foot-pounds Pittsburgh–Des Moines chief engineer J. O. Jackson claimed as acceptable. These tests, however, did not appear to be rigorous, peer reviewed research; they were not published and, therefore, were not open to everyone for discussion. Although the intent was to use the same composition steel for tank 4, it is doubtful that the material used for that tank met the same Charpy impact value. Tests on tank 4 after the accident showed very low Charpy values for the steel in that tank, two to four foot-pounds.

Ironically, at almost the same time as these tanks were being constructed in the 1940s, there was some rigorous laboratory testing being done on low temperature alloy steels including nickel-steel. By 1940 the researchers had concluded that 3½ percent nickel-steel was good to around −200°F. As they continued their work in the mid–1940s they eventually concluded that although one could achieve a 15 foot-pound Charpy impact resistance for *carefully controlled laboratory produced 3½ and 5 percent nickel-steel,* that value could not be consistently reached with commercial heats much below −150°F. That research was published in peer-reviewed journals at the end of the war. So almost at the same time the failure-investigation teams concluded that 3½ percent nickel-steel was not adequate for holding LNG, the research backed up that conclusion.

That same research in the mid–1940s demonstrated that 8½ or nine percent nickel could be used at cryogenic temperatures as low as −300°F. Charpy impact values of over 20 foot-pounds could be achieved. In 1948, to demonstrate that capability in real life situations, some tanks were filled with liquid nitrogen then subjected to impact. When these tanks failed they failed by tearing, that is by ductile failure, rather than by brittle fracture. This confirmed that 8½ or nine percent nickel-steel was ductile and could safely contain LNG. So now a suitable nickel-steel alloy, more economical than aluminum, was available for use with LNG tanks. This was not quite the final step, because the codes still required stress relieving after a tank was constructed for low temperature use. Thus large, field-erected tanks that could be constructed to hold LNG were still precluded, because they could not be stress relieved after construction. This last hurdle was cleared in 1960 with another demonstration. It showed that nine percent nickel-steel, non-stress relieved tanks, properly heat treated, could be built, welded and safely contain LNG. When these tanks were tested to failure they again showed a ductile failure, or leak before failure; they did not fail by brittle fracture. By March of 1962 the ASME accepted properly heat-treated nine percent nickel-steel for use at temperatures as low as −320°F. Thus the second major issue of the failure had now been addressed. Nine percent nickel-steel became the standard for new LNG tanks.

The other lesson learned had to do with the tank design. Tank 4 had a unique design, never used prior to its construction and never used since. The design featured the inner tank bottom suspended from wooden posts (for insulation) to separate it from the outer tank. This suspension design was necessary because the rock wool insulation used could not support the weight of the inner tank as the cork had done for the spherical tanks. Rock wool was used in lieu of cork because by the time tank 4 was constructed wartime restrictions made cork unavailable. This suspended tank bottom contributed to an awkward design, which according to the investigators may have contributed to its failure because the wooden posts would transmit any ground vibrations or shocks to the tank. This design was never considered for any of the new tanks that would soon come online. Instead the new tanks would resemble gasoline or oil storage tanks, cylinders with flat bottoms. A material was found, perlite, that could be used as an aggregate in the concrete base to support the load and act as an insulator. It could also be used in loose granular form to insulate between the double tank walls. The final cylindrical design for tanks that would be used for LNG storage in the future was now basically determined.

Recovery—Concept Vindicated

The LNG comeback started in the 1950s when some tanks of the new design started to show up for cryogenic liquids, although some of them still used aluminum for the inner tank. The real kick-start for the rebound was another surprise. It was led by a Chicago entrepreneur who wanted to barge LNG from the Gulf Coast to his Chicago enterprise because he didn't want to pay for a price increase imposed by his gas supplier. His motto was "Remember Cleveland," and he started his work in 1951. The barge up the Mississippi idea wasn't feasible, but by the mid–1950s his company was working with a British company on shipping LNG from the Gulf Coast in Louisiana to an island near London. The idea was that it should be possible to ship energy in the form of LNG from places where there was a surplus to places where there was a need. In early 1959 the *Methane Pioneer,* a converted World War II Liberty ship, carried an equivalent 115 million cubic feet of natural gas from Louisiana to Canvey Island near London. This was the start of the LNG shipping industry, which was to grow rapidly, as well as the start of the recovery of the LNG industry in general.

By the early 1960s the LNG industry was in full recovery mode. It took 15 to 20 years to recover from the East Ohio accident, but all the lessons were learned. So the observation by the investigators that the underlying concept for LNG was sound, as long as appropriate care was taken, had been validated.

Risk

One other lesson that was learned, although not foreseen by the investigators, was the lesson of improved risk management. It was postulated earlier in this chapter that the modern era in risk management started after the war. Risk was now sought out *prior* to new projects rather than waiting for bad events to happen and then reacting with corrections. The response to this LNG accident, on the cusp of this modern era, demonstrates the "before and after" approach to risk management.

The Cleveland plant was new; a commercial plant like it had never been built before. Everything they did was done for the first time. The engineering approach was sound. They built a pilot plant first to test the concept and the materials (steel and insulation). They had no obvious guidance regarding building codes because nothing like this had been built before. There was concern for safety, so East Ohio went to Columbus to check codes. There was nothing there to preclude them from building, just as there were no local codes to preclude the construction. So without knowing what else to do the regulators approved the construction. This is where the difference between then and now becomes clearer. They rightly saw an opportunity to solve a difficult problem with a novel approach. They didn't, however, *look* for the risks involved with that opportunity. Risk and opportunity are two sides of the same coin; for each opportunity there is risk and vice versa. One must take some risks to take advantage of opportunities or else never make progress. However, the risk must be well understood, and mitigated to the point where the balance is correct. The trip to Columbus was not an attempt to look for or mitigate risk. It was an honest trip to seek assurance that everything was being done safely. It failed, not for lack of concern on the part of either party, but rather for a lack of imagination.

This is not meant to be an indictment of East Ohio. They didn't analyze risk scenarios to look for possible catastrophic failures, but then nobody else did either, not on this project or any others at the time. One example of this was the apparent lack of concern by residents about the large gas tanks in the neighborhood. (As mentioned in Chapter 1, there was some private concern within families about the proximity of the tanks. Also as shown by the letter in Chapter 6, some were concerned about the possible bombing of the tanks. These concerns were easily brushed off and the answers apparently alleviated the concerns.) Risk management hadn't yet progressed to the point where the risk of any endeavor was specifically sought as it is now.

The East Ohio Gas Company L. S. and R. plant was built in the era when the objective for any new endeavor was to maximize the opportunity or return. That is one reason it was placed where it was; in the middle of the city on existing company property close to the gas distribution facilities already available. It was convenient. It failed, coincidentally, during the war. The recovery of the LNG industry took place after the war at the same time that new ideas in risk management were being practiced in the Cold War, nuclear power industry, and space industry. These new ideas included the purposeful identification of risk in new ventures so they could be mitigated prior to implementation. This approach has helped to build an industry stronger than the one in the early days before the accident.

Table 7–2. Recovery Timeline

Date	Event
1938	L. Lee Boyer applies for patent on expanded perlite as an insulating material.
1939	International Nickel starts low temperature metal research.
1940	• ASME Boiler Code requires 15 foot-pounds impact at low temperatures. • Research shows that 3½ percent nickel-steel good to −200°F.
1946	Brophy and Miller (International Nickel) characterize nickel-steel down to −320°F.
1947	Pittsburgh Corning starts making Foamglas insulation.
1948	Perlite insulation starts fast rise in manufacturing.
1949	Chicago LNG plant designed using a "tank farm" concept in a rural area.
1951	William Wood Prince has the idea of moving LNG up the Mississippi by barge to Chicago.
1952	ASME approves use of 9 percent nickel-steel for shop-fabricated, stress relieved cryogenic vessels.
1953	Chicago Bridge and Iron constructs flat-bottomed liquid oxygen cryogenic tank in Ashtabula, Ohio, using perlite and Foamglas.
1954	First Mississippi barge built for moving LNG.
1958	Chicago Bridge and Iron builds flat-bottomed tank at Lake Charles for LNG.
1959	First shipment of LNG across the ocean from Louisiana to Great Britain in the *Methane Pioneer*.
1960	• International Nickel, U.S. Steel, and Chicago Bridge and Iron conduct destruction tests on field-built 9 percent nickel-steel LNG tanks. • American Gas Association starts work on LNG safety code.
1962	ASME Code accepts 9 percent nickel-steel for welded pressure vessels down to −320°F.
1965	A series of new LNG plants starts to come online in the U.S.
1966	NFPA Standard 59A LNG safety standard is published.

8
Breakout: Moving the Energy

After the war from about 1949 until the early 1970s when the first oil shock took place, the U.S. production and consumption of energy increased, rapidly fueling the economic expansion during that period. As seen in figures 8-1 and 8-2, U.S. oil production went from about 11 quadrillion BTU in 1950 to about 20 quadrillion in 1970, almost doubling. However, oil consumption went from around 10 quadrillion to about 35 quadrillion; more than tripling. Thus by the late 1950s and early 1960s the United States was importing oil to help meet its energy needs. The increase in natural gas production and consumption was even more dramatic. Natural gas production and consumption were both about five quadrillion BTU in 1950. By about 1972 they were both about 22 quadrillion BTU, more than quadrupling.

Natural gas production and consumption in the United States as shown in figure 8-1[1] and figure 8-2[2] can be classified in roughly five eras between 1950 and 2010.

In the first era, between 1950 and the peak at 1972, natural gas production and consumption rose over seven percent per year. This was an era of rapid economic expansion, and all sources of energy were sought and exploited. These were the boom years after World War II. In the second era, from 1972 to 1986, production dropped 38 percent from its 1972 peak. This was the result primarily of regulation and the impact of the OPEC oil embargo of 1973. The consumption drop included the impact of the 1974 recession and increased conservation after the oil embargo. The temporary increase in production and consumption in this era, in 1979 and 1980, was due to a 1978 regulation change. In the third era, from 1986 to 2001, both consumption and production increased. Once again this was aided by a federal order and a regulation change. Consumption increased faster than production in this era, and the rapid rise in consumption caused a rapid rise in imported natural gas, as seen in figure 8-6. In the fourth era, from 2001 to 2005, production again slowed, but imports remained high and consumption remained about the same. In the fifth era, from 2005 to 2010, production increased dramatically. This latter rise was primarily due a rise in shale gas production, which also has an impact on the use of LNG in the United States. If one includes natural gas plant liquids, then natural gas had become the primary energy source for the United States, exceeding even that of coal, by 2010. By 2011 natural gas alone had become the primary source of energy in the United States.

The increase in energy demand in the United States in the last half of the twentieth

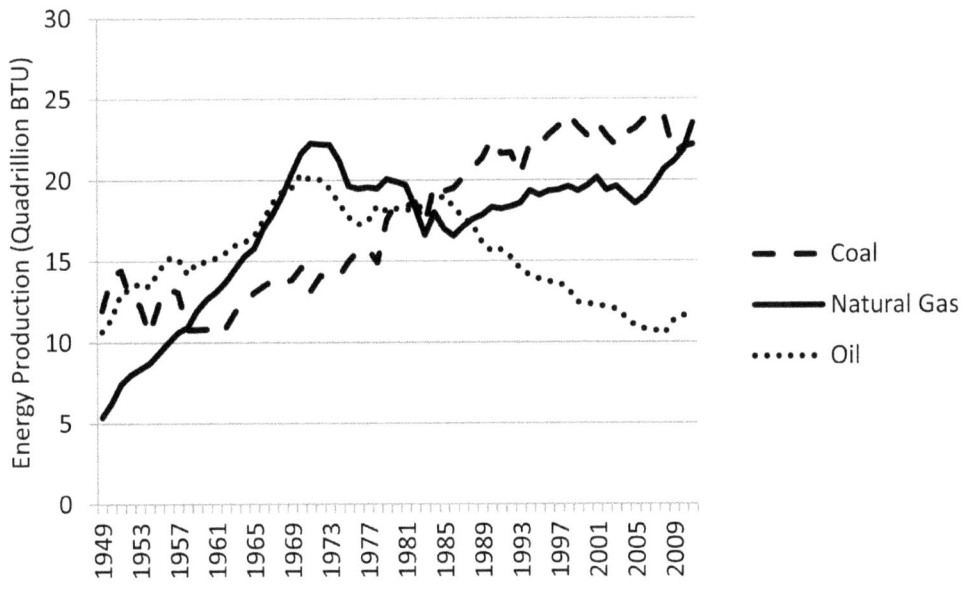

Figure 8-1. U.S. energy production, 1949–2010.

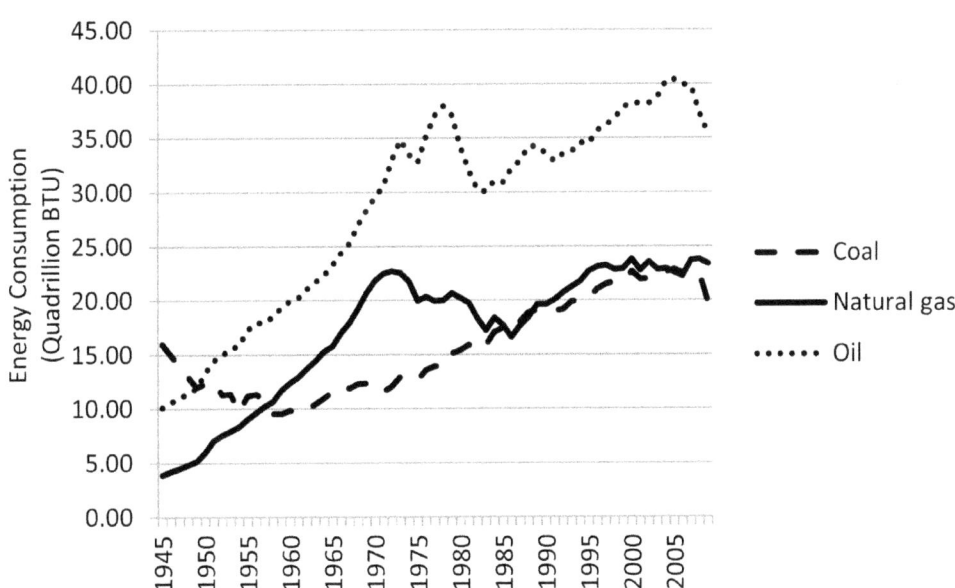

Figure 8-2. U.S. energy consumption, 1945–2009.

century was mirrored throughout the world; more energy was needed and demanded. This need was demonstrated early, when in 1956 the Middle East oil output was already 70 percent higher than the British had predicted it would be, 10 years prior to that. This was the motivation for the *Methane Pioneer* in 1959, the motivation for shipping energy in more ways than just as oil. Oil was the primary means for shipping energy prior to this. Natural gas could now be used as well as oil in moving energy from areas of surplus to areas of need. If shipping LNG was to become a major industry, then LNG had reason to grow domestically also for both base-load and peak-load supply.

However, in the latter half of the twentieth century, state and federal regulations also played an important part in the ups and downs of the natural gas industry.

Natural Gas Regulation

Production and consumption data on natural gas does not tell the whole story. By itself the data do not explain some of the trends shown in figures 8-1 and 8-2. Regulation by state and federal agencies must also be considered. Some regulations can impact supply or demand and have an effect that outlives the original intention.

Natural gas and oil are fundamentally different in the way they were originally moved from the source to the user. Although oil can now move by pipeline, originally it was moved in barrels by truck or rail. Regulation was not a big issue because oil could be moved freely without impacting the state or its citizens. Natural gas, on the other hand, could only be used at the source, for lampblack for example, or moved by pipeline. Pipeline limitations inhibited the development of natural gas in the early stages. Laying pipelines necessarily gets government involved at some level because of rights-of-way and competition. This was true even in the era of manufactured gas, prior to the use of natural gas. A manufactured gas plant could be located in a city, but to distribute the gas the company had to lay lines through the city and gain monopoly status to provide the service. So from the beginning, local governments had to set regulations so the companies would not abuse their monopoly power.

In the oil industry it didn't take Rockefeller and his competitors long to figure out the advantages of moving oil by pipeline; pipelines were used in the early days of the oil industry. However, as things were changing rapidly at the turn of the twentieth century regarding the dissolution of monopolies and trusts, some regulation passed covering oil pipelines. The Hepburn Act of 1906, for example, brought oil pipelines under the Interstate Commerce Act of 1887, which originally had applied only to railroads. However, there are still differences between oil and gas transportation that result in a more significant impact on natural gas than on oil. For example, oil can be carried by common carrier such as truck or train (besides pipeline), it has unregulated entry and exit from or into any state, and it is highly competitive. Natural gas, on the other hand, tends to be a public utility because of the way it is moved by pipeline and distributed to the user. This means it requires approval for construction and is also a natural monopoly.[3] It would be difficult for more than one company to lay pipelines throughout a city.

Between 1911 and 1928 several states tried to assert control over some of the interstate pipelines that had been laid by that time. However, these acts were struck down by the Supreme Court, which invoked the Commerce Clause by saying that states could not regulate interstate commerce; that was reserved to the federal government. By the mid–1930s most of the interstate gas pipelines were controlled by only a few companies; a lot of them also controlled production and distribution of natural gas. This meant control of a huge energy industry was in the hands of a few companies. To address this imbalance Congress passed the Natural Gas Act (NGA) in 1938, which gave the Federal Power Commission (FPC) the authority to regulate interstate natural gas sales. This was the first federal control over natural gas interstate commerce. The NGA did not specify any particular regulation of gas prices at the wellhead, however; they were left unregulated. This changed in a later 1954 Supreme Court decision:

> In this decision, the Supreme Court ruled that natural gas producers that sold natural gas into interstate pipelines fell under the classification of "natural gas companies" in the NGA, and were subject to regulatory oversight by the FPC. This meant that wellhead prices—that is, the rate at which producers sold natural gas into the interstate market—would be regulated much the same as natural gas that was sold by interstate pipelines to local distribution utilities.[4]

The NGA and the court decision put a significant administrative burden on the FPC. The FPC now had to set cost-of-service rates plus add on some fee to allow for a reasonable profit for the gas companies. Although they tried many approaches, they fell behind, so that by the early 1970s many of the rates that had been set by 1959 were well below market value for the gas being sold.[5] This made natural gas a bargain and helped drive the increased demand shown in figure 8-2, the first natural gas era after 1950. As might be expected, this had a perverse affect also. Because the selling price for gas was so low, the producers saw little incentive to search for new reserves. Thus natural gas production peaked in 1972 and started to decline. This was even *prior* to the October 1973 OPEC oil embargo.

This decline in incentive to find new gas and move it interstate led to an interesting quirk in the system. There was little *intrastate* regulation in the early 1970s, so in general the producing states had a sufficient supply of gas but consuming states outside the production areas had shortages, so bad in fact that some schools and factories in the Midwest had to close at times.[6] We were back to the condition that had led to the East Ohio L. S. and R. plant in the first place. Other impacts could be seen on a national level. The percent of new homes in the U.S. built to use natural gas was 54 percent in 1972. By 1978, because of the concern on the availability of natural gas, that had fallen to 37 percent.[7]

Part way through the second era, between 1972 and 1978, natural gas production had fallen about 12 percent. Congress then recognized that the situation had changed, and realized that the original intent to control gas prices for the protection of the consumer had now been overtaken by gas shortages that were hurting the consumer. To address the new imbalance they passed the Natural Gas Policy Act (NGPA) of 1978. In this act the FPC was abolished and the new Federal Energy Regulatory Commission (FERC) was given the jurisdiction over natural gas that the FPC had had. The intention of the NGPA was to create a single natural gas market to equalize supply with demand, and to set a goal of complete deregulation of wellhead prices by 1985.[8] This was the beginning of the era of deregulation, which impacted many industries such as the airline and trucking industries.

The NGPA had an impact. There was a bump in production in 1979 and 1980. Also, the percentage of new homes built to use natural gas immediately turned around and by 1997 it stood at 69 percent, up from its low of 37 percent in 1978.[9] The NGPA had a downside, also; average wellhead prices rose dramatically and therefore consumer gas prices rose. This caused a drop in demand and therefore in production. This can be seen in figures 8-1 and 8-2. Of course the drop in demand had other causes. The recession of 1974, prompted by the OPEC oil embargo of 1973, caused a normal drop in demand. Serious conservation efforts also had an impact on the demand for both oil and natural gas. Thus the second era ended in 1986 with lower levels of production and consumption.

The third era, from 1986 to 2001, was characterized by both more deregulation and a strong increase in consumption. Congress passed the National Gas Wellhead Decontrol Act (NGWDA) in 1989, which meant that wellhead prices were completely deregulated. However, before that in 1985, FERC had issued Order No. 436, known as the open access order, which had major impacts on the flow of gas in interstate pipelines. It established a framework in which interstate pipelines could act solely as transporters of natural gas rather than also acting as gas merchants. Essentially, the pipelines were open to all, and the owners were precluded from using them to protect their own merchant interests; they got away from "bundled" services. It was called open access because the pipeline customers could choose their gas transportation provider separate from the supplier. This helped to increase the new gas hookups mentioned above. The strong increase in consumption in this era spurred the importation of gas shown in figure 8-6.

This completed the last of the gas regulation and deregulation through the end of the century. The last two eras, 2001 to 2005, and 2005 to 2010, were market driven rather than regulation driven. So although throughout its history the natural gas industry has been market driven, there have been periods in which regulation has had an impact on the market.

Moving the Energy—The Start

The British Gas Council's "bold experiment" of importing LNG was tried; it was a huge success. In 1957, even before the first shipment of LNG by the *Methane Pioneer*, studies were showing the feasibility of economically shipping LNG between ports all over the world. Other countries including Germany, France, Sweden, and Japan expressed interest in importing LNG. By the fall of 1957 the British Gas Council declared their intent to import the equivalent of 100 million cubic feet per day. This was about 10 percent of the U.K.'s total gas use, most of which was manufactured from coal or oil.[10] Logically, however, the British Gas Council wouldn't sign the contract until after the first trip of the *Methane Pioneer*.

A year after the first shipment, by March 1960, the *Methane Pioneer* had completed six more shipments of LNG. It was then converted for other uses (eventually LPG storage) and was retired as an LNG carrier in 1972.[11] It had a low capacity, only one-fifth the capacity needed for economical operation, because it was only a pilot project ship.

The pilot project was successful. Just after the arrival of the *Methane Pioneer* at Canvey Island, there was a flurry of excitement and talk about competition. Almost immediately Venezuela announced that two companies, including a subsidiary of Constock Liquid Methane, proposed to build liquefaction plants in Venezuela. One proposal had been made as early as 1957. One U.S. official, the vice chairman of the Federal Power Commission, thought that imported LNG could rival crude oil for imported energy:

> "Every cost estimate I have seen concludes that natural gas from abroad can compete with pipeline gas in the densely populated coastal United States.... The transportation of liquid methane to the Eastern Seaboard and the West Coast of the United States would be at least as appealing a prospect at this time" as are shipments to Western Europe.[12]

Some of this enthusiasm was premature. The Venezuelan plants were never built, for whatever reason. (Neighboring Trinidad and Tobago now has a thriving LNG export market.) The vice chairman was also premature in his predictions. As seen in figure 8-1, natural gas production was still rising rapidly in this country. However, as early as 1969 an import terminal for LNG was built in Everett, Massachusetts, near Boston. Later more import terminals were constructed.

The original intent of Constock after the *Methane Pioneer* experiment was to continue importing LNG to Canvey Island from the Lake Charles, Louisiana, facility on the Gulf Coast. However, there had been a major natural gas discovery in Algeria at Hassi R'Mel in 1956. This is the largest gas field in Algeria and one of the largest in the world. By 1961 it was producing natural gas.[13] This field was obviously closer to both France and the United Kingdom than was Lake Charles, Louisiana. It also potentially had more gas because it was so large. Reportedly, the United Kingdom and France signed contracts for the gas with Algeria in 1961 and 1962, respectively.[14] Although close, this sequence seems unlikely because Algeria was still a French colony in 1961. The more likely sequence is as follows.

Early in 1960, Royal Dutch/Shell joined with Constock to form a new company, Conch International Methane Ltd. By this time the Hassi R'Mel field was being prepared for production. The headquarters of the new company were moved to London to enable the start of LNG deliveries from North Africa to the U.K. Only the technical activities remained in the United States, such as basic research and insulation development. In the spring of 1960 Conch entered into an agreement with France to purchase gas from the Hassi R'Mel gas field and build a liquefaction plant near Arzew, Algeria. The liquefaction plant was financed and built by a new company, CAMEL (Cie Algierieene du Methane Liquid) jointly owned by Conch and French interests. This was right in the middle of the war of Algerian independence from France. This turmoil caused the United Kingdom to hold off its approval until January 1962. In March of 1962 there was a ceasefire in the war, and in July Algeria voted for independence in a referendum. Although this instability caused concern, it was decided the situation was no worse than the oil situation in the Middle East. When Algeria gained its independence it demanded and gained a share of the venture.[15] The French contracted for 50 million cubic feet per day from CAMEL. Thus two thirds of the Arzew output was to go to England and one third to France.

A 320-mile pipeline was built from the Hassi R'Mel field to the CAMEL liquefaction facility at Arzew. The plant was built with three liquefaction streams each of 50 million cubic feet per day capacity to supply the United Kingdom and France as described above. The first one started in operation on September 26, 1964; the second, November 29, 1964. On October 12, 1964, the *Methane Princess* arrived at Canvey Island near London with a load of LNG after a six day trip from Arzew, Algeria. This was the first time LNG had entered world trade, except for the *Methane Pioneer* pilot project. Following the success of the *Methane Pioneer*, Shell had commissioned two new ships specifically for the LNG trade, the *Methane Princess* and the *Methane Progress*. These sister ships were built at British shipyards and each had about five times the capacity of the *Methane Pioneer*, 27,400 cubic meters versus 5,000 cubic meters. The ships were completed in 1964 and entered service the same year. They had aluminum tanks built by Conch. Between them they made approximately 1,000 voyages before being scrapped in the 1990s.[16] The French built their own LNG tanker, the *Jules Verne*. It had seven cylindrical tanks of nine percent nickelsteel and a capacity of 25,840 cubic meters, approximately the same as the *Methane Princess* and *Methane Progress*. The insulation was Klegecell, a closed-cell polyvinylchloride foam. The *Jules Verne* began operating in January 1965 between Algeria and France.[17]

Thus by 1964, 20 years after the East Ohio fire, there was a thriving new LNG industry. It was fed not by local peak-shaving plants but rather by a liquefaction plant built strictly for export to serve the energy-hungry area of northwest Europe. This energy transporting business would continue to grow into a major enterprise supplying parts of the world that had little or no natural gas from areas rich in natural gas. In the meantime the U.S. domestic LNG industry was also set to restart after its 20 year lull.

New LNG Plants—Domestic Production

During the early 1950s, as gas use was increasing, it was still foreseen that demand would continue to grow at five to six percent per year. It was expected to grow even more in the East Coast areas that had not been in on the early use of gas. Many places, such as the northeast United States, had no natural gas because the geology of the area did not allow for its formation. In areas where they had had natural gas for years, space heating was around 80 percent of saturation, that is, about 80 percent of the natural gas market was now covered, but in the coastal areas it was closer to 30 percent. Convenience and price were the attractive features of switching to natural gas. This suggested utilities had to increase their capacity about five percent a year or more to meet peak-shaving demands. Many utilities were running at 30 to 50 percent load factor. This means the average capacity was only 30 to 50 percent of the peak load, because they had to size the pipeline capacity for the peak load. To make it worse, part of the average capacity was interruptible sales. These were sales to industries that agreed to interrupt their gas use in the winter, to allow residential sales; in return for this they received lower rates in the summer. Sales could be increased if peak-shaving could be introduced to allow the load factor to be increased. Depleted gas fields had been successfully used for storage to accommodate peak loads, but these fields were often far from where they were needed and therefore required additional pipeline capacity.[18]

The East Ohio L. S. and R. plant in Cleveland was built in 1940 to meet a particularly pressing need; the need to supply peak gas needs for industrial and residential use during very cold temperature snaps. Industry was still growing in the city at that time and was increasingly being impacted by closure during some very cold winter days so East Ohio could supply residential heating on those days. Peak-shaving was seen as a critical need for both industry and residential needs. There was a cost-benefit analysis between adding more pipelines and building the LNG plant, and the advantages showed the plant to be less expensive so it was chosen. However, it is likely that both more pipelines *and* the LNG plant would have been justified based on the apparent needs of the city. The need only increased during the war, which started for the U.S. just after the original plant was built. Also, more pipelines were added from both West Virginia and eventually the Southwest gas fields, so building a plant to shave the peaks made a lot of sense. These needs did not go away after the Cleveland plant failed.

STUDIES

By the late 1950s and early 1960s things had changed a lot since the first plant was built in Cleveland. For example, there was significantly more gas available, especially from the Southwest. So as the thought turned to increasing the load-factor on the gas pipelines by using LNG for peak-shaving the trade studies became more sophisticated. The investments being considered were larger because the plants being considered were larger. Interestingly, the work being done on the *Methane Pioneer* at the time gave rise to a lot of ideas about moving the natural gas all over the world, even before the maiden voyage of the ship. In 1956 Constock International had started operating the liquefaction plant on the barge in Louisiana in preparation for shipment overseas. At that time the major sources of gas were seen to be the Gulf Coast of the United States, the Persian Gulf area, and Venezuela. The studies seemed to show that LNG could be a competitive way of supplying fuel to the North Sea area, such as the United Kingdom and Europe, and even the northeastern United States. Of course the load factor would have to be kept high, the ships kept moving, just as would be the case for a normal pipeline.[19]

As these early studies speculated on world-wide shipments of LNG, other more rigorous studies were done on LNG plants to supplement peak-shaving for existing utilities. The Cleveland plant had a liquefaction capacity of about four million cubic feet per day, a storage capacity of about 150 million cubic feet (about 250 million after tank 4 was built), and a regasification capacity of 72 million cubic feet per day. One study, for example, compared two different size LNG peak-shaving plants, two million cubic feet per day into 400 million cubic feet of storage and 13 million cubic feet per day into 1,600 million cubic feet of storage, with some standard pipeline contracts and found the LNG plants to be more cost effective. Both of these example plants used much more storage than the Cleveland plant, in one case over six times more storage.[20] These studies showed promise for LNG, despite some concern about the availability of future supplies.

New Plants

Table 8-1 shows the status of the new LNG plants in early 1966. Four had been built in 1965 and were operating, and four others were underway. The first plant built was by Wisconsin Natural Gas; it was approved in December 1964 and went online September 25, 1965. The storage capacity at 250 million cubic feet of gas was about the same as the Cleveland plant after tank 4 had been constructed. In this case, though, all the storage was in one tank that was 82 feet in diameter and 102 feet tall. The outer tank was carbon steel; the inner tank was 5083 aluminum alloy. There was a five-foot annular space that had loose perlite insulation in it. The base was made of load-bearing cored perlite block in which block voids are filled with loose perlite. (Both insulation processes are patented by Chicago Bridge and Iron.)

Table 8-1. Early LNG Plants

Plant	Liq. Capacity MMcf/day	Storage MMcf	Regas. Capacity MMcf/day	Type/Tank	Cost $Million	Year
East Ohio (original)	4	150	72	Cascade/3.5Ni steel	1.25	1941–1944

Plant	Liq. Capacity MMcf/day	Storage MMcf	Regas. Capacity MMcf/day	Type/Tank	Cost $Million	Year
Operating						
San Diego (Chula Vista)	2	600	60	Expander/9Ni steel	2.8	1965
Wisconsin (Oak Creek)	1	250	50	Cascade/aluminum	2	1965
Alabama (Pinson)	4	600	85	9Ni steel	4.2	1965
New Jersey (Carlstadt)	5	1,000	200	Cascade/in-ground	12	1965
Arzew, Algeria	150	1,000	N/A	Cascade/aluminum, 9Ni steel and in-ground	85	1964
Underway						
Brooklyn Union		600	100	Expander/9Ni steel	4.5	1968
Philadelphia		4,000		Cascade/in-ground	20	1971
Memphis (Arlington)	5	1,000	200	Cascade/9Ni steel	7	1967
Massachusetts (Hopkinton)	18.5	3,000	248	Cascade/in-ground	14	1967

Figure 8-3 is a picture of the Wisconsin tank built by CB&I. The tank was located on a slope that led to the impounding area or dike about 500 feet from the tank. Plant property lines were at least 400 feet or more from the tank and at least 100 feet from the impoundment area. The cascade system was used for liquefaction but instead of ammonia and ethylene, the coolants used were propane and ethylene. The daily liquefaction capacity was actually lower than the East Ohio plant at one million cubic feet per day instead of four million. Likewise the regasification capacity was 25 million cubic feet per day compared to East Ohio's 72 million.[21] (The normal peak-shaving capacity was 25 million but it had a 100 percent reserve capability. That meant it could deliver as much as 50 million cubic feet per day in an emergency.) Four LNG plants went up quickly in 1965. All four were peak-shaving plants, as were the following four that were underway in 1966 but were completed a couple of years later.[22]

The storage tanks at the time were a mixture of aluminum, concrete and nine percent nickel-steel. Gradually, after Operation Cryogenics and after the ASME codes allowed properly heat treated nine percent nickel-steel without the need to stress relieve, most of the later tanks were made of nine percent nickel-steel. The first in-ground storage tank was at the Carlstadt, New Jersey, plant near Hackensack. It is a cylindrical hole 115 feet in diameter and 165 feet below ground level. Freeze pipes were installed around the perimeter and propane was used to freeze the earth around the tank. The frozen earth provides a structurally strong support for the walls of the tank and keeps the water out. After it was frozen, a concrete wall was installed around the proposed cavity from six feet below to 13 feet above the cavity. The earth and bedrock were then excavated to form the tank. The roof is nine percent nickel-steel. The LNG is kept two feet below the ground level to preclude spillage and pressurized to keep air out to preclude a combustible mixture.[23]

After the first few plants were constructed there was then a spike in the number of

Figure 8-3. Wisconsin Gas LNG tank (courtesy CB&I).

plants built in the next few years. This is shown in figure 8-4.[24] The figure shows that at least 41 peak-shaving plants, one import terminal, and 26 satellite plants, for a total facility construction of 68, were built between 1965 and 1977. (The Energy Information Administration data on the U.S. LNG facilities that went online between 1965 and 2004 is incomplete. In the data, 22 of the facilities, peak-shaving and satellite, do not list the year of operation. Therefore, some of them are likely to have been in the period covered by figure 8-4. This is why "at least" is used. However, none of these are in 1965 or earlier; these are well documented in the literature.) Peak-shaving plants were built for the same reason East Ohio built the first one, that is, to level the load factor. Satellite plants were built because it was now possible to move the LNG by truck to outlying areas that could not support an entire liquefaction operation. The satellite plants would include storage tanks and regasification facilities to put the regasified LNG into the local gas mains. The gas-

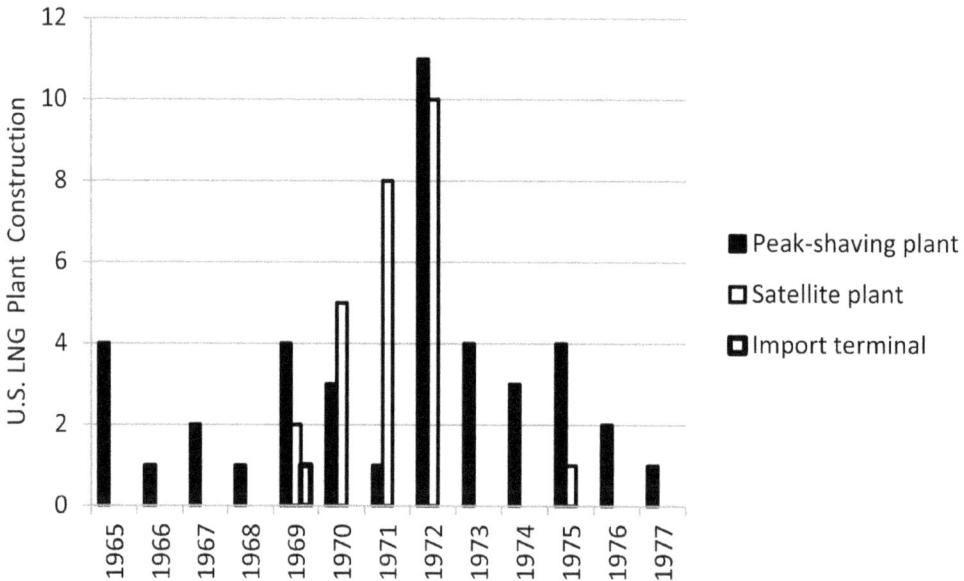

Figure 8-4. U.S. LNG plant construction.

poor East and Northeast regions took advantage of this capability. For example, in Massachusetts alone during that time period, four peak-shaving plants were built as well as 12 satellite plants. One import terminal was also built at Everett, Massachusetts. This terminal could be used to import LNG from anywhere in the world, including that produced on the U.S. Gulf Coast.

The satellite LNG plant is an interesting idea that first showed up in the West in Vancouver, Canada. In 1966 Cryogenic Enterprises built a small liquefaction plant in Richmond, just outside Vancouver, for the purpose of demonstrating the capability of shipping LNG from that plant to a storage tank in Squamish, about 50 miles away. Squamish was a satellite plant; it had no liquefaction capability of its own, neither was it served by a gas pipeline, so its residents had no way to get natural gas. The pilot plant had two above-ground storage tanks with a capacity of about four million cubic feet of gas. The distribution system in Squamish had a storage capacity of two million cubic feet. It was expected to pass through about 10 to 20 million cubic feet per year. The transportation trailer capacity was 500 thousand cubic feet. They had some start-up problems with the LNG plant in Richmond and were not ready on time. In order to get around this construction delay they requested a couple of LNG truckloads from San Diego Gas and Electric (SDG&E). After getting some emergency approvals from the regulatory agencies and making the appropriate truck modifications, they received three million cubic feet of gas by truck from the SDG&E Chula Vista LNG plant within ten days, a 1,500 mile trip. So before their plant was even in operation they had proved the concept of moving LNG by truck from a liquefaction plant to a satellite plant.[25] The first U.S. satellite plant was built in LaCrosse, Wisconsin, in 1969. The storage tank built by CB&I had a capacity of 250 million cubic feet and the vaporization capability was 21 million cubic feet per day.[26]

Post Surge

The initial surge in new plants, however, did not last. By 2004 there were a total of 57 peak-shaving plants and 39 satellite plants, an increase of only 28 facilities over the 27 years from 1978 through 2004.[27] Part of the reason can be seen in figures 8-1 and 8-2. The U.S. domestic production of both crude oil and natural gas peaked in 1972. This was immediately followed by the OPEC oil embargo and subsequent energy crisis of 1973. Both natural gas production and consumption dropped at that point and continued to decrease for the next ten years. The decreased consumption was partly due to increased conservation and partly due to using more coal; coal production continued to rise during that time. This slowdown meant lower load factors and, therefore, less need for new LNG plants.

However, ever since these LNG plants were constructed there has been a continuous addition and withdrawal of LNG over the years. Figure 8-5 shows the net LNG withdrawals in the United States from 1980 through 2010. The Energy Information Administration shows no data from 1965 through 1979, probably because it was not collected. One data point, in 1969, shows 2,581 million cubic feet added and withdrawn that year. This was most likely the startup of the Kenai, Alaska, export facility. Figure 8-5 demonstrates that the peak-shaving and satellite plants across the United States are operating as planned to reduce the load factor and to provide natural gas to satellite areas with no gas pipelines or LNG production of their own.[28] LNG is produced on off-peak hours and either stored for use on cold days to cover the peak load or shipped to satellites for base-load natural gas use in those areas.

In 2004, for example, the 57 liquefaction and storage facilities in the United States produced, and added to storage, 52 billion cubic feet of natural gas in the form of LNG, but withdrew about 51 billion cubic feet. Of course most of it was withdrawn to shave peak loads and to supply the satellite plants. The original East Ohio plant had a storage

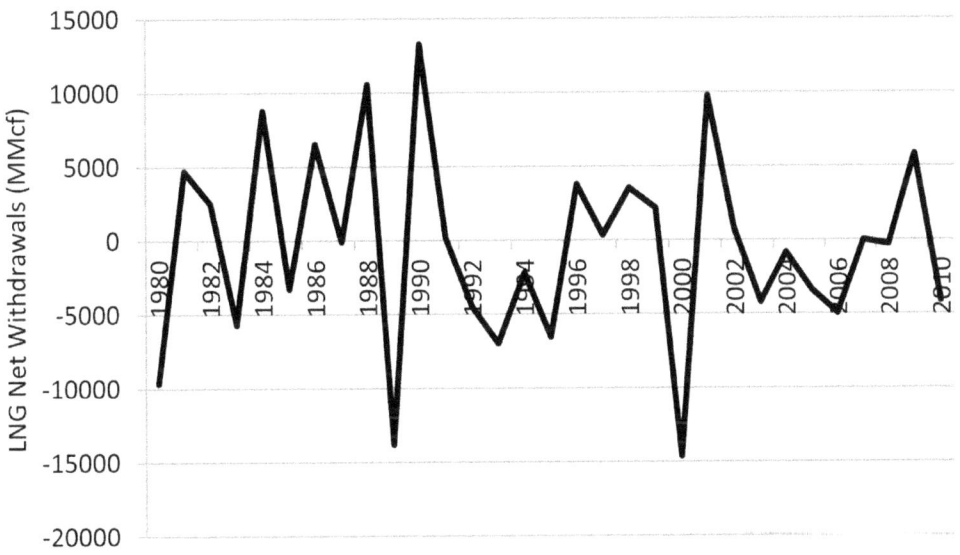

Figure 8-5. LNG net withdrawals from storage.

capacity of 150 million cubic feet and cycled through perhaps two refills per winter season or about 0.3 billion cubic feet, 0.57 percent of the 52 billion cubic feet stored in 2004. The modern LNG liquefaction plants are also safer, have a greater liquefaction capability, and much larger storage on average. The average modern plant has about six times the storage capacity of the original East Ohio plant, approximately 900 million cubic feet. This larger size is evident in table 8-1 also. Clearly, for the last three decades from 1980, the LNG industry has been fully functional in liquefying and regasifying natural gas. Although there is no data from 1965 to 1980, 1965 could probably be listed as the year when the industry had fully recovered; see table 8-1 and figure 8-5. It was now operating as the original planners had hoped in 1940 when the first plant was built in Cleveland, although on a scale they probably never imagined.

Imports

LNG use from 1980 to 2010 was fairly constant even through the decline of natural gas production and consumption (figures 8-1 and 8-2) from 1972 to 1985, and through the subsequent rise in both production and consumption from 1985. However, things were changing again. Even as the production of U.S. natural gas rose after 1985, the rise in consumption was even greater. The same thing was happening with natural gas that had happened to oil a couple of decades earlier: when consumption outpaced production, natural gas had to be imported. This is shown in figure 8-6.[29]

U.S. natural gas imports rose from about five percent of consumption in 1985 to about 20 percent in 2000. The reason for the sharp rise in imports in 1985 is discussed above under natural gas regulation. Most of the natural gas was imported by pipeline, about equally from Canada and Mexico. This sharp increase caused little notice, probably

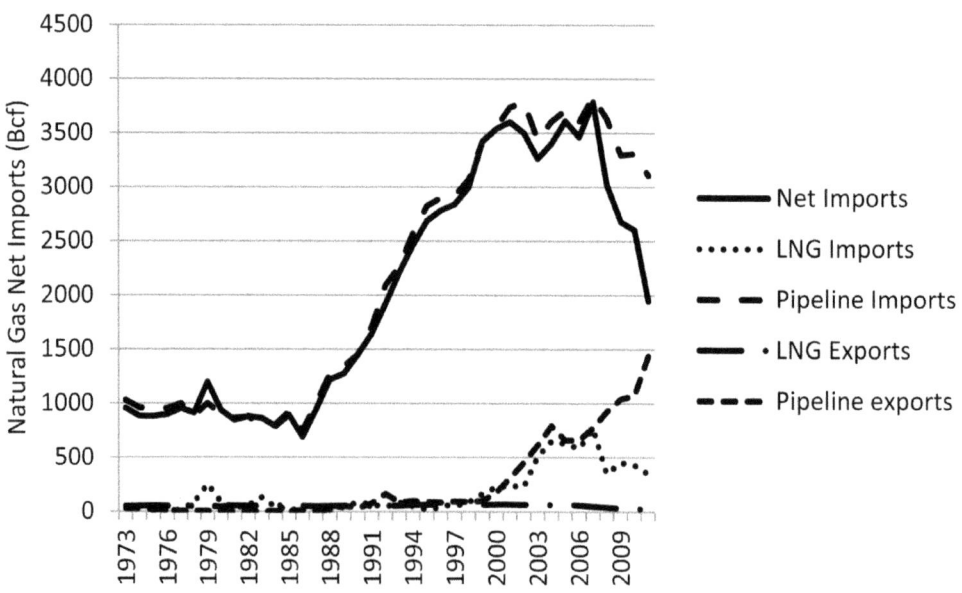

Figure 8-6. U.S. natural gas imports.

because Canada and Mexico are close, friendly neighbors. There was no imminent threat of an OPEC-style embargo as there was for oil from the Middle East. Nevertheless, there was a legitimate concern that U.S. natural gas reserves were dwindling and that the United States would become a major gas importing country. In 1972 the estimated U.S. reserves were 266 trillion cubic feet (Tcf). By 1996 the EIA was estimating the reserves at 166.5 trillion cubic feet. However, in recent years, because of new discoveries and shale gas, the estimates have gone up rapidly. The 2010 reserve estimate is 304 trillion cubic feet, almost double the 1996 estimate.[30] Reserves are defined as quantities that can be recoverable with reasonable certainty in future years. Technology has a lot to do with this, however. Improvements in the technology and exploration have made it possible to recover gas that was not available years ago. For example, to find a new barrel of oil or gas reserve cost 15 dollars in 1977; by 1996 that had fallen to five dollars.[31] These improvements in gas recovery technology continue to happen at a rapid rate today.

Increased consumption, natural gas deregulation, plentiful gas abroad, and the now known ability to move LNG across the ocean all contributed to more interest in import terminals in the United States to receive the gas expected to come in. Although figure 8-6 shows that from 1985 to about 2003 most of the gas imported to the United States was via pipelines from Canada and Mexico, that was expected to change; more imports were expected from overseas.

Marine Terminals—U.S. LNG Imports

Once the *Methane Pioneer* had demonstrated the feasibility of transporting LNG overseas and the Aznew, Algeria, LNG plant was exporting LNG to northwest Europe, thinking in the United States started to include the possibility of importing LNG. This meant building terminals specifically to import LNG. U.S. import terminal construction can be divided into roughly two phases: the early-mid 1970s, which corresponded to the first peak in natural gas production and consumption, and the early 2000s, when natural gas reached a peak in consumption that surpassed the 1972 peak. Four terminals were constructed in the first period. Table 8-2 shows the location and the year of either authorization or first operation.[32]

Table 8-2. U.S. LNG Marine Terminals

Name Company	Location	Year: Authorization or First Delivery	Type	Jurisdiction
Everett LNG Distrigas	Boston, MA	1969	Import	FERC
Kenai ConocoPhillips	AK	1969	Export	FERC
Cove Point LNG Dominion CP	MD	1970s	Import	FERC
Elba Island LNG El Paso Energy	GA	1972	Import	FERC

Name Company	Location	Year: Authorization or First Delivery	Type	Jurisdiction
Lake Charles				
Trunkline LNG	Lake Charles, LA	1977	Import	FERC
Guayanilla Bay LNG				
Eco Electrica	Penuelas, PR	1996	Import	FERC
Gulf Gateway Energy Bridge				
Excelerate energy	Gulf of Mexico	2004	Import/offshore	MARAD/USCG
Cameron LNG				
Sempra LNG	Hackberry, LA	2008	Import	FERC
Freeport LNG				
Freeport LNG	Freeport, TX	2008	Import	FERC
Sabine Pass				
Cheniere	Sabine, LA	2008	Import	FERC
Northeast Gateway				
Excelerate Energy	Boston, MA	2008	Import/offshore	MARAD/USCG
Neptune				
Suez	Boston, MA	2010	Import/offshore	MARAD/USCG
Gulf LNG				
Gulf LNG Energy	Pascougla, MS	2011	Import	FERC
Golden Pass LNG				
Golden Pass LNG	Sabine Pass, TX	2011	Import	FERC

- FERC: Federal Energy Regulatory Commission
- MARAD/USCG: Maritime Administration/U.S. Coast Guard
- The PR plant imported LNG is not used in the continental U.S. but to power an electricity plant in PR.

These terminals were the first built for operational import or export of LNG. The very first plant was the experimental one built on Lake Charles, Louisiana, to demonstrate the feasibility of shipping LNG overseas. This was the one that supplied the LNG to the *Methane Pioneer* in 1959 for its first voyage to Canvey Island near London, which then opened the global LNG shipping industry.

The first import terminal was built in New England, in Everett, Massachusetts, near Boston. New England and the East Coast had always been short of natural gas; the geology did not support the formation of natural gas as did that of Appalachia. The plant was started in 1969 by Distrigas and was completed in 1971. It has been operating longer than any other LNG terminal in the United States and between 1971 and 2003 received approximately half of the LNG imported into the United States. In December 2010 it was the first to have received 1,000 shipments. An example of its importance to New England is the fact that it meets approximately 20 percent of that area's annual gas demand. Additionally, it can supply about 15 percent of the area's peak gas needs. In addition to the regasification done at Everett, LNG is shipped from Everett to satellite facilities around New England to be used by the local distribution companies. The regasification facility can sustain a throughput rate of 715 million cubic feet per day. The storage capacity is 3.4 billion cubic feet in two large storage tanks. This facility alone shows how far back things have come since the fire. Started about 25 years after the fire, the storage capacity of this one plant is over 1,000 times as much as the original East Ohio plant.[33] Massachusetts leads the nation with 14 satellite plants, about 34 percent of the total. It also has six peak-shaving plants.[34]

Alaska is rich in natural gas but it is what is known as "stranded gas." This means there is no good way to get it to market. The gas that has been found with the oil production in the state is simply re-stored underground. At least it is not flared as natural gas was in the past when immediate use could not be found for it. However, in 1962 the North Cook Inlet gas field was discovered in southern Alaska, about 60 air miles from Anchorage. Being near the water in the south gave easy access to it via water routes. At that time there were no U.S. import terminals, so there was no place for the gas to go in the lower 48 states. However, there was a ready market in energy-poor Japan. This was about the time the LNG recovery was starting, so by 1969 the Kenai Liquefied Natural Gas Plant began operations. It is on the Kenai Peninsula in southern Alaska on Cook Inlet. It receives gas from the Tyonek platform in the northern waters of the inlet. This plant, which produced about 34 million cubic feet of gas in 2011, has been shipping LNG to two Japanese utilities since 1969. It also provides local delivery in south-central Alaska in peak demand and emergency situations.[35]

To complete the initial rush of construction of import terminals three more quickly followed. They were at Cove Point, Maryland, on the Chesapeake Bay, Elba Island, Georgia, and Lake Charles, Louisiana. Figure 8-7 shows a picture of the present Cove Point import terminal.

All four of the first group of import terminals were built in the 1970s, when domestic gas production was falling. The decreased production was caused by regulation that damp-

Figure 8-7. Cove Point, Maryland, LNG terminal (courtesy of Dominion Resources).

ened the search for domestic supplies, by the recession, and by the intense conservation efforts spurred by the OPEC oil embargo. However, there was also a desire to become more independent of oil shocks and therefore to be less dependent on oil for energy. Importing LNG to supplement U.S. natural gas production seemed to be a good investment to supply what was expected to be a rise in natural gas consumption. This motivated the construction of these LNG import terminals. Initially these terminals were expected to import from Algeria, which was the first LNG export terminal and had started operation in 1964; that is exactly what happened. These imports peaked in 1979 with approximately 250 billion cubic feet coming in from Algeria that year. This was about 1.3 percent of U.S. gas demand.[36]

This boom in imports was short-lived, however. The NGPA of 1978, which started the United States down the deregulation path, started to have an impact as early as 1979. From 1979 to 1981 there was a small bump in production. Production then dropped further until 1985, when full deregulation kicked in, and it has risen ever since. However, this small bump in 1979–1981 was enough to have an impact on LNG imports. In 1980 imported LNG dropped to approximately 100 billion cubic feet, less than half the value of the prior year. Another reason for the decline was a price dispute with Algeria, which at that time was the sole exporter of LNG. Imports were therefore very sensitive to the U.S. production levels. This sensitivity showed up quickly. In 1980 both Cove Point and Elba Island were mothballed, and Lake Charles and Everett suffered from very low utilization.[37] This is reflected in table 8-2, which shows no LNG import terminal activity for several years after that, from 1977 to 2004. Figure 8-6 also shows the blip in LNG imports in the 1979–1981 timeframe but then essentially close to zero for several years.

However, by 1985 both natural gas production and consumption again started to rise rapidly. The consumption rose so rapidly that it quickly eclipsed production and resulted in a rapid increase in gas imports as shown in figure 8-6. There were many reasons for this. One, of course, was the deregulation of natural gas in 1985 that encouraged more domestic production. The average wellhead price (adjusted for inflation) dropped dramatically after 1985, leading to cheaper gas and more consumption.[38] One of the reasons for the increased consumption can be seen in figure 8-8, which shows that electricity generated by natural gas increased from about 2,700,000 billion BTU in 1986 to over 8,000,000 billion BTU in 2011; that is a tripling.[39] Oil use for electrical generation, on the other hand, decreased to only 290,000 billion BTU in the same timeframe. This clearly represents cheaper gas and more expensive oil. The other advantages of natural gas were the lesser dependence on OPEC, and its cleaner burning properties. Although coal was still the primary energy source for generating electricity in that interval, its use started to decline after 2005.

As consumption rose, especially for electricity production, gas prices started to rise. Also as late as 2004 the EIA was predicting a steady rise in imports for the foreseeable future.[40] Rising imports would suggest that importing it in the form of LNG would probably become more competitive. This was made more attractive by the opening of the first Atlantic Basin LNG plant in Trinidad and Tobago in 1999.[41] This close-by source would certainly increase the competition.

Once again the path of LNG in the United States changed. Imported LNG again became competitive. This caused the two mothballed plants, Elba Island and Cove Point, to be reactivated in 2001 and 2003, respectively. Within a few years all the original four

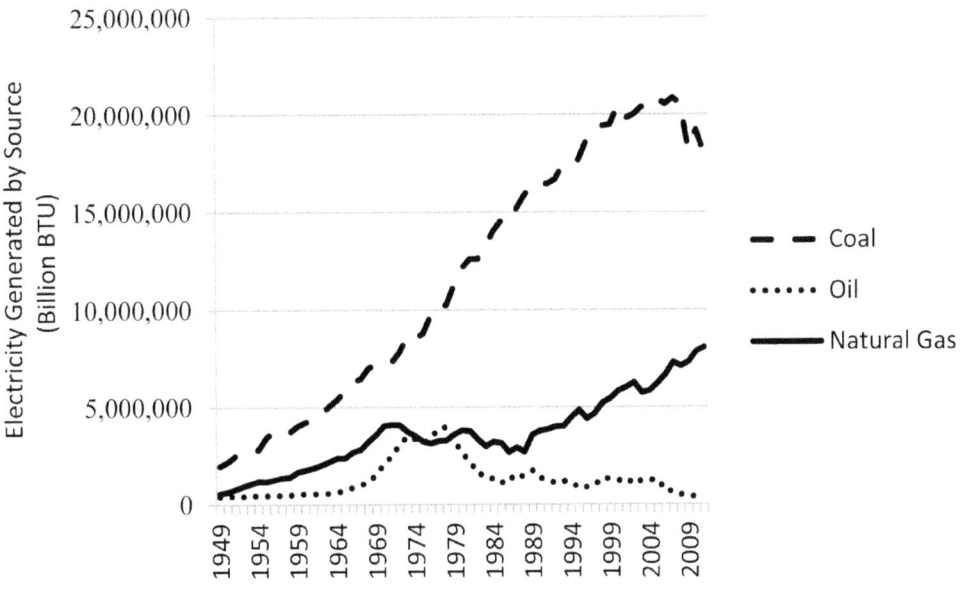

Figure 8-8. Electricity generated by source.

import terminals expanded their operations. The motivation was there for all the new facilities listed in table 8-2 authorized or opening from 2004 to 2011.

By the middle of the first decade of the twenty-first century, United States energy use was still climbing. The anticipation was that to meet these increasing energy needs the country would have to continue importing natural gas. Some of the imports would logically come from gas-rich nations overseas and thus be in the form of LNG. This meant the expansion of existing terminals and the addition of new ones as shown in table 8-2. The world-wide trade in LNG was flourishing and the United States would participate as a major importer. However, by the end of the same decade the natural gas industry would take a new direction once again.

International LNG

The LNG industry started in the United States as a means to store natural gas close to where it was needed for peak use rather than building an excessive number of pipelines that could supply peak use but would then be idle much of the time. Studies showed that even for the first plant in Cleveland in 1940, this was an economical way to handle peak loads. Cleveland was close enough to the gas fields of Appalachia that most of its gas could be supplied by pipeline, and peak-shaving was only a small part of the total need. This was true even during the war, when a great deal of gas was needed for the war production effort. When that plant failed in 1944, Cleveland abandoned LNG for storage underground. There were still some shortages, but within a few years additional pipeline gas from Texas and the Southwest became available, and the restoration of an LNG capability was not necessary in Cleveland.

However, there were some parts of the world where the issue of energy wasn't peak loads but getting any natural gas energy in the first place. The United Kingdom, for example, had good supplies of coal but essentially no oil or natural gas. (This was true until the mid–1960s and early 1970s, when oil and natural gas were discovered and exploited in the North Sea.) The same was true for other parts of northwest Europe. The British could, and did, manufacture gas from coal, but it had all the disadvantages of manufactured gas. It was expensive, odiferous, and left a lot of dangerous residue. They were stranded without natural gas and its attendant advantages.

This situation emphasized once again one of the problems with natural gas; it could not be easily moved long distances to where it might be needed. If you lived reasonably close by, even hundreds of miles, you could get it by pipeline. Pipelines are expensive and use a lot of right-of-way territory, but they are effective in moving the gas. For peak loads it was often possible to store the gas in underground caverns or depleted wells. Thus the "haves" could effectively extract, move, and use natural gas energy, but the "have-nots" could not. Pipelines were the only way one could *move* the gas energy even in the United States, which in the 1940s had plentiful gas supplies, although not always in the most convenient places. The East Ohio Gas Company fire in 1944 put a damper on any thought of using stored or movable LNG energy for several years afterward. This turned around by the actions of William Wood Prince and the *Methane Pioneer* as told in Chapter 7.

The international trade that started in Algeria in 1964 has grown faster outside the United States than it has within the United States for the reasons already discussed. By 2012 there were 31 liquefaction plants across the world in 18 different countries; these are the exporting countries (see table 8-3).[42]

Table 8-3. LNG Capacity and Exports by Country, 2010

Country	Liquefaction Capacity MMtpa	Exports MMtpa
Qatar	69.2	57.5
Indonesia	34.1	23.6
Malaysia	23.9	23.1
Australia	19.3	19.1
Nigeria	21.9	18.1
Trinidad	15.5	15.2
Algeria	19.9	14.3
Russia	9.6	10.6
Oman	10.8	8.7
Egypt	12.2	7.1
Brunei	7.2	6.7
UAE	5.8	5.8
Yemen	6.7	4.3
Equatorial Guinea	4.5	4.1
Norway	4.5	3.5
Peru	3.7	1.3
U.S.	1.5	0.6
Libya	0.7	0.2
Total	270.9	223.8

Qatar has by far the greatest number at six. Many are in exporting countries of the Middle East or Southeast Asia, including Australia. Additionally there were 10 under construction, seven of which were in Australia. Fifteen more are being planned. There is still some uncertainty in this market for various reasons such as politics, supply and demand, and U.S. shale gas production. This is evidenced by the fact that one plant under construction had been suspended and four plants being planned were either suspended or cancelled.[43]

At the same time, there were 90 regasification terminals spread over 23 importing countries. There are 18 under construction, with six of these being in China. Additionally, there were 26 regasification terminals in the planning stages. However, there were also 21 being planned that have been cancelled or suspended; eleven of these are in the United States. This is because of new shale gas reserves that are being exploited.

Table 8-4. LNG Imports by Country, 2010

Country	Imports MMtpa
Japan	70.6
S. Korea	34.1
Spain	20.5
UK	14.2
Taiwan	11.6
France	10.5
China	9.5
India	9.3
U.S.	8.5
Italy	6.7
Turkey	5.9
Belgium	4.5
Mexico	4.4
Chile	2.3
Portugal	2.2
Kuwait	2.1
Brazil	2.0
Canada	1.5
Argentina	1.3
Greece	0.9
Dominican Republic	0.6
Puerto Rico	0.6
UAE	0.1
Total	**223.8**

The trade volume in LNG in 2010 was approximately 230 MMtpa, up from about 180 MMtpa in 2009 and from about 20 MMtpa in 1980.[44] (MMtpa is one million tonnes per year. One tonne [metric] is 1,000 kilograms or 2,205 pounds [English].) For comparison, the 150 million cubic feet of gas in the original East Ohio spheres was equivalent to about 0.006 MMtpa. The LNG liquefaction capacity and exports by country are shown in table 8-3. This data, as of 2010, shows the small role in U.S. LNG exports compared to other countries. It is slightly different for imports as shown in table 8-4, also as of 2010.[45]

The numbers show a large and thriving industry, well integrated into the world energy economy. Because it is a major player in that economy, it both affects and is affected by it. For example, the recent economic slowdown caused by the world economic crisis of 2008 was reflected in a glut of LNG on the market. On the other hand, when the Japanese tsunami crisis hit in 2011 and Japan had to look to other sources of energy after the nuclear power plant accident, it turned to importing more LNG to supply the county's energy needs. These numbers have changed over the years and are likely to change in the future. Some of the original users such as the United Kingdom, France, and Spain continue to import LNG for energy. Japan will also likely to continue be a major importer. The Netherlands, however, had, since the first imports, discovered its own gas field and does not need to depend on importing LNG. Norway now is an exporter for the same reason. China will likely uncover more natural gas of its own, but its expanding energy needs might retain the need to import LNG from the Middle East and Africa. It is also likely that more gas will be unlocked in South America, meaning less dependence on importing LNG.

Shipping

The movement of base-load LNG from a producing country to a user country requires not only the liquefaction capability at one end and the regasification capability at the other but the means of transport. In fact, it was the transportation concept, not the liquefaction/regasification concept, which had to be proven, this was done by the *Methane Pioneer*. Once the *Methane Pioneer* experiment was successful the transportation system had to develop along with the other two capabilities. All three, the liquefaction/export, transportation, and import/regasification, had to develop together so as to be able to maintain the balanced system and avoid either a glut or shortage at one end or the other of the shipping "pipeline."

As the LNG trade grew, so did the number and size of the ships. Between 1969 and 1975 about 18 ships were built, ranging from about 26,000 cubic meters to about 90,000 cubic meters in capacity. From about 1975 to 2005 the "standard" size carriers averaged from 125,000 to 155,000 cubic meters' capacity. Prior to 2009 there were about 274 standard or small (<100,000 cubic meters) tankers in service.[46] As the LNG capacity, especially in Qatar for example, grew rapidly in recent years, the fleet also took a dramatic jump in size and number. Qatargas pioneered the development of two new super-size tankers for long hauls. These are the Q-Flex, with a capacity from 210,000 to 217,000 cubic meters, and the Q-Max, with a capacity of greater than 260,000 cubic meters. At the end of 2010 the fleet included 31 Q-Flex and 14 Q-Max LNG tankers.[47]

Some of the ships have a membrane construction in which the LNG containment compartment is built right into the ship as part of its structure. They look like a familiar cargo ships. Others, such as shown in figure 8-9, have spherical containment tanks. For example, the *Artic Princess* (not shown) was delivered in 2006 and was, briefly, the largest LNG carrier at the time. It is 288 meters long and has a capacity of 147,000 cubic meters of LNG carried in four spherical tanks, each with a diameter of 42 meters. A full LNG load could deliver enough natural gas for one year for a city with a population of 45,000.[48]

Although the U.S. is not a major part of the LNG trade today, as seen in tables 8-3 and 8-4, it was the source of the two major innovations that started this global industry. The first was the simple idea of liquefying the natural gas so it could be easily stored and used when needed. The second was the idea of shipping LNG by barge, then by ship, to move it where it was needed. Both contributed to the key attribute of LNG that made it so important in world trade, transportability. This can be easily seen in table 8-3, which

Figure 8-9. LNG container ship (courtesy ConocoPhillips).

shows the "haves" as exporters, and table 8-4, which shows the "have-nots" as importers. To get from one to the other the LNG had to be transportable.

The advantages conferred by portability caused the LNG industry to get off the ground. After some fits and starts the world trade in LNG has been increasing steadily since at least 1980. In the last few years it has jumped dramatically, from about 75 MMtpa in 1996 to about 225 MMtpa in 2010; a tripling.[49] In 2011, of all the natural gas consumed, 10 percent had been transported between the producer and the market in the form of LNG.[50] According to some, the LNG product is not yet commoditized, that is, a mass-produced unspecialized product—such as oil—because it is still dominated by long- and short-term contracts that move the LNG from point to point. However, it seems clear that commoditization will be a near term event and LNG will be traded on world markets as other commodities.

The experiment to liquefy, store, and regasify natural gas started by Hope Natural Gas in Cornwell, West Virginia, in 1939, and commercialized in 1940 by the East Ohio Gas Company in Cleveland, was successful. After the fire it took an interregnum of almost 20 years to work out the problems and realize the advantages of LNG again, but it happened and the breakout has been quite impressive.

Looking Ahead

It is not possible to look ahead regarding LNG with any certainty. A good example of this is the mothballing of two U.S. import terminals, Cove Point and Elba Island, only a couple of years after they opened. This happened because of decline of demand and a pricing dispute with Algeria, the primary producer at the time. They reopened a few years later because of more demand and different sources. The Atlantic trade in LNG became more profitable for the United States when the close-by LNG plant opened in Trinidad. Compounding the difficulty in predicting these twists and turns in the LNG market is the fact that the industry is very capital intensive. It is very expensive to build a liquefaction plant, accounting for all the factors such as long-term gas supply, the liquefaction and storage of the gas, the siting of the terminal and transfer of the LNG to the marine transports, the adequate shipping capability, and a reliable source for the product. As LNG grows more toward a commodity status, these dramatic swings will settle down. Oil is seen as a necessary ingredient in the global economy, so there is never a question of whether it will go away or not. However, even oil is subject to fluctuations in the economy, rising on demand and falling with a poor economy; but the oil infrastructure is there and it will continue to supply global energy. LNG is reaching the same point. There are more liquefaction plants, export and import terminals, ships, and regasification plants being built to support a sound LNG infrastructure.

As natural gas use expands as a supplier of global energy, so too does the technology in the field. This is especially true in the LNG trade. One of the problems in the past with the use of natural gas was the rigidity of its production and use. It was usually produced locally and used locally, or distributed via pipeline. The use of LNG has broken that bond, and now it can be shipped all over the world. However, there are still constraints on the system, imposed either by regulation or location, that can preclude expansion. Anything that can add flexibility to the system can improve the chances of getting gas to the consumer more economically.

A number of recent technological innovations have been made to provide more flexibility in the system. One is to provide a liquefaction capability onboard a ship; a floating liquefaction plant. These ships can be moved to receive gas from offshore, where it may not be convenient to have a land-based LNG plant, liquefy the gas and transfer it to an LNG carrier. They can also be used in "stranded gas" situations where there is no other way to move the gas. These ships are being built to recover gas from offshore areas, liquefy it, and move it either to onshore facilities or to LNG carriers. They will more likely use the expander cycle to liquefy the gas because it is lighter and more efficient for a floating platform. They are quick to develop, compared to land-based plants, often just because of the regulatory process, which can draw out construction of the latter facilities.[51] Similarly, floating storage and regasification units (FSRU) are ships that have been designed to deliver the natural gas as a liquid or gas.[52] They can unload the LNG at a conventional terminal as a liquid or regasify it onboard the ship and unload the gas through a subsea buoy or gas manifold. They are loaded in the first place at traditional LNG terminals. These capabilities add to the flexibility of the system, just as the offshore terminals listed in table 8-2 have been doing for years. The offshore terminals avoid many of the problems associated with siting a land-based LNG plant.

Niche Markets

It is not possible to talk about new technology in the area of LNG without talking about its use in what are now niche, or emerging, markets. Natural gas will undoubtedly be used in the future the same way it is used now, mainly for residential heating, industrial operations, and electricity generation. It is well suited for these applications. However, even in the early days of the reemergence of LNG, in the 1960s, when the transportation of LNG itself was first being tried, there was speculation about other uses in transportation. In an observation in 1967 by cryogenics expert Anker Gram,

> The potential of LNG is so enormous it is difficult to cut the future into phases. Maybe the next one is when the supersonic aircraft starts using LNG as fuel. This is only a matter of time. An official study in the U.S. has already concluded that a savings of 30 percent per seat-mile can be effected by switching from JP4 to LNG.[53]

We know that that early speculation was premature, but the very next year there were serious proposals to use LNG to power turbine driven engines for large, open-pit ore haulers. Again the economic analysis showed this to be cost effective. LNG expert Robert Petsinger said in 1968,

> If the economics of LNG work out favorably, it may be possible to convert the diesel-electric locomotives and open-pit earthmoving fleets to LNG operations on a broad basis to justify investment in LNG gas and distribution plants to service the equipment.[54]

Fast forward a few years to the present, and you see these proposals becoming reality. At present there are 22,000 heavy-duty trucks on the road using LNG as a fuel. This is still small compared to the total number on the road, because so far there is only one 15-liter engine available suitable for the heavy-duty trucks, and there is still not an extensive fueling system in operation. The latter situation is changing. At least two companies are setting up a network of LNG fueling stations on major truck routes from Houston to Los Angeles and Atlanta to Chicago, adding to the ones already there. This will encourage more truckers to switch now that more stations will be available. This should happen because it is estimated that the LNG is about 30 percent cheaper than diesel on an energy equivalent basis. With natural gas becoming more plentiful, this trend toward more LNG trucks should continue.[55]

Although not as close as fleets of LNG powered trucks, aircraft using LNG as a fuel are being considered and developed. NASA, looking at technologies for generations to come, has some ideas from U.S. aircraft manufacturers that use LNG as a fuel. NASA is looking at a target of a 60 percent reduction in fuel burn compared to today's aircraft. (Fuel burn is the rate at which fuel is burnt during a flight; usually given in tonnes per hour.) The LNG fuel not only helps achieve this but is a greener (cleaner) fuel, which will be very important also. This may be a long way off in the United States, but in Russia they have already tested an LNG powered aircraft, the Tupolev 155. In April 1988 the TU 155 was test flown using hydrogen as a fuel. The aircraft was modified and the next January it was flown using LNG as the fuel. Hydrogen has many advantages as a fuel. It is green and contains a lot of energy. However, it is bulky and expensive, so it doesn't compare well with LNG in these characteristics. The Russians are specifically looking at LNG as a fuel because of the good long-term prospects of the natural gas supply. Their approach to the chicken-and-egg problem, that is the aircraft need for LNG fueling stations, is to build a series of aircraft that can run on either jet fuel or LNG. Thus, if an LNG aircraft lands at a place where LNG is not available, normal jet fuel can be used to refuel it. They are presently developing a series of LNG-powered aircraft.[56]

The Japanese Aerospace Exploration Agency (JAXA) is developing the GX rocket, the first one to use LNG as a fuel.[57] Hydrogen is the preferred fuel for the large stages of heavy-lift vehicles. It is not only a high performance fuel but is also cleaner. However, because of its low density it is bulky. Therefore, LNG has some advantages as a fuel in some circumstances. For example, it is less evaporative in space and therefore suitable for a vehicle spending a lot of time there, such as a probe to a planet. It is definitely less expensive than hydrogen to produce. The higher density means the propellant tank can be smaller. For these reasons LNG might have a niche to fill in rocketry.

The use of LNG in these transportation areas will always be small compared to its other uses. However, it does have the potential to impact these areas significantly because it not only is a greener fuel than petroleum-based fuels but also holds out the promise of being cheaper in the long run.

Shale Gas

The most recent development in natural gas production is the recovery of shale gas. Most natural gas discussed so far has been what is called conventional gas. This is gas that is found in isolated pockets underground either as non-associated, or dry gas, or as associated gas, which is found with oil. These pockets are tapped and the gas is extracted. However, in certain areas, often under a sandstone layer, there is what is called an unconventional gas source—shale. A schematic diagram in figure 8-10 shows typical locations for both conventional and unconventional natural gas.

According to Geology.com,

> Shale is a fine grained sedimentary rock that forms from the compaction of silt and clay-size mineral particles that we commonly call "mud." This composition places shale in a category

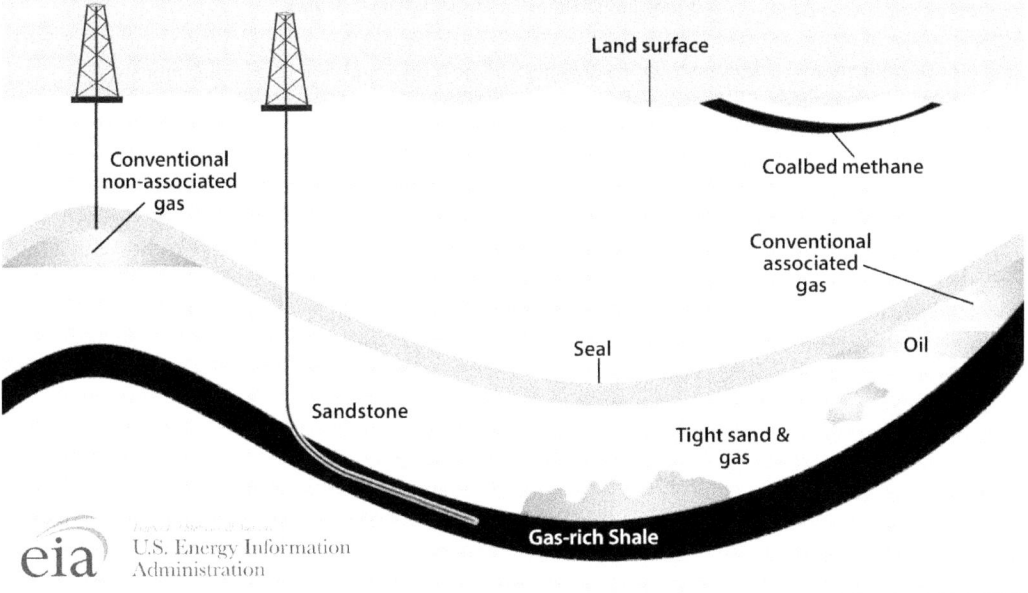

Figure 8-10. Shale gas schematic (U.S. Energy Information Administration and the U.S. Geological Survey).

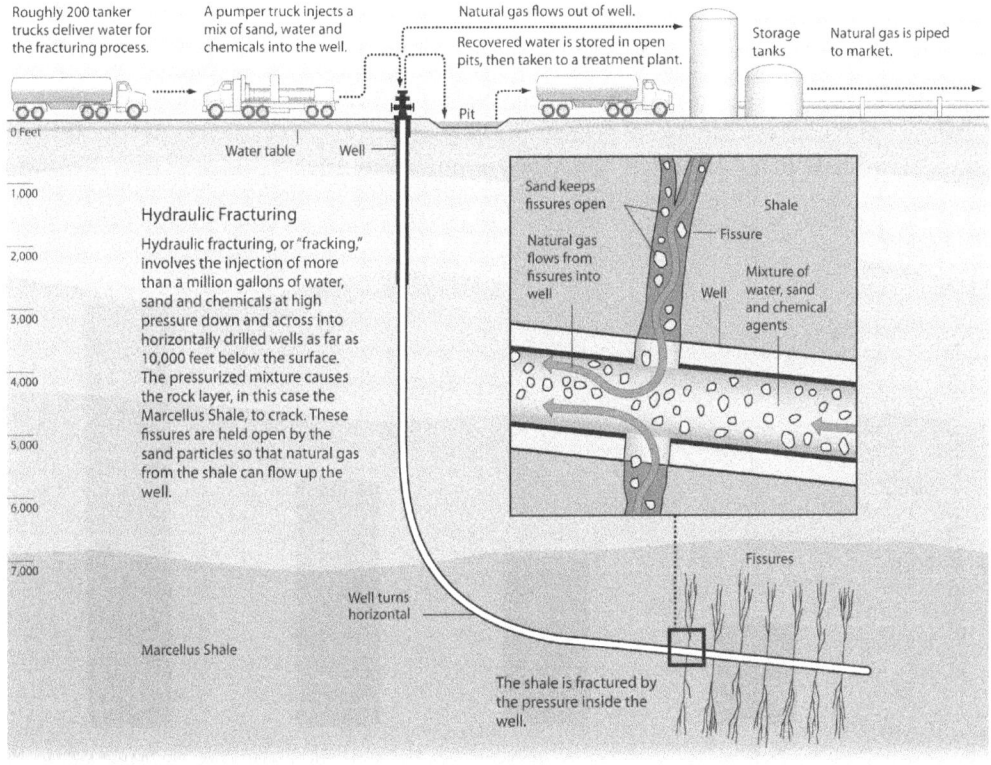

Figure 8-11. Hydraulic fracturing (illustration by Al Granberg, courtesy ProPublica).

of sedimentary rocks known as "mudstones." Shale is distinguished from other mudstones because it is fissile and laminated ... is made up of many thin layers. "Fissile" means the rock readily splits into thin pieces along the laminations.[58]

Natural gas is often trapped between these laminated layers. The fact that the shale is fissile means it can be readily split and the gas released. It is only recently that methods have been available to split this shale and release the gas. One method is to horizontally drill in a shale layer, to get maximum access to the gas in the layer, and then hydraulically fracture it. This is called *fracking*. Hydraulic fracturing is effected by drilling into the gas-rich shale (figure 8-10)[59] and then injecting, under high pressure, a mixture of water, chemicals, and sand (figure 8-11).[60]

The high pressure fluid opens the fissures and the sand particles keep them open. This allows the gas to flow out of the well. The gas is collected as usual, and the water and chemicals are first collected in pits and then hauled away for treatment. The fracking process has opened up access to a lot of natural gas. However, it is a controversial process because of the large amounts of water needed, the difficulty of safely disposing of the treated water and chemicals, and doubts by some on the safety of the chemicals used. There have even been claims, in Ohio, that the process has led to minor earthquakes, because it disturbs the underlying shale by lubricating the layers and thus making it likely to slide. This is still an open debate.

The process has been so effective, and shows the potential for so much more recoverable gas, that it might once again change the import/export equation for the United States. The steep rise in U.S. natural gas production from 2005 to 2010, as shown in figure 8-1, is almost all due to the production of shale gas. Figure 8-12 shows the steep rise in the production of shale gas in the U.S. between 2007 and 2010; it almost quintupled in that period (an increase of almost 48 percent per year).[61]

The shale plays of North America are quite extensive, covering large parts of

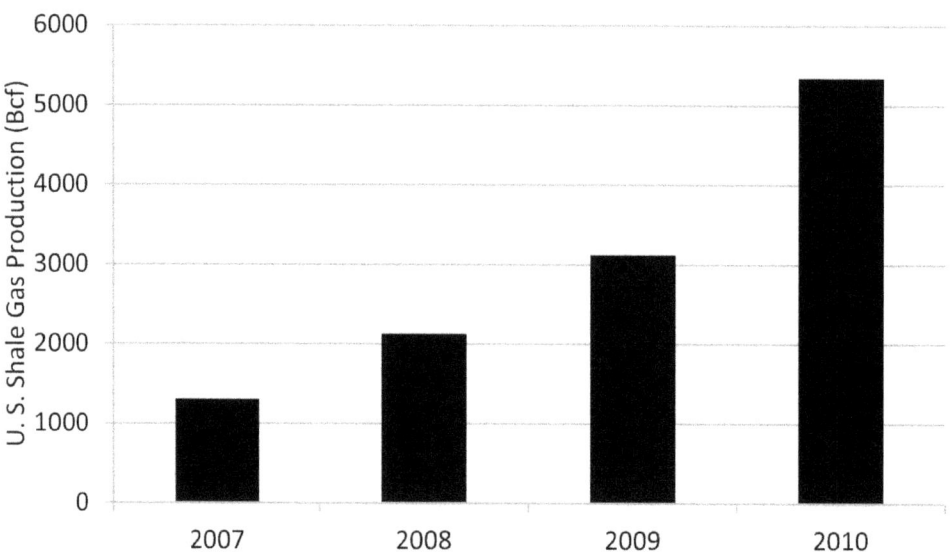

Figure 8-12. U.S. shale gas production.

the United States, Canada, and Mexico. Some of the largest are in the United States, such as the Barnett Field in Texas, and the Marcellus Field, which covers most of Appalachia.[62]

The share of shale gas of the total U.S. natural gas production went from about three percent of total production in 2005 to almost 25 percent in 2010.[63] The EIA predicts (AEO2011, Annual Energy Output for 2011) that total shale gas production will grow fourfold from 2009 to 2035. However, there is a high degree of uncertainty because of the uncertainty regarding the amount of recoverable shale gas from known reserves. The history of shale gas production is so short that long term projections are difficult. Nevertheless, working with present knowledge, the EIA projections are shown in figure 8-13.[64] This projection shows that shale gas is expected to be about 49 percent of all U.S. natural gas production by 2035. (This chart excludes Alaska and coalbed methane production for clarity.)

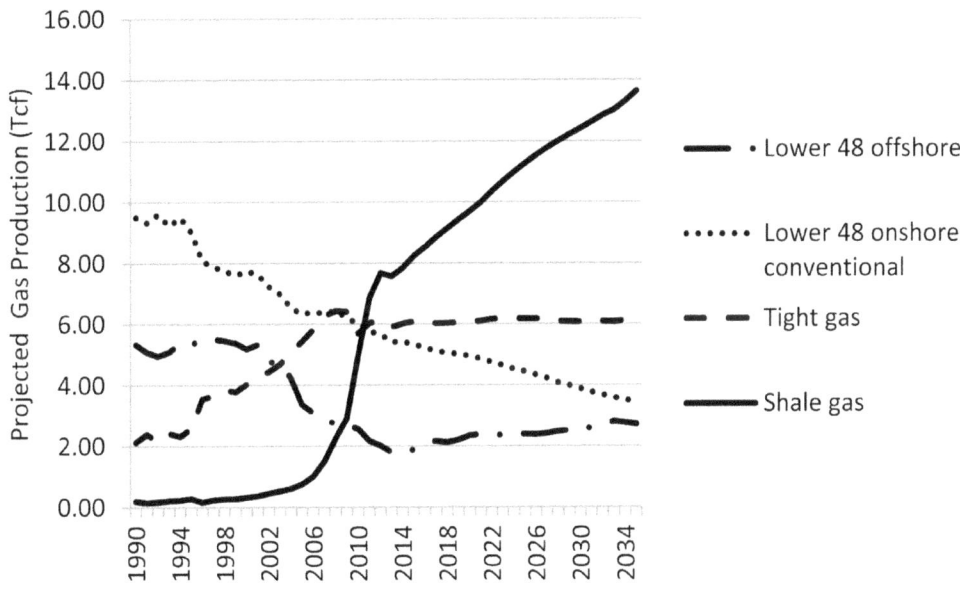

Figure 8-13. Projected U.S. natural gas production, 1990–2035.

Because conventional gas production in the lower 48 was decreasing and consumption was increasing, predictions of only a few years ago were looking at importing more natural gas in the form of LNG. Table 8-2 shows the recent increase of import marine terminals anticipating this surge in imports. However, as might be expected with this new shale gas resource, the United States might not only keep up with its own needs but might be able to export gas. This is shown in figure 8-14, which shows the EIA expectation that by about 2020 the United States might be exporting natural gas, probably in the form of LNG.[65] The sharp drop in natural gas imports shown in figure 8-6, starting in 2007, is another indication of the impact of the shale gas boom.

The boom in shale gas in the United States will probably have an impact on the several new import terminals shown in table 8-2. If the boom continues many of these may have reduced imports and/or be mothballed as Cove Point and Elba Island were in 1980, when imports of LNG dropped. There is another possible scenario that may have been presaged in early 2012 when Cheniere Energy, the operator of the Sabine Pass at Sabine, Louisiana, received approval to add an LNG *export* terminal to that facility, the first new export facility in the United States in a generation. Considering the expectations of U.S. shale gas projections and the likelihood that the United States may become an LNG exporter in the coming years, it seems quite possible that more facilities will consider building export facilities in parallel with their import facilities.

Figure 8-14. U.S. projected production and consumption, 1990–2035.

As with any boom, nothing is certain. An example of this uncertainty is the Kenai, Alaska, export facility and what happened to it in a little over a year. In February 2011 ConocoPhillips announced it was shuttering the Kenai LNG export terminal. It didn't have any LNG contracts with Tokyo, there was a glut of LNG in Asia, and it was only sending out a single ship. The plant, in operation over 40 years, was being mothballed. A few months later the tsunami hit Japan. In June of 2012 ConocoPhillips announced it had resumed LNG shipments to Japan, revitalizing the dormant plant.[66] The mothballed plant had been reopened.

The U.S. natural gas reserves have increased significantly, if one accounts for the shale gas reserves. This has implications for the world trade in LNG and further repercussions coming back to the United States. The International Gas Union in the World LNG Report of 2010 has already acknowledged that the shale gas development "means that a significant source of demand for global LNG supplies has disappeared."[67] Thus the reduction in demand from the United States could mean a glut of global supplies for some time. They cite the EIA forecasts for three AEOs for 2025 U.S. natural gas imports:

- AEO 2005: 180 billion cubic meters
- AEO 2008: 75 billion cubic meters
- AEO 2011: ~10 billion cubic meters

Although the United States is a leader in the field, shale gas is not, of course, a resource unique to the United States. In 2011 the EIA did an initial assessment of shale gas potential in 32 countries (excluding large parts of Africa, the Middle East, Central Asia and Siberia). Significant potential fields were identified in Europe, North Africa, China, Australia, and South America.[68] The EIA observed,

- The initial shale gas technically recoverable resource (TRR) estimates for the 32 countries outside the U.S. is 5,760 Tcf.
    - More than six times EIAs 862 Tcf TRR estimate for U.S. shale gas.
- Together with U.S. shale gas, world shale gas TRR of 6,622 Tcf raises total estimated world TRR by over 40 percent to 22,600 Tcf.[69]

This has further implications for future LNG trade. There are a number of countries that depend now on imports that potentially have significant shale gas deposits. These include France, Poland, Turkey, Ukraine, South Africa, Morocco, and Chile. Presumably, if these countries start to extract their shale gas reserves, they would either reduce or eliminate their imports. Once again the direction and quantity of the LNG global trade could change. Shale gas is starting to make an impact on the energy field and one way or another will impact the LNG industry.

Ironically, this might have a negative impact on global climate change, as discussed in the next section.

Transition Fuel

Humans left Africa about 50,000 years ago with some prototype language. They eventually populated the entire world as hunters and foragers. Agriculture started about 10,000 years ago. Written history was initiated perhaps 5,000 years ago. Give or take a few hundreds or thousands of years, these are all very short spans relative to the age of the Earth. If humans are to survive for even a few more thousand years we will have to learn to live in harmony with the natural world better than we have done so far. Within an even shorter span than listed above, a few hundred years, the innovative human population has learned to extract energy from the earth to provide great advances in human comfort and productivity. These resources, wood, coal, oil, and natural gas, have been very beneficial in supporting life on Earth.

One cannot predict the human condition in 2,000 to 3,000 years. It is difficult to make a reasonable prediction for even a few years. However, if humanity is to survive to that future, a couple of things seem evident. One of these is that, as vast as reserves of coal or natural gas are, they are finite and they are not being replenished. Thus, eventually, the hydrocarbons we use for energy will be exhausted. One wonders what the last barrel of oil will cost. However, long before these resources are exhausted we will have to go back to the only continuous source of energy we have: the sun. Except for fossil fuels, geothermal energy, and nuclear power, the sun is the source of all the energy available on Earth including wind, water, and solar energy. Assuming there will be human life 2,000 to 3,000 years from now, we don't know exactly how they will use the sun, but we do know they will not be able to depend on hydrocarbons as we do today.

The second thing that is evident if we expect humanity to be long-lived is that climate change, global warming induced by humankind, needs to be slowed and stopped. Carbon dioxide, which is being produced in great amounts in the atmosphere because it is a product of burning fossil fuels, is a greenhouse gas. It is called this because it acts like the glass on a greenhouse, a glass building used to nurture plants. Certain wavelengths of the energy received on Earth from the sun are absorbed by the Earth. However, the Earth then radiates energy back into space at other wavelengths. The glass on a greenhouse stops the radiation of this energy, causing the temperature in the greenhouse to rise so the plants can be nurtured. The carbon dioxide layer in the atmosphere has exactly the same effect, causing the Earth as a whole to become warmer.

Some changes have occurred and more will occur, but if greenhouse gases continue to build up in the atmosphere the Earth would eventually look like Venus. The atmosphere of Venus is estimated to be about 96 percent carbon dioxide, with the remainder nitrogen. The surface temperature is estimated to be about 500°C (900°F). This could be the result of a "runaway greenhouse effect," that is, the build-up of carbon dioxide in the atmosphere trapping the heat on the surface and raising surface temperatures:

> In fact, we believe that if this sequence were to take place on the Earth, the resulting temperature and pressure of the atmosphere left behind would not be very different from that for present-day Venus: the atmospheric temperature would be hundreds of degrees Celsius and the pressure would be maybe 100 times greater than it is today.... We have to be extremely concerned about processes such as burning of fossil fuels in large volumes that might (we don't know for sure because the scientific questions are complex) have the potential to trigger a runaway greenhouse effect and produce on the Earth atmospheric conditions such as those found on Venus.[70]

These are extreme conditions, and presumably changes would be made well before this kind of impact was felt.

Even though these extreme scenarios—depletion of fossil fuels and extreme climate change caused by burning of these fossil fuels—seem a long way off, weaning humanity from the use of these fuels is necessary to avoid both of these outcomes. Somehow moving to energy sources such as the sun, nuclear, and geothermal should be made to happen in the near future to preclude further global warming.

Neither the political will nor the technology exists to make this transition immediately, although the technology is rapidly changing. However, it is possible to consider this transition, which will be a long one, as a gradual switch to cleaner fuels leading up to the implementation to totally renewable fuels derived from the sun. Clearly the point here is to promote the use of natural gas as one of the cleaner fuels. Natural gas is a hydrocarbon fossil fuel, which means burning it will produce greenhouse gases such as carbon dioxide. Because of this, and the fact that it will eventually be depleted, it is *not* a long-term solution to the energy future. But it is a cleaner burning fuel than other fossil fuels.

If one burns hydrogen (H) there is only water as a byproduct; no carbon emissions. If readily available, hydrogen would be a very good fuel. As carbon is added to the molecule of the fuel being used, burning that fuel will result in more carbon emissions and more greenhouse gases. Methane, the largest constituent of natural gas, is as good as it gets for a fossil fuel. There are four atoms of hydrogen to one of carbon in methane (CH_4). Gasoline, a mixture of various alkanes, has more carbon atoms compared to methane. Octane (C_8H_{18}), for example, has more carbon per molecule than methane and, therefore, contributes more carbon dioxide to the atmosphere when it burns. Coal is almost all carbon (C) with small amounts of hydrogen, oxygen, sulfur. When it burns it produces large amounts of the greenhouse gas carbon dioxide, but also other gases such as sulfur dioxide and nitrogen oxide. Compared to oil and coal, natural gas is a relatively clean fuel.

This is why the recent surge in natural gas production due to fracking is both good news and bad news. The good news is that if we could very quickly replace coal and oil with natural gas, we would be burning a cleaner fuel, which would slow the greenhouse gas buildup in the atmosphere. This could provide time to switch to clean fuels. The bad news is that, besides the environmental concerns about extracting it, the availability of a great deal more fossil fuel, even natural gas, could prolong the fossil fuel age and result in a much hotter planet in the future.

This relatively clean-burning fuel, coupled with the vast amount of recently discovered shale gas reserves, holds the promise that natural gas can be a transition fuel that moves us from the fossil fuel economy to a cleaner one that depends only on renewable resources. In some senses this is already happening, in the electric power industry for example. The EIA in its AEO 2011 shows that in the 2009, capacity for electricity generation from natural gas accounts for about 34 percent, just slightly ahead of coal at 30 percent. However, when they project capacity additions out to 2035, natural gas represents 60 percent of these additions and coal only six percent.[71] One can see the same trends in figures 8-1, 8-2 and 8-8, which show decreasing coal use.

Since the start of the natural gas industry in the late nineteenth century, natural gas has had many fluctuations in supply and demand. The relatively recent capability of LNG to make natural gas energy transportable has increased its use around the world, making energy available where there is no natural supply. This mobility, added to the apparent increased supply of natural gas from shale formations, and the fact that it is a relatively clean burning fuel, provide the potential for natural gas to be almost an ideal fuel to transition human energy needs to a totally renewable energy future.

Chapter Notes

Chapter 1

1. *Before the Mayor's Board of Inquiry East Ohio Gas Company Fire: Transcript of Testimony and Proceedings Taken at Investigation of East Ohio Gas Company Fire*, Transcript of the East Ohio Gas Company Explosion 1944, Ohio Historical Society State Archives 1600, pp. 89–90.
2. B. E. Boyle, "The Lessons of Tragedy: The East Ohio Gas Company Fire," *Timeline* (Columbus, Ohio) 12.5 (September–October 1995): 27–29.
3. P. L. Nelson, *Inferno on the East Side: The Incident Revisited, a Half Century Later,* 1997, Western Reserve Fire Museum at Cleveland, Cleveland, Ohio, p. 5.
4. Ibid., p. 2.
5. J. Clark and R. Miller, "Liquefaction, Storage, and Regasification of Natural Gas," *American Gas Journal,* November 1940, p. 55.
6. "Gas Tanks Exploded on Oct. 20, 1944," *The Plain Dealer* (Cleveland, Ohio), October 16, 1994, p. 21A.
7. A. Cimperman Strazar, "Memories That Will Remain Forever," *Ameriska Dominivia (American Home) Anniversary Edition* (Cleveland, Ohio), September 1987, p. 6.
8. John Penca, interview with author, June 6, 2012.
9. The Dominion East Ohio Gas Company Records, Box 134, Folder 1, YHC MSS 0164, Ohio Historical Society, Youngstown Historical Center of Industry and Labor.
10. J. Small, "He Stands Alone—He Flinches—His Family Three Charred Bodies," unknown Cleveland newspaper (*The Cleveland News, The Cleveland Press,* or *The Plain Dealer*) and unknown date (week or weeks after the fire).
11. The Dominion East Ohio Gas Company Records, YHC MSS 0164, Ohio Historical Society, Youngstown Historical Center of Industry and Labor, Box 133, Folder 4.
12. T. Gerdel, "130 Were Killed in Cleveland Holocaust 20 Years Ago," *Cleveland Plain Dealer,* October 19, 1964, Cleveland Plain Dealer Historical Archives, http://www.NewsLibrary.com.
13. "Gas Tanks Exploded on Oct. 20, 1944," p. 21A.
14. J. Z. Girod, "Disaster as Seen Through the Eyes of Justine Girod," *Ameriska Dominivia (American Home) Anniversary Edition* (Cleveland, Ohio), September 1987, p. 3.
15. Nelson, *Inferno on the East Side,* p. 4.
16. "Gas Tanks Exploded on Oct. 20, 1944," p. 21A.
17. B. E. Boyle, "The Lessons of Tragedy," pp. 31–32.
18. D. Robertson, *The Greatest Thing Since Sliced Bread,* New York: Harper, 2008.
19. B. E. Boyle, "The Lessons of Tragedy," p. 36.
20. "A Neighborhood on Fire: Honey Vegel Submits Story on Tragedy," *American Home Newspaper 1994 Special Edition* (Cleveland Ohio), October 1994, p. 1.
21. R. Seltzer, "Robinson Says Gas Supply to Improve by Late 1948," *Cleveland Press,* 1947 (unknown day), Cleveland Press Collection, Special Collections, Michael Schwartz Library, Cleveland State University.
22. "*All* NEW Gas Heating Installations PROHIBITED," *Cleveland Press,* September 1947 (unknown day), Cleveland Press Collection, Special Collections, Michael Schwartz Library, Cleveland State University.
23. D. Von Drehle, *Triangle: The Fire That Changed America,* New York: Atlantic Monthly Press, 2003.
24. "Cites E. Ohio, City, State in Gas Blast," *Cleveland Press,* July 24, 1945, Cleveland Press Collection, Special Collections, Michael Schwartz Library, Cleveland State University.

Chapter 2

1. Woodenergy.ie, "List and Values of Wood Fuel Parameters—Part 3," 2013, http://www.woodenergy.ie/woodasafuel/listandvaluesofwoodfuelparameters-part3/.
2. The Engineering Toolbox: "Fuels—Higher Calorific Values," 2013, http://www.engineeringtoolbox.com/fuels higher-calorific-values-d_169.html.

3. W. Rosen, *The Most Powerful Idea in the World* (New York: Random House, 2010), p. 84.

4. Engineering Toolbox: "Fuels—Higher Calorific Values."

5. The National Academies Press: "1. Chemical composition of Petroleum Hydrocarbon Sources," 2013, http://www.nap.edu/openbook.php?record_id=314&page=17.

6. D. Yergin, *The Prize: The Epic Quest for Oil, Money, and Power* (New York: Simon & Schuster, 1991).

7. NaturalGas.org, "Background," 2012, http://naturalgas.org/overview/background.asp.

8. Ibid.

9. R. C. Burruss and R. T. Ryder, "Composition of Crude Oil and Natural Gas Produced from 14 Wells in the Lower Silurian 'Clinton' Sandstone and Medina Group, Northeastern Ohio and Northwestern Pennsylvania," Open-File Report 03-409 (Preliminary), U.S. Geological Survey, Reston, Virginia, [2003].

10. NaturalGas.org, "Background."

11. Columbia Gas and Electric Corporation, *The Story of Natural Gas*, 1927, Dominion East Ohio Gas Company Records, Box 159, Folder 26, p. 3, YHC MSS 0164, Ohio Historical Society, Youngstown Historical Center of Industry and Labor.

12. M. W. H. Peebles, *Evolution of the Gas Industry*, New York: New York University Press, 1980, p. 5.

13. D. A. Waples, *The Natural Gas Industry in Appalachia: A History from the First Discovery to the Maturity of the Industry* (Jefferson, North Carolina: McFarland, 2005), p. 7.

14. Ibid.

15. Columbia Gas and Electric Corporation, *Story of Natural Gas*, p. 4.

16. Waples, *Natural Gas Industry*, p. 7.

17. Ibid., p. 8.

18. T. Ferris, *The Science of Liberty: Democracy, Reason, and the Laws of Nature* (New York: Harper, 2010), p. 81.

19. C. Castaneda, *Invisible Fuel: Manufactured and Natural Gas in America, 1800–2000* (New York: Twayne, 1999), p. 38.

20. Waples, *Natural Gas Industry*, p. 8.

21. Ibid., p. 10.

22. R. Holmes, *The Age of Wonder* (New York: Vintage, 2010), p. 351.

23. Ibid., p. 356.

24. Ibid., p. 337.

25. Department of the Environment (UK), "Gas Works, Coke Works and Other Coal Carbonization Plants," 1995, http://enfo.agt.bme.hu/drupal/sites/default/files/SCHO0195BJKP-e-e_0.pdf, p. 2.

26. Peebles, *Evolution*, p. 7.

27. Waples, *Natural Gas Industry*, p. 25.

28. Ibid., p. 26.

29. Peebles, *Evolution*, p. 10.

30. Ibid., p. 8.

31. Ibid., p. 10.

32. Waples, *Natural Gas Industry*, p. 29.

33. Ibid.

34. L. Stotz and A. Jamison, *History of the Gas Industry* (New York: Stettiner, 1938), p. 4.

35. Ibid., p 6.

36. Heritage Research Center, Ltd, "What Is Manufactured Gas?" 2012, http://www.heritageresearch.com/documents/More%20About%20Manufactured%20Gas.pdf; Engineering Toolbox, "Gaseous Fuels and Chemical Compositions," 2013, http://www.engineeringtoolbox.com/chemical-composition-gaseous-fuels-d_1142.html.

37. A. Hatheway, "History and Chronology of Manufactured Gas Plants," 2012, http://www.hatheway.net/history.htm.

38. The Engineering Toolbox, "Fuel Gases—Heating Values," 2013, http://www.engineeringtoolbox.com/heating-values-fuel-gases-d_823.html.

39. Heritage Research Center, Ltd, "What Is Manufactured Gas?"

40. Ibid.

41. Waples, *Natural Gas Industry*, p. 27.

42. Heritage Research Center, "Manufactured Gas—The Genie's Legacy," 2013, http://www.heritageresearch.com/ourlibrary/histories/manufactured_gas.html.

43. Ibid.

44. Cotton Times, "Understanding the Industrial Revolution," 2013, http://www.cottontimes.co.uk/timeline1.html.

45. United States Census Bureau, *Census of Population and Housing: U.S. Census Data from the Fifth Census (1830) and the Sixth Census (1840)*.

46. Waples, *Natural Gas Industry*, p. 13.

47. Ibid.

48. Stotz and Jamison, *History of the Gas Industry*, p. 70.

49. Waples, *Natural Gas Industry*, p. 14.

50. Castaneda, *Invisible Fuel*, p. 38.

51. B. Cline, "The History of Kerosene," *History Magazine*, August/September 2007, http://www.bevcline.com/kerosene.pdf.

52. American Chemical Society, "The Development of the Pennsylvania Oil Industry," 2013, http://www.acs.org/content/acs/en/education/whatischemistry/landmarks/pennsylvaniaoilindustry.html.

53. Castaneda, *Invisible Fuel*, p. 41.

54. American Chemical Society, "The Development of the Pennsylvania Oil Industry."

55. Castaneda, *Invisible Fuel*, p. 41.

56. Waples, *Natural Gas Industry*, p. 19.

57. Ibid., p. 20.

58. Ibid., p. 22.

59. Castaneda, *Invisible Fuel*, p. 43.

60. Waples, *Natural Gas Industry*, p. 22.

61. T. Hrastar, *The Gilded Age: 1865–1900*, lecture notes, The Growth of Modern America Series (n.p., 2012).

62. J. M. Perry, "Some Data on Railroads," 2013, http://cprr.org/Museum/Railroad_Statistics.pdf.

63. U.S. Patent and Trademark Office, "U.S. Patent Activity Calendar Years 1790 to the Present," March 19, 2013, http://www.uspto.gov/web/offices/ac/ido/oeip/taf/h_counts.pdf.

64. United States Census Bureau, *Census of Population and Housing: 1860 U.S. Census and 1900 U.S. Census*.

65. Teachers College, Columbia University, "Re-

form of NYC Public Schools, 1896," http://www.tc.edu/faculty/waite/teach/texts/txt01.htm.

66. Automotive Engineer, "Nicolaus Otto Developed the Four-Stroke Combustion Engine," 2010, http://ae-plus.com/milestones/nicolaus-otto-developed-the-four-stroke-combustion-engine.

67. *Encyclopedia Britannica*, s.v. "Gottlieb Daimler," 2013, http://www.britannica.com/EBchecked/topic/149896/Gottlieb-Daimler.

68. *Encyclopedia Britannica*, s.v. "Henry Ford," 2013, http://www.britannica.com/EBchecked/topic/213223/Henry-Ford.

69. Energy Information Administration, "History of Energy Consumption in the United States, 1635–1945," 2013, http://www.eia.gov/totalenergy/data/annual/index.cfm#appendices.

70. Yergin, *The Prize*, p. 36.

71. R. W. Hidy and M. E. Hidy, *Pioneering in Big Business 1882–1911* (New York: Harper, 1955), p. 13.

72. Yergin, *The Prize*, pp. 37–40.

73. Encyclopedia of Cleveland History, "BP America—The Encyclopedia of Cleveland History," 2013, http://ech.case.edu/cgi/article.pl?id=BA.

74. Yergin, *The Prize*, p. 43.

75. Castaneda, *Invisible Fuel*, p. 70.

76. The Random House Dictionary of the English Language, unabridged 1966 ed., s.v. "trust."

77. Ibid.

78. Hidy and Hidy, *Pioneering in Big Business*, pp. 47–49.

79. *Encyclopedia Britannica*, s.v. "Standard Oil Company and Trust," 2012, http://www.britannica.com/EBchecked/topic/562986/Standard-Oil-Company-and-Trust.

80. Castaneda, *Invisible Fuel*, p. 71.

81. *Encyclopedia Britannica*, s.v. "Standard Oil Company and Trust," 2012, http://www.britannica.com/EBchecked/topic/562986/Standard-Oil-Company-and-Trust.

82. Waples, *Natural Gas Industry*, pp. 69–70.

83. Ibid., p. 71.

84. J. R. Kelso, *The Spirit of Progress: The Story of the East Ohio Gas Company and the People Who Made It*, Newcomen Publication 1317 (New York: Newcomen Society of the United States, 1988), p. 9.

85. Dominion, "From Gas Lights to New Energy Heights," 1998, http://www.dom.com/about/pdf/hngc_history.pdf, p. 4.

86. Dominion, "History of Hope Natural Gas Company" (n.p., c. 1964), pp. 3–4.

87. Castaneda, *Invisible Fuel*, p. 71.

88. Dominion, *History of Hope*, p. 3.

89. "Fifty Years of Service: Commemorating a Half Century of East Ohio's Contribution to Better Living," 1948, Dominion East Ohio Gas Company Records, YHC MSS 0164, Ohio Historical Society, Youngstown Historical Center of Industry and Labor.

90. Kelso, *Spirit of Progress*, p. 10; Waples, *Natural Gas Industry*, p. 74.

91. Ohio Historical Society, "The Dominion East Ohio Gas Company: History of the Dominion East Ohio Gas Company," 2005, http://www.ohiohistory.org/resource/archlib/dominion/history.html.

92. Waples, *Natural Gas Industry*, p. 73.

93. Dominion, *History of Hope*, p. 4.

94. Encyclopedia of Cleveland History, "East Ohio Gas Co.—The Encyclopedia of Cleveland History," 2004, http://ech.case.edu/cgi/article.pl?id=EOGC.

95. Dominion, *History of Hope*, p. 11.

96. Encyclopedia of Cleveland History, "East Ohio Gas Co."

97. "History of the East Ohio Gas Company," September 1953, Dominion East Ohio Gas Company Records, YHC MSS 0164, Ohio Historical Society, Youngstown Historical Center of Industry and Labor, Box 159, Folder 15.

98. "History of the East Ohio Gas Company," and Dominion, *History of Hope*, p. 11.

99. Encyclopedia of Cleveland History, "East Ohio Gas Co."

100. "History of the East Ohio Gas Company."

101. Kelso, *Spirit of Progress*, p. 10.

102. "History of the East Ohio Gas Company."

103. Stotz and Jamison, *History of the Gas Industry*, p. 302.

104. Kelso, *Spirit of Progress*, p. 10.

105. Waples, *Natural Gas Industry*, pp. 75, 113.

106. M. Brignano and H. McCullough, *The Spirit of Progress: The Story of the East Ohio Gas Company and the People Who Made It* (Cleveland: East Ohio Gas Company, 1988), pp. 20, 24.

107. Dominion, *History of Hope*, pp. 9–10.

108. U.S. Energy Information Administration, "Natural Gas Compressor Stations on the Interstate Pipeline Network: Developments Since 1996," Energy Information Administration, Office of Oil and Gas, November 2007, http://www.eia.gov/pub/oil_gas/natural_gas/analysis_publications/ngcompressor/ngcompressor.pdf.

109. Ibid.

110. Dominion, *History of Hope*, p. 10.

111. Ibid., p. 12.

112. Ibid., pp. 12–14.

113. *Encyclopedia Britannica*, s.v. "Standard Oil Company and Trust."

114. *Encyclopedia Britannica*, s.v. "holding company," 2012, http://www.britannica.com/EBchecked/topic/269181/holding-company.

115. Yergin, *The Prize*, p. 98.

116. Ibid., p. 110.

117. Dominion, *From Gas Lights*, p. 8.

118. Kelso, *Spirit of Progress*, p. 13.

Chapter 3

1. U.S. Energy Information Administration, "Total Energy: Annual Energy Review: Table E1. Estimated Primary Energy Consumption in the United States, Selected Years, 1635–1945," September 2012, http://www.eia.gov/totalenergy/data/annual/showtext.cfm?t=ptb1601.

2. J. M. Gould, *Output and Productivity in the Electric and Gas Utilities, 1899–1942*, part 2: "Manufactured and Natural Gas," National Bureau of Eco-

nomic Research (NBER), 1946, http://www.nber.org/chapters/c4273.pdf, pp. 79–125.

3. Library of Congress, "The Life of Thomas A. Edison," 2013, http://memory.loc.gov/ammem/edhtml/edbio.html.

4. *Encyclopedia Britannica*, s.v. "Bunsen burner," 2013, http://www.britannica.com/EBchecked/topic/84759/Bunsen-burner.

5. M. W. H. Peebles, *Evolution of the Gas Industry*, New York: New York University Press, 1980, p. 66.

6. Engineering Toolbox, "Fuel Gases—Heating Values," 2013, http://www.engineeringtoolbox.com/heating-values-fuel-gases-d_823.html.

7. L. Stotz and A. Jamison, *History of the Gas Industry* (New York: Stettiner, 1938), pp. 89–90.

8. Ibid., p. 90.

9. D. A. Waples, *The Natural Gas Industry in Appalachia: A History from the First Discovery to the Maturity of the Industry* (Jefferson, North Carolina: McFarland, 2005), p. 22.

10. M. Brignano and H. McCullough, *The Spirit of Progress: The Story of the East Ohio Gas Company and the People Who Made It* (Cleveland: East Ohio Gas Company, 1988), p. 12.

11. Waples, *Natural Gas Industry*, p. 22.

12. Brignano and McCullough, *Spirit of Progress*, p. 12.

13. Waples, *Natural Gas Industry*, p. 45.

14. Ibid., p. 22.

15. R. W. Hidy and M. E. Hidy, *Pioneering in Big Business 1882–1911* (New York: Harper, 1955), pp. 172–73.

16. Waples, *Natural Gas Industry*, p. 46.

17. The Encyclopedia of Cleveland History, "The History of Cleveland History Timeline," 2013, http://ech.cwru.edu/timeline.html.

18. Brignano and McCullough, *Spirit of Progress*, p. 19.

19. Gould, *Output and Productivity*, pp. 100–101.

20. D. Tabler, "The World's Largest Carbon Factory," Appalachian History, April 30, 2010, http://www.appalachianhistory.net/2010/04/worlds-largest-carbon-factory.html.

21. Ford Model T, "Production," 2013, http://web.bryant.edu/~ehu/h364proj/fall_98/coppola/production.html.

22. Waples, *Natural Gas Industry*, pp. 26–27.

23. Peebles, *Evolution*, p. 55.

24. Federal Trade Commission, *Report to the Senate on Public Utility Corporations*, Senate document no. 92, 70th Congress, 1st Session, Part 84-A, 1935, pp. 93, 95, from: C. J. Castenada, *Invisible Fuel: Manufactured and Natural Gas in America, 1800–2000*. New York: Twayne, 1999, p. 104.

25. Waples, *Natural Gas Industry*, p. 22.

26. Stotz and Jamison, *History of the Gas Industry*, p. 89.

27. Ibid.

28. Brignano and McCullough, *Spirit of Progress*, p. 15.

29. Waples, *Natural Gas Industry*, p. 183.

30. Stotz and Jamison, *History of the Gas Industry*, pp. 120–21.

31. Ibid., p. 176.

32. Ibid., pp. 178–80.

33. Waples, *Natural Gas Industry*, p. 185.

34. Ibid., p. 186.

35. Stotz and Jamison, *History of the Gas Industry*, p. 88.

36. Waples, *Natural Gas Industry*, pp. 127–28.

37. Hidy and Hidy, *Pioneering in Big Business*, p. 392.

38. G. M. Saybolt, *Obtaining Naphtha from Natural Gas*, U.S. Patent No. 989,927, filed September 1, 1906, issued April 18, 1911.

39. Waples, *Natural Gas Industry*, p. 128.

40. LPGA Times, "The First Fifty Years of LP-Gas: An Industry Chronology. Chapter 1: The Dream of LP-Gas Becomes Reality," January 1962, p. 17.

41. Ibid.

42. Innovateus, "What Is Ethane?" 2013, http://www.innovateus.net/science/what-ethane.

43. Waples, *Natural Gas Industry*, pp. 126–27.

44. Dominion, *History of Hope Natural Gas Company* (n.p., c. 1964), p. 19.

45. Ibid., p. 15.

46. Ibid., p. 17.

47. Ibid., p. 18.

48. Ibid.

49. Brignano and McCullough, *Spirit of Progress*, p. 28.

50. J. R. Kelso, *The Spirit of Progress: The Story of the East Ohio Gas Company and the People Who Made It*, Newcomen Publication 1317 (New York: Newcomen Society of the United States, 1988), p. 11.

51. Brignano and McCullough, *Spirit of Progress*, p. 33.

52. Dominion, *History of Hope*, p. 18.

53. Ibid.

54. Ibid.

55. Waples, *Natural Gas Industry*, p. 154.

56. Kelso, *Spirit of Progress*, p. 11.

57. Waples, *Natural Gas Industry*, p. 155.

58. Dominion, *History of Hope*, p. 20.

59. "Iroquois Gas Corporation," *Iroquois Gas News*, November 1959, p. 2, as cited by Waples, *Natural Gas Industry*, pp. 36–37.

60. Waples, *Natural Gas Industry*, p. 114, 119.

61. Ibid., pp. 118–19.

62. L. C. White, "History of Petroleum and Natural Gas Developments and Statistics of Production," in *West Virginia Legislative Handbook and Manual and Official Register*, ed. John T. Harris (1917), p. 599.

63. J. A. Bownocker, "Depletion of Natural Gas in the Appalachian Fields," presented at the annual meeting of the Natural Gas Association of America, Cleveland, Ohio, May 20–21, 1919, p. 257.

64. Ibid., p. 253.

65. Ibid., pp. 270–71.

66. U.S. Bureau of Mines, *Natural Gas Annuals and Minerals Yearbook*, various years, as cited in Castaneda, *Invisible Fuel*, p. 121.

67. Ibid.

68. Dominion, *History of Hope*, p. 22.

69. Brignano and McCullough, *Spirit of Progress*, p. 43.

70. The Encyclopedia of Cleveland History, "Cleaveland, Moses," 2000, http://ech.case.edu/ech-cgi/article.pl?id=CM10.
71. The Encyclopedia of Cleveland History, "Industry," http://ech.case.edu/ech-cgi/article.pl?id=I4.
72. Ibid.
73. The Encyclopedia of Cleveland History, "The History of Cleveland History Timeline."
74. "History of the East Ohio Gas Company," September 1953, Dominion East Ohio Gas Company Records, YHC MSS 0164, Ohio Historical Society, Youngstown Historical Center of Industry and Labor, Box 159, Folder 15.
75. Brignano and McCullough, *Spirit of Progress*, p. 43.
76. Ibid.
77. Ibid., p. 45.
78. Stotz and Jamison, *History of the Gas Industry*, p. 170.
79. Ibid., pp. 122–25.
80. Ibid., pp. 225–26.
81. Dominion, *History of Hope*, pp. 22–23.
82. Ibid., p. 23.
83. Economic History Association, "An Overview of the Great Depression," February 5, 2010, http://eh.net/?s=An+Overview+of+the+Great+Depression; United States History, "Unemployment Statistics During the Great Depression," 2013, http://www.u-s-history.com/pages/h1528.html.
84. Economic History Association, "Economic Recovery in the Great Depression," EH.net Encyclopedia, February 5, 2010, http://eh.net/encyclopedia/article/Steindl.GD.Recovery.
85. Dominion, *History of Hope*, pp. 26–28.
86. Brignano and McCullough, *Spirit of Progress*, pp. 47–48.
87. A. R. Tussing and C. C. Barlow, *The Natural Gas Industry: Evolution, Structure, and Economics* (Cambridge, MA: Ballinger, 1984), p. 97; Peebles, *Evolution*, p. 59.
88. Waples, *Natural Gas Industry*, pp. 155–56; Tussing and Barlow, *Natural Gas Industry*, pp. 29–30.
89. Peebles, *Evolution*, pp. 55–56.
90. Tussing and Barlow, *Natural Gas Industry*, table 3–2, pp. 34–35.
91. Brignano and McCullough, *Spirit of Progress*, p. 45.
92. Waples, *Natural Gas Industry*, p. 157.
93. Tussing and Barlow, *Natural Gas Industry*, map 3–2, p. 38.
94. "History of the East Ohio Gas Company."
95. Dominion, *History of Hope*, pp. 32–34; Waples, *Natural Gas Industry*, p. 170.
96. M. Gannon, *Operation Drumbeat: The Dramatic True Story of Germany's First U-Boat Attacks Along the American Coast in World War II* (New York: Harper and Row, 1990).
97. Waples, *Natural Gas Industry*, p. 171.
98. Ibid., pp. 28–30.
99. E. Richardson, "History Lessons: Gas Holders," *Blogdowntown*, Southern California Public Radio, November 21, 2006, http://blogdowntown.com/2006/11/2417-history-lesson-gas-holders.
100. California Historical Society Digital Archives/ USC California Digital Archive, "Panoramic view of downtown Los Angeles, showing City Hall in background, ca. 1945," 2004, http://digitallibrary.usc.edu/cdm/singleitem/collection/p15799coll65/id/3767/rec/23.
101. Brignano and McCullough, *Spirit of Progress*, p. 53.
102. J. O. Jackson, "Liquefied-Gas-Storage containers," *Gas Age*, April 22, 1943, p. 39.
103. Waples, *Natural Gas Industry*, pp. 161–65.
104. Brignano and McCullough, *Spirit of Progress*, p. 52.
105. Waples, *Natural Gas Industry*, p. 165.
106. Dominion, *History of Hope*, pp. 15–27.
107. J. O. Jackson, "Liquefied-Gas-Storage Containers."

Chapter 4

1. T. Ferris, *The Science of Liberty: Democracy, Reason, and the Laws of Nature* (New York: Harper, 2010).
2. Purdue University, "Gases, Liquids, and Solids," 2013, http://www.chem.purdue.edu/gchelp/liquids/character.html.
3. R. Holmes, *The Age of Wonder* (New York: Vintage, 2010), pp. 449–50.
4. J. R. Elliot and C. T. Lira, *Introductory Chemical Engineering Thermodynamics* (New Jersey: Prentice Hall, 1998), p. 1.
5. Dictionary.com, s.v. "Chaos," 2013, http://dictionary.reference.com/browse/chaos.
6. Online Etymology Dictionary, s.v. "gas (n.)," 2013, http://www.etymonline.com/index.php?term=gas.
7. D. A. Waples, *The Natural Gas Industry in Appalachia: A History from the First Discovery to the Maturity of the Industry* (Jefferson, North Carolina: McFarland, 2005), p. 24; C. Castaneda, *Invisible Fuel: Manufactured and Natural Gas in America, 1800–2000* (New York: Twayne, 1999), p. 4.
8. NNDB, "Jan Baptist van Helmont," 2013, http://www.nndb.com/people/852/000103543/.
9. J. B. West, "Robert Boyle's Landmark Book of 1660 with the First Experiments on Rarefied Air," *Journal of Applied Physiology* 98: 31.
10. NNDB, "Evangelista Torricelli," 2013, http://www.nndb.com/people/605/000087344/.
11. J. B. West, "Robert Boyle's Landmark Book," p. 32; Catholic University of America, "Robert Boyle," http://faculty.cua.edu/may/Boyle.pdf; *Encyclopedia Britannica*, s.v. "Robert Boyle," 2012, http://www.britannica.com/EBchecked/topic/76496/Robert-Boyle.
12. W. Rosen, *The Most Powerful Idea in the World* (New York: Random House, 2010), pp. 11–13.
13. J. B. West, "Robert Boyle's Landmark Book," p. 33.
14. Ibid., p. 36.
15. *Encyclopedia Britannica*, s.v. "Boyle's Law," 2011, http://www.britannica.com/EBchecked/topic/76517/Boyles-law.

16. *Encyclopedia Britannica*, s.v. "Guillaume Amontons," 2012, http://www.britannica.com/EBchecked/topic/21241/Guillaume-Amontons.
17. F. W. Sears and M. W. Zemansky, *College Physics: Mechanics, Heat, and Sound* (Cambridge MA: Addison-Wesley, 1952), pp. 318–19.
18. Sears and Zemansky, *College Physics*, p. 321.
19. G. J. Van Wylen, R. E. Sonntag, and C. Borgnakke, *Fundamentals of Classical Thermodynamics*, 4th ed. (New York: John Wiley and Sons, 1994), pp. 47–54.
20. M. Fowler, "Kinetic Theory of Gases: A Brief Review," Modern Physics, 2008, http://galileo.phys.virginia.edu/classes/252/kinetic_theory.html.
21. S. G. Brush, "History of the Kinetic Theory of Gases," 2003, http://punsterproductions.com/~sciencehistory/pdf/ITALENC.pdf.
22. Ibid.
23. Sears and Zemansky, *College Physics*, p. 329.
24. Ibid.
25. The Classical Library, "Francis Bacon 1561–1626," 2013, http://www.classicallibrary.org/bacon/index.htm.
26. C. Christopoulou, "Robert Boyle's Experiments on Cold: A Study of the Role of Chemical Experiments," 6th International Conference on the History of Chemistry, August 28–September 1, 2007, http://www.euchems.eu/fileadmin/user_upload/binaries/49_Christopoulou_tcm23-139407.pdf.
27. Hubpages, "What Is Absolute Zero?" 2013, http://kirstenblog.hubpages.com/hub/What-is-Absolute-zero.
28. W. Thomson (Lord Kelvin), "On an Absolute Thermometric Scale," *Philosophical Magazine*, October 1848, pp. 100–106, in *Mathematical and Physical Papers*, ed. Sir William Thomson, vol. 1. Cambridge University Press, 1882, http://zapatopi.net/kelvin/papers/on_an_absolute_thermometric_scale.html.
29. W. Thomson, "On an Absolute Thermometric Scale," footnote 6.
30. T. Thomson, *A System of Chemistry in Four Volumes*, vol. 2 (Edinburgh: Printed for Bell and Bradfute, and E. Balfour; London: G. and J. Robinson, 1802), p. 24.
31. F. Accum, *System of Theoretical and Practical Chemistry*, vol. 1 (London: Printed for the author, 1803), p. 319.
32. M. Faraday, F.R.S., *The Liquefaction of Gases: Papers by Michael Faraday, F.R.S. (1823–1845)*, Alembic Club Reprints No. 12 (Edinburgh: William F. Clay; London: Simkin Marshal, Hamilton, Kent, 1896), pp. 26–29.
33. J. Hamilton, *A Life of Discovery: Michael Faraday, Giant of the Scientific Revolution* (New York: Random House, 2002), pp. 36, 45.
34. Holmes, *The Age of Wonder*, p. 402.
35. M. Faraday, "Liquefaction of Gases: On Fluid Chlorine," excerpts from papers by Michael Faraday, F.R.S. (Transactions of the Royal Society of London, read March 13, 1823), 2003, http://campus.udayton.edu/~hume/Faraday/faraday3.htm.
36. W. L. Hardin, *The Rise and Development of the Liquefaction of Gases* (New York: Macmillan, 1899), p. 24.
37. Hardin, *Rise and Development*, pp. 24–27.
38. Ibid., p. 29.
39. T. O. Sloane, *Liquid Air and the Liquefaction of Gases* (1899; reprint, Bradley, IL: Lindsay, 1988), p. 140.
40. Faraday, *Liquefaction of Gases*, p. 39.
41. Hardin, *Rise and Development*, p. 20.
42. Faraday, *Liquefaction of Gases*, pp. 33–39.
43. Le Moyne College, "Joseph Black (1728–1799)," excerpted in *A Source Book in Physics*, by William Francis Magie (New York: McGraw-Hill, 1935), 2013, http://web.lemoyne.edu/~giunta/blackheat.html.
44. Sears and Zemansky, *College Physics*, p. 336.
45. Ibid., p. 339.
46. Hardin, *Rise and Development*, pp. 65–69.
47. Ibid., p. 61.
48. *Encyclopedia Britannica*, s.v. "Thomas Andrews," 2013, http://www.britannica.com/EBchecked/topic/24010/Thomas-Andrews.
49. Hardin, *Rise and Development*, p. 71.
50. Sears and Zemansky, *College Physics*, p. 335.
51. Hardin, *Rise and Development*, p. 81.
52. Sears and Zemansky, *College Physics*, p. 336.
53. Hardin, *Rise and Development*, p. 113.
54. Ibid., p. 114.
55. Ibid., p. 118.
56. Sears and Zemansky, *College Physics*, pp. 332–33.
57. Hardin, *Rise and Development*, p. 120.
58. Ibid., pp. 130–31.
59. Ibid., p. 159–164.
60. W. Thomson (Lord Kelvin), *Mathematical and Physical Papers: Collected from Different Scientific Periodicals from May, 1841, to the Present Time*, vol. 1 (Cambridge University Press, 1882), pp. 334–35.
61. University of Iowa, "Intermediate Thermodynamics; Thermodynamic Properties," 2013, http://www.engineering.uiowa.edu/~me140/Lecture/Thermodynamic%20Properties.pdf; University of Arizona, Department of Chemistry and Biochemistry, "The Joule Expansion," 2013, http://www.chem.arizona.edu/~salzmanr/480a/480ants/jadjte/jadjte.html.
62. NNDB, "Karl von Linde," 2013, http://www.nndb.com/people/861/000268057/.
63. The Linde Group, "Cryogenic Air Separation–History and Technological Progress," 2013, http://www.linde-le.de/process_plants/air_separation_plants/documents/L_2_1_e_09_150dpi.pdf.
64. B. K. Choudhury, *Process Design of Turboexpander Based Nitrogen Liquefier*, Master's Thesis, Department of Mechanical Engineering, National Institute of Technology, Rourkela, India, 2009, p. 9.
65. P. E. Haynes, "Liquefaction and the Fuel-Gas industry," *Gas Age*, May 8, 1941, pp. 44–45.
66. R. Sham, T. Jindal, and B. Pabla, "Cryogenic Processes—A Review," *International Journal of Engineering Science and Technology (IJEST)* 3.1 (January 2011): 603, http://www.ijest.info/issue.php?file=vol03issue01.
67. Ibid., pp. 604, 607.
68. Wolfram Research, "Kamerlingh-Onnes, Heike

(1853–1926)," 2013, http://scienceworld.wolfram.com/biography/Kamerlingh-Onnes.html.

69. Hardin, *Rise and Development*, pp. 181–83.

Chapter 5

1. R. W. Wilson and H. R. Newsom, "Helium: Its Extraction and Purification," *Journal of Petroleum Technology*, April 1968, p. 341.

2. Jefferson Lab, "The Element Helium," 2012, http://education.jlab.org/itselemental/ele002.html.

3. *The Economist*, "Value of Helium Gas for War Balloons is Revealed by the Navy Department: Had Been Camouflaged as 'Argon,'" vol. 61, January 4, 1919.

4. American Chemical Society, "The Gas That Wouldn't Burn," 2012, http://acswebcontent.acs.org/landmarks/landmarks/helium/thegas.html.

5. Inter-American Corporation, "Helium Processing History," 2012, http://www.helium-corp.com/processing/history.

6. Ibid.; *Economist*, "Value of Helium Gas."

7. Ibid.; Inter-American Corporation, "Helium Processing History."

8. Wilson and Newsom, "Helium."

9. Neenah Wisconsin, "History of Building Codes," BuildingCodeHistory.pdf.

10. A. M. Greene, Jr., *History of the ASME Boiler Code* (New York: American Society of Mechanical Engineers, 1953), p. 5.

11. Y. H. Leong, "The Birth of a Code: ASME Boiler and Pressure Vessel Code," Pressure Systems Interest Group, 2010, http://www.psig.sg/Birth%20of%20a%20Code.html.

12. Ibid.

13. Greene, *History of the ASME Boiler Code*, p. 57.

14. Ibid., p. 63.

15. Ibid., p. 86.

16. Ibid., p. 109.

17. American Society of Mechanical Engineers, *Rules for Construction of Unfired Pressure Vessels*, Section VIII, ASME Boiler Construction Code (New York, 1940), p. 68.

18. American Society of Mechanical Engineers, *Addenda to A.S.M.E. Boiler Construction Code, Unfired Pressure Vessel Code* (New York, August 31, 1936).

19. American Society of Mechanical Engineers, *A.S.M.E. Boiler Construction Code*, Section 8, Unfired Pressure Vessels (New York, 1937).

20. American Society of Mechanical Engineers, *Rules for Construction*, p. 68.

21. G. L. Cabot, *Means for Handling and Transporting Liquid Gas*, U.S. Patent No. 1,140,250, filed October 12, 1914, and issued May 18, 1915.

22. G. L. Cabot and J. J. Cabot, *Apparatus for Condensing Gas Under High Pressure*, U.S. Patent 1,225,574, filed October 26, 1914, and issued May 8, 1917.

23. J. A. Clark and R. W. Miller, "Liquefaction, Storage, and Regasification of Natural Gas," *American Gas Journal*, November 1940, p. 51.

24. Ibid.

25. University of Cambridge, "The Ductile-Brittle Transition," 2012, http://www.doitpoms.ac.uk/tlplib/BD6/printall.php.

26. T. A. Siewert, M. P. Manahan, C. N. McCowan, J. M. Holt, F. J. Marsh, and E. A. Ruth, "The History and Importance of Impact Testing, May 1, 2002," 2002, http://www.nist.gov/manuscript-publication-search.cfm?pub_id=851287.

27. W. V. Howard, "Experiment with Liquefied Natural Gas Storage," *Oil and Gas Journal*, May 9, 1940.

28. *Before the Mayor's Board of Inquiry East Ohio Gas Company Fire: Transcript of Testimony and Proceedings Taken at Investigation of East Ohio Gas Company Fire*, Transcript of the East Ohio Gas Company Explosion 1944, Ohio Historical Society State Archives 1600, p. 498.

29. Howard, "Experiment."

30. *Before the Mayor's Board of Inquiry*, p. 500.

31. Clark and Miller, "Liquefaction," p. 51.

32. Ibid.

33. Howard, "Experiment."

34. Clark and Miller, "Liquefaction," p. 51.

35. Ibid.

36. Ibid., p. 52.

37. Cleveland building permit number E26310 for 3 spheres to store liquid natural gas (63 feet O. D.), June 15, 1940.

38. *Before the Mayor's Board of Inquiry*, pp. 393–96.

39. Ibid., pp. 405–06.

40. Ibid., p. 498.

41. Ibid., p. 499.

42. Ibid., pp. 500–01.

43. J. O. Jackson, "Welded Liquefied Natural Gas Storage Tanks," *Welding Journal* 20.12 (December 1941): 834.

44. J. O. Jackson, *Method and Apparatus for Storing Gaseous Materials in the Liquid State*, U.S. Patent No. 2,328,647, filed August 6, 1941, issued September 7, 1943.

45. J. O. Jackson and H. C. Cooper, *Low Temperature Storage Tank*, U.S. Patent No. 2,329, 765, filed November 12, 1941, issued September 21, 1943.

46. J. O. Jackson, *Welded Steel Structure*, U.S. Patent No. 2,337,049, filed January 6, 1942, issued December 21, 1943.

47. P. E. Haynes, "Liquefaction and the Fuel-Gas Industry," *Gas Age*, May 8, 1941, p. 45.

48. Clark and Miller, "Liquefaction," p. 51.

49. Ibid.

50. L. S. Twomey, *Method of Liquefying and Storing Fuel Gases*, U.S. Patent No. 2,082,189, filed May 9, 1934, issued June 1, 1937.

51. Clark and Miller, "Liquefaction," p. 51.

52. M. A. Elliott, C. W. Seibel, F. W. Brown, R. T. Artz, and L. B. Berger, *Report on the Investigation of the Fire at the Liquefaction, Storage, and Regasification Plant of the East Ohio Gas Co., Cleveland Ohio, October 20, 1944*, United States Department of the Interior, Bureau of Mines, Report of Investigations (R. I.) 3876, February 1946, figure 3.

53. Hope Natural Gas Company, letter to J. French Robinson, president of East Ohio Gas Company, Oc-

tober 30, 1944, Folder 9, Dominion East Ohio Gas Company Records, YHC MSS 0164, Ohio Historical Society, Youngstown Historical Center of Industry and Labor.

54. J. A. Clark, "Progress Report on Liquefaction, Storage and Regasification of Natural Gas," *Gas Age*, May 22, 1941, p. 22.

55. J. F. Robinson, "The Storage of Natural Gas," *Gas Age*, February 10, 1944, p. 24.

56. Elliott et al., *Report*, figure 5.

57. Clark, "Progress Report," p. 35.

58. Huppi.com, "Timelines of the Great Depression," 2013, http://www.huppi.com/kangaroo/Timeline.htm.

59. Clark and Miller, "Liquefaction," p. 52.

60. Ibid., p. 51.

61. G. E. Barnes, M. M. Braidech, and K. H. Donaldson, *Report of the Technical Consultants Board of Inquiry for the Mayor of Cleveland on the East Ohio Gas Company Fire*. Cleveland, Ohio, July 1945, Case Western Reserve University Archives, pp. 11–12.

62. W. E. Steinwedell, "Liquefaction, Storage, and Regasification of Natural Gas For Peak Loads," *American Gas Journal* 158.1 (January 1943): 11.

63. The Dominion East Ohio Gas Company Records, Box 130, Folder 9, YHC MSS 0164, Ohio Historical Society, Youngstown Historical Center of Industry and Labor.

64. Clark, "Progress Report," p. 22.

65. Ibid.

66. *Before the Mayor's Board of Inquiry*, p. 395.

67. Ibid.

68. Ibid., p. 434.

69. Barnes et al., *Report*, sheet 4.

70. Ibid., pp. 21, 80.

71. The Dominion East Ohio Gas Company Records, Box 129, Folder 9, YHC MSS 0164, Ohio Historical Society, Youngstown Historical Center of Industry and Labor; ibid.

72. *Before the Mayor's Board of Inquiry*, p. 471.

73. *Brief for the Appellant, Florence V. Foley v. Pittsburgh–Des Moines Company,* Supreme Court of Pennsylvania, No. 83, March Term, 1949, Marvin Clinton Harrison Papers (MS 3799), Western Reserve Historical Society, Cleveland, Ohio, p. 60.

74. Ibid., p. 61.

75. U.S. Environmental Protection Agency, "11.18 Mineral Wool Manufacturing—Final Section—July 1993," in *Technology Transfer Network—AP 42*, 5th ed., vol. 1, ch. 11: "Mineral Products Industry," http://www.epa.gov/ttnchie1/ap42/ch11/final/c11s18.pdf.

76. *Before the Mayor's Board of Inquiry*, pp. 436–37.

77. M. Braidech, "Cleveland, The Center of the Natural Gas Industry," *Chemical and Engineering News* 22.5 (March 10, 1944): 328.

Chapter 6

1. S. R. Gerber, *Coroner's Report on East Ohio Gas Company Disaster, October 20, 1944*, Cuyahoga County, Cleveland Ohio, July 1945, p. 7.

2. G. E. Barnes, M. M. Braidech, and K. H. Donaldson, *Report of the Technical Consultants Board of Inquiry for the Mayor of Cleveland on the East Ohio Gas Company Fire. Cleveland, Ohio, July 1945,* Case Western Reserve University Archives.

3. M. A. Elliott, C. W. Seibel, F. W. Brown, R. T. Artz, and L. B. Berger, *Report on the Investigation of the Fire at the Liquefaction, Storage, and Regasification Plant of the East Ohio Gas Co., Cleveland Ohio, October 20, 1944*, United States Department of the Interior, Bureau of Mines, Report of Investigations (R. I.) 3876, February 1946.

4. American Home Publishing Company, "Gas Tanks Are Safe in Case of an Air Raid," *American Home*, July 28, 1942, Dominion East Ohio Gas Company Records, Box 129, Folder 5, YHC MSS 0164, Ohio Historical Society, Youngstown Historical Center of Industry and Labor.

5. Thomas A. Burke Papers, Container 1, Folder 29, Western Reserve Historical Society, Cleveland, Ohio,

6. Ibid., Folder 30.

7. *Before the Mayor's Board of Inquiry East Ohio Gas Company Fire: Transcript of Testimony and Proceedings Taken at Investigation of East Ohio Gas Company Fire*, Transcript of the East Ohio Gas Company Explosion 1944, Ohio Historical Society State Archives 1600.

8. Barnes et al., *Report*.

9. *Before the Mayor's Board of Inquiry*, pp. 39–73.

10. Barnes et al., *Report*, p. 34.

11. Ibid., pp. 35–36.

12. Ibid., pp. 55–56.

13. Ibid., pp. 34–35.

14. Ibid., p. 55.

15. Ibid., pp. 34, 55.

16. Ibid., p. 55.

17. Ibid., p. 56.

18. *Before the Mayor's Board of Inquiry*, pp. 93, 294.

19. Ibid., pp. 436–37.

20. Ibid., pp. 439–40.

21. Ibid., pp. 107–08.

22. Ibid., p. 394.

23. Barnes et al., *Report*, p. 45.

24. J. O. Jackson, Pittsburgh Des Moines Steel Company, letter to W. G. Hagan, East Ohio Gas Company, July 3, 1944, Dominion East Ohio Gas Company Records, Box 130, Folder 9, YHC MSS 0164, Ohio Historical Society, Youngstown Historical Center of Industry and Labor.

25. A. M. Greene, Jr., *History of the ASME Boiler Code* (New York: American Society of Mechanical Engineers, 1953), p. 112.

26. *Before the Mayor's Board of Inquiry*, p. 142.

27. Ibid., pp. 99–100.

28. Ibid., p. 414.

29. Barnes et al., *Report*, p. 57.

30. A. Hurlich, "Low Temperature Metal," *Chemical Engineering*, November 25, 1963, p. 323.

31. Barnes et al., *Report*, p. 81.

32. Elliott, Seibel, Brown, Artz, and Berger, *Report*, p. 14.

33. Barnes et al., *Report*, p. 81.

34. Ibid.

35. Ibid.
36. Ibid., p. 92.
37. Hurlich, "Low Temperature Metal."
38. *Brief for the Appellant, Florence V. Foley v. Pittsburgh–Des Moines Company,* Supreme Court of Pennsylvania, No. 83, March Term, 1949, Marvin Clinton Harrison Papers (MS 3799), Container 19, Folder 412, Western Reserve Historical Society, Cleveland, Ohio, p. 67.
39. Dr. Siewert, email to author, October 4, 2011.
40. *Brief for the Appellant,* p. 63.
41. Justia U.S. Law, "183 F.2d 467: Moran, v. Pittsburgh-des Moines Steel Co. et al," 2013, http://law.justia.com/cases/federal/appellate-courts/F2/183/467/266790/.
42. Jackson, Pittsburgh Des Moines Steel Company, letter to W. G. Hagan.
43. L. Hammer, "Letter Hints of Gas Blast," *Cleveland Press,* October 20, 1949, Cleveland Press Collection, Special Collections, Michael Schwartz Library, Cleveland State University.
44. Justia U.S. Law, "183 F.2d 467: Moran."
45. Hammer, "Letter Hints of Gas Blast."
46. S. J. Rosenberg and D. H. Gagon, *Effect of Grain Size and Heat Treatment upon Impact-Toughness at Low Temperatures of Medium Carbon Forging Steel,* National Bureau of Standards, Research Paper RP1410, August 1941, http://nvlpubs.nist.gov/nistpubs/jres/27/jresv27n2p159_A1b.pdf.
47. M. Gensamer, *Metallurgy of the Cleveland Liquefied Gas Tank Failure, Report of the Technical Consultant to the East Ohio Gas Co.,* January 15, 1945, referenced as Case 16 in "A Critical Survey of Brittle Failure in Carbon Plate Steel Structures Other Than Ships," by M. E. Shank. In *Symposium on the Effect of Temperature on the Brittle Behavior of Metals with Particular Reference to Low Temperatures,* ed. A. L. Tarr (Philadelphia: American Society for Testing Materials, June 28–39, 1953), p. 69.
48. Barnes et al., *Report,* pp. 58–59.
49. Ibid., sheet no. 6.
50. Elliott et al., *Report,* p. 29.
51. Ibid., p. 28.
52. Barnes et al., *Report,* p. 109.
53. Ibid., p. 82.
54. *Before the Mayor's Board of Inquiry,* pp. 406, 410.
55. Barnes et al., *Report,* p. 80.
56. Elliott et al., *Report,* p. 28.
57. Barnes et al., *Report,* p. 62.
58. Ibid.
59. Ibid., p. 112.
60. Elliott et al., *Report,* p. 37.
61. Barnes et al., *Report,* pp. 63–71.
62. Ibid., pp. 97–103.
63. Ibid., p. 8.
64. Ibid., pp. 105–06.
65. Leagle, *Foley v. The Pittsburgh-Des Moines Co.,* 2013, http://www.leagle.com/xmlResult.aspx?xmldoc=1949364363Pa1_1364.xml&docbase=CSLWAR1-1950-1985.
66. Elliott et al., *Report,* p. 32.
67. Barnes et al., *Report,* p. 113.
68. Elliott et al., *Report,* p. 32.
69. *Before the Mayor's Board of Inquiry,* p. 105.
70. Barnes et al., *Report,* p. 114.
71. Science Daily, "Superheating," 2013, http://www.sciencedaily.com/articles/s/superheating.htm.
72. Barnes et al., *Report,* p. 115.
73. P. E. Haynes, "Liquefaction and the Fuel-Gas Industry," *Gas Age,* May 8, 1941, p. 49.
74. Barnes et al., *Report,* p. 115.
75. *Before the Mayor's Board of Inquiry,* pp. 523–24.
76. NASA, *NASA Systems Engineering Handbook (2007),* NASA/SP-2007-6105, Rev 1 (Washington, D.C.: NASA, 2007), p. 142.
77. *Before the Mayor's Board of Inquiry,* pp. 487–88.
78. Barnes et al., *Report,* p. 116.

Chapter 7

1. A. Silverman, "34 Dead, Scores Missing, 10,000 Driven Out in Blast," *Cleveland Plain Dealer,* October 21, 1944, p. 1.
2. Cleveland Public Administration Library, *The City Record,* October 25, 1944, p. 1290; November 15, 1944, p. 1413; and December 6, 1944, p. 1488.
3. Iowa Department of Public Safety, "History of Fire and Fire Codes," 2013, http://www.dps.state.ia.us/fm/inspection/history/History_of_Fire_and_Fire_Codes.pdf.
4. H. C. Brearley, *The History of the National Board of Fire Underwriters: Fifty Years of a Civilizing Force* (New York: Frederick A. Stokes, 1916), pp. 7–8.
5. Ibid., p. 9.
6. Ibid., p. 12.
7. Ibid., p. 13.
8. Ibid., pp. 78–79.
9. Ibid., p. 80.
10. Ibid., pp. 87–88.
11. Ibid., p. 93.
12. The National Fire Protection Association, "History," 1996, http://www.nfpa.org/itemDetail.asp?categoryID=500&itemID=18020&URL=About%20NFPA/Overview/History&cookie%5Ftest=1.
13. Ibid.
14. Ibid.
15. Ibid.
16. Ibid.
17. Ibid.
18. Brearley, *History of the National Board,* p. 91.
19. National Fire Protection Association, *National Fire Codes for Flammable Liquids, Gases, Chemicals and Explosives* (Boston: National Fire Protection Association, 1943), p. 10.
20. Safety Emporium, "Flash Point Definition," 2013, http://www.ilpi.com/msds/ref/flashpoint.html.
21. Center for Energy Economics, "LNG Safety and Security," November 2006, http://www.beg.utexas.edu/energyecon/lng/documents/CEE_LNG_Safety_and_Security.pdf, p. 13.
22. National Fire Protection Association, *National Fire Codes,* p. 18.

23. Ibid., p. 23.

24. *Before the Mayor's Board of Inquiry East Ohio Gas Company Fire: Transcript of Testimony and Proceedings Taken at Investigation of East Ohio Gas Company Fire,* Transcript of the East Ohio Gas Company Explosion 1944, Ohio Historical Society State Archives 1600, pp. 488–89.

25. *LPGA Times,* "The First Fifty Years of LP-Gas: An Industry Chronology. Chapter 3: The Years of Slow Growth," March 1962, p. 21.

26. National Fire Protection Association, *National Fire Codes,* p. 152.

27. Chief of Division, Ohio Department of Industrial Relations, Division of Boiler Inspection, letter to Dr. S. R. Gerber, coroner of Cuyahoga County, Cleveland Ohio, December 27, 1944, Dominion East Ohio Gas Company Records, Box 132, Folder 15, YHC MSS 0164, Ohio Historical Society, Youngstown Historical Center of Industry and Labor.

28. Ibid.

29. H. H. Fitzgerald, "Clearance Standards for LNG Storage," in *American Gas Association Operating Section Conference, 1962,* CEP-62-6.

30. National Board of Fire Underwriters, "Standard of the National Board of Fire Underwriters for the Storage and Handling of Liquefied Petroleum Gases at Utility Gas Plants," Pamphlet NBFU No. 59, July 1954, p. 2; H. H. West and M. S. Mannan, "LNG Safety Practice and Regulations: From the 1944 East Ohio Tragedy to Today's Safety Record," AIChE meeting, Houston Texas, AIChE Topical Conference on Natural Gas Utilization and LNG Gas Transportation, April 2001.

31. Ibid.

32. National Fire Protection Association, "Standard for the Production Storage and Handling of Liquefied Natural Gas (LNG)," NFPA 59A (Quincy, Massachusetts: National Fire Protection Association, 2009), p. 59A-1.

33. West and Mannan, "LNG Safety Practice."

34. National Fire Protection Association, "Standard," pp. 59A-9–17.

35. Code of Federal Regulations (CFR) Title 49—Transportation, Part 193—Liquefied Natural Gas Facilities: Federal Safety Standards (DOT 49-CFR-193), October 1, 1996, ed.

36. West and Mannan, "LNG Safety Practice."

37. G. E. Barnes, M. M. Braidech, and K. H. Donaldson, *Report of the Technical Consultants Board of Inquiry for the Mayor of Cleveland on the East Ohio Gas Company Fire. Cleveland, Ohio, July 1945,* Case Western Reserve University Archives, pp. 8b–8c.

38. Ibid., pp. 6–7.

39. M. A. Elliott, C. W. Seibel, F. W. Brown, R. T. Artz, and L. B. Berger, *Report on the Investigation of the Fire at the Liquefaction, Storage, and Regasification Plant of the East Ohio Gas Co., Cleveland Ohio, October 20, 1944,* United States Department of the Interior, Bureau of Mines, Report of Investigations (R. I.) 3876, February 1946, p. 40.

40. Ibid., p. 41.

41. R. H. Ormston, "Liquefaction: The Answer to Storage?" *Gas Age,* February 25, 1954, p. 33.

42. K. Felkins, H. P. Keighly, Jr., and A. Jankovic, "The Royal Mail Ship Titanic: Did a Metallurgical Failure Cause a Night to Remember?" *JOM* 50.1 (1998): 12–18, http://www.tms.org/pubs/journals/jom/9801/felkins-9801.html; V. Bassett, "Causes and Effects of the Rapid Sinking of the Titanic," *Undergraduate Engineering Review,* 1998, http://www.writing.eng.vt.edu/uer/bassett.html.

43. Ibid.

44. T. N. Armstrong and A. P. Gagenebin, "Impact Properties of Some Low Alloy Nickel Steels at Temperatures Down to -200 Degrees Fahr.," *Transactions of the American Society for Metals* 28 (January–December 1940).

45. T. N. Armstrong and G. R. Brophy, "Some Properties of Low Carbon 8½ Per Cent Nickel Steel," in *Part I: Materials, Proceedings of the National Conference on Petroleum Mechanical Engineering,* (ASME, 1947), p. 3.

46. G. R. Brophy and A. J. Miller, *Steels and Structural Embodiments Thereof for Use at Low Temperatures,* U.S. Patent No. 2,451,469, filed August 2, 1946, and issued October 19, 1948.

47. Ibid.

48. Ibid.

49. T. N. Armstrong, "Impact Tests of Pressure Vessels at -320°F," *Welding Research, Welding Research Supplement,* January 1949, pp. 34s–38s.

50. W. S. "Nine Percent Nickel—28 Years of Reliable Service in Liquefied Natural Gas Containment," 2013, http://www.nickelinstitute.org/en/Technical Literature/Technical%20Series/NinePercentNickel_28YearsofReliableServiceinLNGContainment_10030_.aspx, p. 2.

51. United States Steel, *Low Temperature and Cryogenic Steels: Materials Manual,* 2nd revised printing (Pittsburgh: United States Steel Corporation, February 1967), p. 7.

52. P. B. Petty, "Metals for Service at Subzero Temperatures," *Chemical and Metallurgical Engineering,* June 1945, p. 103.

53. Ibid.

54. L. P. Zick, J. W. Crosett, and W. T. Lankford, "Nickel-Steel Tank Tests at Minus 320," *Mechanical Engineering,* July 1963.

55. Ibid.

56. *Cleveland Press,* "ALL NEW Gas Heating Installations PROHIBITED!" September 1947 (n.d.).

57. R. Seltzer, "Robinson Says Gas Supply to Improve by Late 1948," *Cleveland Press,* 1947 (n.d.).

58. "East Ohio Gets O.K. on 25,000 Gas Heat Units," *Cleveland Press,* April 7, 1949.

59. "Work Halted in Big Plant; Near Zero Due," *Cleveland Press,* March 1950 (n.d.).

60. *GAS Magazine,* "The Chicago Liquefaction and Storage Plan," October 1949, p. 92.

61. C. M. Sliepcevich, "Liquefied Natural Gas—A New Source of Energy, Part I, Ship Transportation," *American Scientist* 53.2 (June 1965): 266.

62. C. V. Spangler, "A Safer Way to Stockpile Natural Gas," *Gas,* May 1950, p. 62.

63. National Institute of Standards and Technology, "Cryogenics Technologies Group: About Cryo-

genics," 2013, http://cryogenics.nist.gov/AboutCryogenics/about%20cryogenics.htm.

64. Ibid.

65. *The New York Times*, "Liquid Air and Some of Its Uses," June 6, 1897.

66. National Institute of Standards and Technology, "Cryogenic Engineering," 2013, http://nvlpubs.nist.gov/nistpubs/sp958-lide/107-110.pdf.

67. Cryogenic Society of America, Inc., "History of Cryogenics," 2008, http://www.cryogenicsociety.org/resources/cryo_central/history_of_cryogenics.

68. NASA, *Liquid Hydrogen as a Propulsion Fuel, 1945–1959*, NASA SP-4404, http://history.nasa.gov/SP-4404/ch6-4.htm.

69. Perlite.info, "What Is Perlite?" 2011, http://www.perlite.info/hbk/0034409.htm; Perlite.info, "Early History," http://www.perlite.info/hbk/0031443.html.

70. O. North and A. Marks, "Perlite," *Bureau of Mines/Minerals Yearbook Metals and Minerals (Except Fuels) 1952*, vol. 1, 1955, http://images.library.wisc.edu/EcoNatRes/EFacs/0041/0001/XL/0798.gif, pp. 788–93.

71. Foamglas, "Foamglas® Insulation/ Production and Fabrication," 2013, http://www.foamglas.com/industry/en/products_product_information/production_fabrication; D. Rostoker, "Specialty Cellular Glass Products and Their Application," *Proceedings from the First Industrial Energy Technology Conference, Houston, TX, April 22–25, 1979*, http://repository.tamu.edu/bitstream/handle/1969.1/93794/ESL-IE-79-04-119.pdf?sequence=1, pp. 1021–1025.

72. Pittsburgh Corning, "A History of Innovation," 2013, http://pittsburghcorning.com/about-us/company-history.aspx.

73. Mark D. Butts, CB&I, email to author, September 17, 2012.

74. A. R. Young, "Liquefaction and Storage of Natural Gas for Peak Shaving," CEP-59-17, American Gas Association (AGA) Operating Section Conference, 1959, p. 191.

75. Mark D. Butts, CB&I, email to author, September 17, 2012.

76. Sliepcevich, "Liquefied Natural Gas," p. 267.

77. C. L. Kelly, "Liquefied Natural Gas, Part I," *Petroleum Times*, January 31, 1958, p. 84.

78. Ibid.

79. Ibid.

80. Ibid.

81. Ibid.

82. Sliepcevich, "Liquefied Natural Gas," p. 269.

83. Photo courtesy of American Merchant Marine at War, www.usmm.org.

84. Sliepcevich, "Liquefied Natural Gas," p. 277.

85. Kelly, "Liquefied Natural Gas," p. 85.

86. N. N. Taleb, *The Black Swan: The Impact of the Highly Improbable* (New York: Random House, 2010), p. xxii.

87. N. Silver, *The Signal and the Noise: Why So Many Predictions Fail but Some Don't* (New York: Penguin, 2012).

88. P. L. Bernstein, *Against the Gods: The Remarkable Story of Risk* (New York: John Wiley, 1998), p. 8.

89. Ibid., pp. 3, 63.

90. Ibid., p. 4.

91. H. Markowitz, "Portfolio selection," *Journal of Finance* 7.1 (March 1952).

92. Stanford University, "Von Neumann and the Development of Game Theory," 2013, http://www-cs-faculty.stanford.edu/~eroberts/courses/soco/projects/1998-99/game-theory/neumann.html.

93. NASA, *Probabilistic Risk Assessment Procedures Guide for NASA Managers and Practitioners*, NASA/SP-2011-3421, 2nd ed. (Washington, D.C.: December 2011), p. 1–1.

94. "Reactor Safety Study, Report WASH-1400, Nuclear Regulatory Commission, 1975," in NASA, *Probabilistic Risk Assessment*, p. 3–2.

95. NASA, *Probabilistic Risk Assessment*, p. 2–1.

Chapter 8

1. U.S. Energy Information Administration, "Total Energy: Annual Energy Review: Table 1.2: Primary Energy Production by Source, 1949–2010," 2012, http://www.eia.gov/totalenergy/data/annual/showtext.cfm?t=ptb0102.

2. U.S. Energy Information Administration, "History of Energy Consumption in the United States, 1775–2009," 2011, http://www.eia.gov/todayinenergy/detail.cfm?id=10#.

3. S. Reed, "The History of Oil Pipeline Regulation," Association of Oil Pipelines, September 17, 2009, http://www.ferc.gov/help/pub-ref-rm/history-oil-pipeline-regulation.pdf.

4. NaturalGas.org, "The History of Regulation," 2013, http://www.naturalgas.org/regulation/history.asp.

5. Ibid.

6. Ibid.

7. U.S. Energy Information Administration, "25th Anniversary of the 1973 Oil Embargo: Energy Trends Since the First Major U.S. Energy Crisis," http://www.eia.gov/pressroom/archive/speeches/25thann/sld008.htm.

8. NaturalGas.org, "History of Regulation."

9. U.S. Energy Information Administration, "25th Anniversary."

10. C. M. Sliepcevich, "Liquefied Natural Gas—A New Source of Energy, Part I, Ship Transportation," *American Scientist* 53.2 (June 1965): 277.

11. P. G. Noble, "A Short History of LNG Shipping 1959–2009," Texas Section–SNAME, February 10, 2009, http://higherlogicdownload.s3.amazonaws.com/SNAME/1dcdb863-8881-4263-af8d-530101f64412/UploadedFiles/c3352777fcaa4c4daa8f125c0a7c03e9.pdf.

12. *Oil and Gas Journal*, "Huge Growth Seen for Liquid Methane Both Here and Abroad," vol. 57.11 (March 9, 1959).

13. OilVoice, "Hassi R'Mel," 2013, http://www.oilvoice.com/well/Hassi_RMel/3c9efe40b2bb.aspx.

14. M. D. Tusiani and G. Shearer, *LNG: A Nontechnical Guide* (Tulsa: Pennwell Corporation, 2007), p. 14.

15. Sliepcevich, "Liquefied Natural Gas," p. 278.
16. Noble, "Short History"; H. A. McKinley, "The Prospects for Liquefied Natural Gas in the European Energy Market," Symposium on Petroleum Economics and Evaluation, February 8–9, 1965, Dallas, Texas, Society of Petroleum Engineers, OnePetro, http://www.onepetro.org/mslib/servlet/onepetropreview?id=00001108.
17. Sliepcevich, "Liquefied Natural Gas," p. 282; Tusiani and Shearer, *LNG*, p. 139.
18. A. R. Young, "Liquefaction and Storage of Natural Gas for Peak Shaving," CEP-59-17, American Gas Association (AGA) Operating Section Conference, 1959, p. 187.
19. P. B. Lederman and B. W. Williams, "Economics of Gas Liquefaction," *Gas Age*, November 14, 1957, p. 43.
20. Young, "Liquefaction and Storage," figs. 13 and 14.
21. *Cryogenic Engineering News*, "First Commercial LNG Plant On Stream," December 1965–January 1966, pp. 26–27.
22. C. M. Sliepcevich, "Liquefied Natural Gas—A New Source of Energy, Part II, Peak Load Shaving and Other Uses," *American Scientist* 53.3 (September 1965): 308; D. Hale, "$46,000,000 in LNG Projects Underway," *American Gas Journal*, August 1966, p. 30; U.S. Energy Information Administration, "LNG facilities," spreadsheet from the EIA (www.eia.gov) to author, September 14, 2012.
23. H. E. Vaughan, "Liquefied Natural Gas Projects Today," *Hydrocarbon Processing* 44.3 (March 1965): 136.
24. U.S. Energy Information Administration (EIA), "LNG facilities."
25. A. Gram, "LNG Enters Its Fourth Stage of Development," *Gas*, June 1967, p. 41.
26. CBI Industries, *The Bridge Works: A History of Chicago Bridge and Iron Company* (Chicago: Mobium, 1987), p. 201; U.S. Energy Information Administration (EIA), "LNG facilities."
27. Energy Information Administration, "U.S. LNG Markets and Uses: June 2004 Update," 2004, http://www.eia.gov/pub/oil_gas/natural_gas/feature_articles/2004/lng/lng2004.pdf.
28. U.S. Energy Information Administration, "U.S. Natural Gas LNG Storage Net Withdrawals," 2013, http://www.eia.gov/dnav/ng/hist/na1350_nus_2a.htm.
29. U.S. Energy Information Administration, "U.S. Natural Gas Imports and Exports 2011," 2012, http://www.eia.gov/naturalgas/importsexports/annual/.
30. U.S. Energy Information Administration, "Natural Gas, U.S. Dry Natural Gas Proved Reserves," 2013, http://www.eia.gov/dnav/ng/hist/rngr11nus_1a.htm.
31. U.S. Energy Information Administration, "25th Anniversary of the 1973 Oil Embargo."
32. Federal Energy Regulatory Commission, Office of Energy Projects, "North American LNG Import/Export Term: Existing," October 12, 2012, http://ferc.gov/industries/gas/indus-act/lng/LNG-existing.pdf; Federal Energy Regulatory Commission, "Existing FERC Jurisdictional LNG Import/Export Terminals," April 19, 2012, http://ferc.gov/industries/gas/indus-act/lng/exist-term/cameron.asp.
33. GDF SUEZ Energy North America, 2013, http://www.suezenergyna.com/ourcompanies/lngnadomac.shtml.
34. U.S. Energy Information Administration, "LNG Facilities."
35. Conoco-Phillips, "Kenai Liquefied Natural Gas Plant and North Cook Inlet Gas Field, Alaska," 2013, http://alaska.conocophillips.com/EN/news/media/Documents/FactSheet-KenaiLNGNorthCookInlet.pdf.
36. Dominion, "History of LNG," 2013, https://www.dom.com/business/gas-transmission/cove-point/history-of-lng.jsp.
37. Ibid.
38. M. M. Foss, "The Role of LNG in North American Natural Gas Supply and Demand," Center for Energy Economics, September 2004, http://www.beg.utexas.edu/energyecon/lng/documents/CEE_Role_of_LNG_in_Nat_Gas_Supply_Demand_Final.pdf, p. 21.
39. U.S. Energy Information Administration, "Total Energy: Annual Energy Review: Table 8.4a. Consumption for Electricity Generation by Energy Source: Total (All Sectors), 1949–2011," 2012, http://www.eia.gov/totalenergy/data/annual/index.cfm#electricity.
40. Foss, "Role of LNG," p. 26.
41. Dominion, "History of LNG."
42. International Gas Union, "World LNG Report 2010," 2010, http://www.igu.org/igu-publications/IGU%20World%20LNG%20Report%202010.pdf, p. 6.
43. Global LNG Info, "World's LNG Liquefaction Plants and Regasificaton Terminals," 2013, http://www.globallnginfo.com/World%20LNG%20Plants%20&%20Terminals.pdf.
44. International Gas Union, "World LNG Report 2010," p. 5.
45. Ibid., p. 8.
46. Noble, "Short History."
47. International Gas Union, "World LNG Report 2010," p. 30.
48. GlobalSecurity.org, "LNG Tanker History," 2013, http://www.globalsecurity.org/military/systems/ship/tanker-lng-history.htm.
49. International Gas Union, "World LNG Report 2010," p. 5.
50. BG Group, "The Global LNG Market—a Look Back and a Look Forward," 2013, http://www.bg-group.com/InvestorRelations/Presentations/Pages/Global-LNG-Market.aspx.
51. P. Wouter, "FLEXLNG: Developing the World's First Floating LNG Production Vessels," FPSO 2009 Conference, Oslo, Norway, 2013, http://intsok.com/style/downloads/Flex-L-PDF-Flex-LNG.pdf.
52. Marine Insight, "What Is a Floating Storage Regasification Unit (FSRU)?" 2013, http://www.marineinsight.com/marine/types-of-ships-marine/what-is-floating-storage-regasification-unit-fsru/.
53. Gram, "LNG," p. 43.
54. R. Petsinger, "LNG Serves Industry's Needs," *Oil and Gas Journal*, November 25, 1968, p. 142.

55. Bloomberg, "Trucks Run on Natural Gas in Pickens Clean Energy Drive: Freight," 2012, http://www.bloomberg.com/news/2012-02-29/trucks-run-on-natural-gas-in-pickens-clean-energy-drive.html; C. Helman, "Shell Investing $300M to Fuel LNG-Powered Trucks," *Forbes*, June 13, 2012, http://www.forbes.com/sites/christopherhelman/2012/06/13/shell-investing-300m-to-fuel-lng-powered-trucks/.

56. G. Warwick, "LNG Propulsion—A Cool Idea?" *Aviation Week*, March 19, 2012, http://www.aviationweek.com/Blogs.aspx?; Tupolev, "Cryogenic Aircraft: Development of Cryogenic Fuel Aircraft," 2013, http://www.tupolev.ru/english/Show.asp?SectionID=82.

57. Y. Torono, "LNG Propulsion System Flight Demonstration Project," Japanese Exploration Agency (JAXA), 2013, http://theknowledgeworld.com/world-of-aerospace/JAXA-Japan-Aerospace-Agency.htm.

58. Geology.com, "Shale," 2013, http://geology.com/rocks/shale.shtml.

59. R. Newell, "Shale Gas and the Outlook for U.S. Natural Gas Markets and Global Gas Resources," Organization for Economic Cooperation and Development, June 21, 2011, Paris, France, U.S. Energy Information Administration, p. 3.

60. ProPublica, "What Is Hydraulic Fracturing?" 2013, http://www.propublica.org/special/hydraulic-fracturing-national.

61. U.S. Energy Information Administration, "Shale Gas Production," 2013, http://www.eia.gov/dnav/ng/ng_prod_shalegas_s1_a.htm.

62. Newell, "Shale Gas," p. 9.

63. International Gas Union, "World LNG Report 2010," p. 20.

64. U.S. Energy Information Administration, "Annual Energy Output 2011 with Projections to 2035," 2010, http://www.eia.gov/oiaf/aeo/gas.html.

65. U.S. Energy Information Administration, "Annual Energy Outlook 2013: Natural Gas from Executive Summary," figure 2, "Total U.S. natural gas production, consumption, and net imports in the Reference case, 1990–2040 (trillion cubic feet)," 2013, http://www.eia.gov/forecasts/aeo/source_natural_gas_all.cfm.

66. P. Epler, "ConocoPhillips Shuttering Kenai LNG Plant," *Alaska Dispatch*, February 10, 2011, http://www.alaskadispatch.com/article/conocophillips-shuttering-kenai-lng-plant. Alaska Dispatch, "ConocoPhillips Resurrects Shipments of LNG from Alaska to Japan," June 14, 2012, http://www.alaskadispatch.com/article/conocophillips-resurrects-shipments-lng-alaska-japan, p. 21.

67. World LNG Report 2010, p. 21.

68. Newell, "Shale Gas," p. 25.

69. Ibid., p. 28.

70. "A Runaway Greenhouse Effect?" http://csep10.phys.utk.edu/astr161/lect/venus/greenhouse.html.

71. Newell, p. 21.

Selected Bibliography

Accum, F. *System of Theoretical and Practical Chemistry*. Volume 1. London: Printed for the author, 1803.
Alaska Dispatch. "ConocoPhillips Resurrects Shipments of LNG from Alaska to Japan." June 14, 2012. http://www.alaskadispatch.com/article/conocophillips-resurrects-shipments-lng-alaska-japan.
American Chemical Society. "The Development of the Pennsylvania Oil Industry." 2013. http://www.acs.org/content/acs/en/education/whatischemistry/landmarks/pennsylvaniaoilindustry.html.
_____. "The Gas That Wouldn't Burn." 2012. http://acswebcontent.acs.org/landmarks/landmarks/helium/thegas.html.
American Home Newspaper (Cleveland, Ohio). "A Neighborhood on Fire: Honey Vegel Submits Story on Tragedy." Special edition. October 1994.
American Home Publishing Company. "Gas Tanks Are Safe in Case of an Air Raid." *American Home*, July 28, 1942. Dominion East Ohio Gas Company Records, Box 129, Folder 5, YHC MSS 0164. Ohio Historical Society, Youngstown Historical Center of Industry and Labor.
American Society of Mechanical Engineers. *Addenda to ASME Boiler Construction Code, Unfired Pressure Vessel Code*. New York, August 31, 1936.
_____. *ASME Boiler Construction Code*. Section 8, Unfired Pressure Vessels. New York, 1937.
_____. *Rules for Construction of Unfired Pressure Vessels, Section VIII, ASME Boiler Construction Code*. New York, 1940.
Armstrong, T. N. "Impact Tests of Pressure Vessels at -320°F." *Welding Research, Welding Research Supplement*, January 1949.
Armstrong, T. N., and G. R. Brophy. "Some Properties of Low Carbon 8½ Per Cent Nickel Steel." In *Part I: Materials, Proceedings of the National Conference on Petroleum Mechanical Engineering*, ASME, 1947.
Armstrong, T. N., and A. P. Gagenebin. "Impact Properties of Some Low Alloy Nickel Steels at Temperatures Down to -200 Degrees Fahr." *Transactions of the American Society for Metals* 28 (January–December 1940).
Automotive Engineer. "Nicolaus Otto Developed the Four-Stroke Combustion Engine." 2010. http://ae-plus.com/milestones/nicolaus-otto-developed-the-four-stroke-combustion-engine.
Barnes, G. E., M. M. Braidech, and K. H. Donaldson. *Report of the Technical Consultants Board of Inquiry for the Mayor of Cleveland on the East Ohio Gas Company Fire*. Cleveland, Ohio, July 1945. Case Western Reserve University Archives.
Bassett, V. "Causes and Effects of the Rapid Sinking of the Titanic." *Undergraduate Engineering Review*. 1998. http://www.writing.eng.vt.edu/uer/bassett.html.
Before the Mayor's Board of Inquiry East Ohio Gas Company Fire: Transcript of Testimony and Proceedings Taken at Investigation of East Ohio Gas Company Fire. Transcript of the East Ohio Gas Company Explosion 1944. Ohio Historical Society State Archives 1600.
Bernstein, P. L. *Against the Gods: The Remarkable Story of Risk*. New York: John Wiley, 1998.
BG Group. "The Global LNG Market—A Look Back and a Look Forward." 2013. http://www.bg-group.com/InvestorRelations/Presentations/Pages/Global-LNG-Market.aspx.
Bloomberg. "Trucks Run on Natural Gas in Pickens Clean Energy Drive: Freight." 2012. http://www.bloomberg.com/news/2012-02-29/trucks-run-on-natural-gas-in-pickens-clean-energy-drive.html.
Bownocker, J. A. "Depletion of Natural Gas in the Appalachian Fields." Presented at the annual meeting of the Natural Gas Association of America, Cleveland, Ohio, May 20–21, 1919.
Boyle, B. E. "The Lessons of Tragedy: The East Ohio Gas Company Fire." *Timeline* (Ohio Historical Society, Columbus, Ohio) 12.5 (September–October 1995).

Braidech, M. "Cleveland, the Center of the Natural Gas Industry." *Chemical and Engineering News* 22.5 (March 10, 1944).

Brearley, H. C. *The History of the National Board of Fire Underwriters: Fifty Years of a Civilizing Force.* New York: Frederick A. Stokes, 1916.

Brief for the Appellant, Florence V. Foley v. Pittsburgh–Des Moines Company. Supreme Court of Pennsylvania, No. 83, March Term, 1949. Marvin Clinton Harrison Papers (MS 3799), Container 19, Folder 412. Western Reserve Historical Society, Cleveland, Ohio.

Brignano, M., and H. McCullough. *The Spirit of Progress: The Story of the East Ohio Gas Company and the People Who Made It.* Cleveland: East Ohio Gas Company, 1988.

Brophy, G. R., and A. J. Miller. *Steels and Structural Embodiments Thereof for Use at Low Temperatures.* U.S. Patent No. 2,451,469, filed August 2, 1946, and issued October 19, 1948.

Brush, S. G. "History of the Kinetic Theory of Gases." 2003. http://punsterproductions.com/~sciencehistory/pdf/ITALENC.pdf.

Burruss, R. C., and R. T. Ryder. "Composition of Crude Oil and Natural Gas Produced from 14 Wells in the Lower Silurian 'Clinton' Sandstone and Medina Group, Northeastern Ohio and Northwestern Pennsylvania." Open-File Report 03-409 (Preliminary), U.S. Geological Survey, Reston, Virginia, [2003].

Cabot, G. L. *Means for Handling and Transporting Liquid Gas.* U.S. Patent No. 1,140,250, filed October 12, 1914, and issued May 18, 1915.

Cabot, G. L., and J. J. Cabot. *Apparatus for Condensing Gas Under High Pressure.* U.S. Patent No. 1,225,574, filed October 26, 1914, and issued May 8, 1917.

California Historical Society Digital Archives/USC California Digital Archive (2004). Retrieved from: http://digitallibrary.usc.edu/cdm/singleitem/collection/p15799coll65/id/3767/rec/23.

Castaneda, C. *Invisible Fuel: Manufactured and Natural Gas in America, 1800–2000.* New York: Twayne, 1999.

Catholic University of America. "Robert Boyle." http://faculty.cua.edu/may/Boyle.pdf.

CBI Industries. *The Bridge Works: A History of Chicago Bridge and Iron Company.* Chicago: Mobium, 1987.

Center for Energy Economics. "LNG Safety and Security." November 2006. http://www.beg.utexas.edu/energyecon/lng/documents/CEE_LNG_Safety_and_Security.pdf.

Chief of Division, Ohio Department of Industrial Relations, Division of Boiler Inspection. Letter to Dr. S. R. Gerber, Coroner of Cuyahoga County, Cleveland Ohio, December 27, 1944. Dominion East Ohio Gas Company Records, Box 132, Folder 15, YHC MSS 0164. Ohio Historical Society, Youngstown Historical Center of Industry and Labor.

Choudhury, B. K. *Process Design of Turboexpander Based Nitrogen Liquefier.* Master's Thesis, Department of Mechanical Engineering, National Institute of Technology, Rourkela, India, 2009.

Christopoulou, C. "Robert Boyle's Experiments on Cold: A Study of the Role of Chemical Experiments." The 6th International Conference on the History of Chemistry, August 28–September 1, 2007. http://www.euchems.eu/fileadmin/user_upload/binaries/49_Christopoulou_tcm23-139407.pdf.

Clark, J., and R. Miller. "Liquefaction, Storage, and Regasification of Natural Gas." *American Gas Journal,* November 1940.

———. "Liquefaction, Storage, and Regasification of Natural Gas." *Oil and Gas Journal, Engineering and Operating Section,* October 17, 1940.

Clark, J. A. "Progress Report on Liquefaction, Storage and Regasification of Natural Gas." *Gas Age,* May 22, 1941.

Classical Library. "Francis Bacon 1561–1626." 2013. http://www.classicallibrary.org/bacon/index.htm.

Cleveland Plain Dealer. "Gas Tanks Exploded on Oct. 20, 1944." October 16, 1994. Cleveland, Ohio.

Cleveland Press. "ALL NEW Gas Heating Installations PROHIBITED!" September 1947 (n.d.). Cleveland, Ohio. Cleveland Press Collection, Special Collections, Michael Schwartz Library, Cleveland State University.

———. "Cites E. Ohio, City, State in Gas Blast." July 24, 1945. Cleveland, Ohio. Cleveland Press Collection, Special Collections, Michael Schwartz Library, Cleveland State University.

———. "East Ohio Gets O.K. on 25,000 Gas Heat Units." April 7, 1949.

———. "Work Halted in Big Plant; Near Zero Due." March 1950 (n.d.).

Cline, B. "The History of Kerosene." *History Magazine.* August/September 2007. http://www.bevcline.com/kerosene.pdf.

Code of Federal Regulations (CFR) Title 49—Transportation, Part 193—Liquefied Natural Gas Facilities: Federal Safety Standards (DOT 49-CFR-193). October 1, 1996, ed.

Columbia Gas and Electric Corporation. *The Story of Natural Gas.* Prepared as a textbook for the Public Schools of West Virginia. 1927. Dominion East Ohio Gas Company Records, Box 159, Folder 26, p. 3, YHC MSS 0164. Ohio Historical Society, Youngstown Historical Center of Industry and Labor.

Conoco-Phillips. "Kenai Liquefied Natural Gas Plant and North Cook Inlet Gas Field, Alaska." 2013. http://alaska.conocophillips.com/EN/news/media/Documents/FactSheet-KenaiLNGNorthCookInlet.pdf.

Cotton Times. "Understanding the Industrial Revolution." 2013. http://www.cottontimes.co.uk/timeline1.html.

Cryogenic Engineering News. "First Commercial LNG Plant On Stream." December 1965–January 1966.

Cryogenic Society of America, Inc. "History of Cryogenics." 2008. http://www.cryogenicsociety.org/resources/cryo_central/history_of_cryogenics.

Department of the Environment (UK). "Gas Works, Coke Works and Other Coal Carbonization Plants." Department of the Environment Industry Profile, sponsored by Contaminated Land and Liabilities Division. 1995. http://enfo.agt.bme.hu/drupal/sites/default/files/SCHO0195BJKP-e-e_0.pdf.

Dominion. *From Gas Lights to New Energy Heights.* 1998. http://www.dom.com/about/pdf/hngc_history.pdf.

———. *History of Hope Natural Gas Company.* N.p., c. 1964.

———. "History of LNG." 2013. https://www.dom.com/business/gas-transmission/cove-point/history-of-lng.jsp.

Economic History Association. "An Overview of the Great Depression." February 5, 2010. http://eh.net/?s=An+Overview+of+the+Great+Depression.

The Economist. "Value of Helium Gas for War Balloons Is Revealed by the Navy Department: Had Been Camouflaged as 'Argon.'" Vol. 61 (January 4, 1919).

Elliot, J. R., and C. T. Lira. *Introductory Chemical Engineering Thermodynamics.* New Jersey: Prentice Hall, 1998.

Elliott, M. A., C. W. Seibel, F. W. Brown, R. T. Artz, and L. B. Berger. *Report on the Investigation of the Fire at the Liquefaction, Storage, and Regasification Plant of the East Ohio Gas Co., Cleveland Ohio, October 20, 1944.* United States Department of the Interior, Bureau of Mines, Report of Investigations (R. I.) 3876. February 1946.

Encyclopedia of Cleveland History. "BP America—The Encyclopedia of Cleveland History." 2013. http://ech.case.edu/cgi/article.pl?id=BA.

———. "Cleaveland, Moses—The Encyclopedia of Cleveland History." 2000. http://ech.case.edu/ech-cgi/article.pl?id=CM10.

———. "East Ohio Gas Co.—The Encyclopedia of Cleveland History." 2004. http://ech.case.edu/cgi/article.pl?id=EOGC.

———. "The History of Cleveland History Timeline." 2013. http://ech.cwru.edu/timeline.html.

Engineering Toolbox. "Fuel Gases—Heating Values." 2013. http://www.engineeringtoolbox.com/heating-values-fuel-gases-d_823.html.

———. "Fuels—Higher Calorific Values." 2013. http://www.engineeringtoolbox.com/fuels-higher-calorific-values-d_169.html.

———. "Gaseous Fuels and Chemical Compositions." 2013. http://www.engineeringtoolbox.com/chemical-composition-gaseous-fuels-d_1142.html.

Epler, Patti. "ConocoPhillips shuttering Kenai LNG plant." Alaska Dispatch, February 10, 2011. http://www.alaskadispatch.com/article/conocophillips-shuttering-kenai-lng-plant.

Faraday, M. "Liquefaction of Gases: On Fluid Chlorine." Excerpts from papers by Michael Faraday, F.R.S. Transactions of the Royal Society of London, read March 13, 1823. 2003. http://campus.udayton.edu/~hume/Faraday/faraday3.htm.

Faraday, M., F.R.S. *The Liquefaction of Gases: Papers by Michael Faraday, F.R.S. (1823–1845).* Alembic Club Reprints No. 12. Edinburgh: William F. Clay; London: Simkin Marshal, Hamilton, Kent, 1896.

Federal Energy Regulatory Commission, Office of Energy Projects. "North American LNG Import/Export Term: Existing." October 12, 2012. http://ferc.gov/industries/gas/indus-act/lng/LNG-existing.pdf.

Felkins, K., H. P. Keighly Jr., and A. Jankovic. "The Royal Mail Ship Titanic: Did a Metallurgical Failure Cause a Night to Remember?" *JOM* 50.1 (1998): 12–18. http://www.tms.org/pubs/journals/jom/9801/felkins-9801.html.

Ferris, T. *The Science of Liberty: Democracy, Reason, and the Laws of Nature.* New York: Harper, 2010.

"Fifty Years of Service: Commemorating a Half Century of East Ohio's Contribution to Better Living." 1948. Dominion East Ohio Gas Company Records, YHC MSS 0164, Ohio Historical Society, Youngstown Historical Center of Industry and Labor.

Fitzgerald, H. H. "Clearance Standards for LNG Storage." In *American Gas Association Operating Section Conference, 1962,* CEP-62–6.

Foamglas. "Foamglas® Insulation/ Production and Fabrication." 2013. http://www.foamglas.com/industry/en/products_product_information/production_fabrication.

Ford Model T. "Production." 2013. http://web.bryant.edu/~ehu/h364proj/fall_98/coppola/production.html.

Foss, M. M. "The Role of LNG in North American Natural Gas Supply and Demand." Center for Energy Economics. September 2004. http://www.beg.utexas.edu/energyecon/lng/documents/CEE_Role_of_LNG_in_Nat_Gas_Supply_Demand_Final.pdf.

Fowler, M. "Kinetic Theory of Gases: A Brief Review." Modern Physics. 2008. http://galileo.phys.virginia.edu/classes/252/kinetic_theory.html.

Gannon, M. *Operation Drumbeat: The Dramatic True Story of Germany's First U-Boat Attacks Along the American Coast in World War II.* New York: Harper and Row, 1990.

GAS Magazine. "The Chicago Liquefaction and Storage Plan." October 1949.

GDF SUEZ Energy North America. "Our Companies" 2013. http://www.suezenergyna.com/ourcompanies/lngna-domac.shtml.

Gensamer, M. *Metallurgy of the Cleveland Liquefied Gas Tank Failure, Report of the Technical Consultant to the East*

Ohio Gas Co., January 15, 1945. Referenced as Case 16 in "A Critical Survey of Brittle Failure in Carbon Plate Steel Structures Other Than Ships," by M. E. Shank, in *Symposium on the Effect of Temperature on the Brittle Behavior of Metals with Particular Reference to Low Temperatures*, ed. A. L. Tarr. Philadelphia: American Society for Testing Materials, 1954.

Geology.com. "Shale." 2013. http://geology.com/rocks/shale.shtml.

Gerber, S. R. *Coroner's Report on East Ohio Gas Company Disaster, October 20, 1944*. Cuyahoga County, Cleveland Ohio, July 1945.

Gerdel, T. "130 Were Killed in Cleveland Holocaust 20 Years Ago." *Cleveland Plain Dealer,* October 19, 1964, Cleveland, Ohio. Cleveland Plain Dealer Historical Archives. http://www.NewsLibrary.com.

Girod, J. Z. "Disaster as Seen Through the Eyes of Justine Girod." *Ameriska Dominivia (American Home) Anniversary Edition* (Cleveland, Ohio), September 1987.

Global LNG Info. "World's LNG Liquefaction Plants and Regasificaton Terminals." 2013. http://www.global lnginfo.com/World%20LNG%20Plants%20&%20Terminals.pdf.

GlobalSecurity.org. "LNG Tanker History." 2013. http://www.globalsecurity.org/military/systems/ship/tanker-lng-history.htm.

Gould, J. M. *Output and Productivity in the Electric and Gas Utilities, 1899–1942*. Part 2: "Manufactured and Natural Gas." National Bureau of Economic Research (NBER). 1946. http://papers.nber.org/books/goul46-1.

Gram, A. "LNG Enters Its Fourth Stage of Development." *GAS,* June 1967.

Greene, A. M., Jr. *History of the ASME Boiler Code*. New York: American Society of Mechanical Engineers, 1953.

Hale, D. "$46,000,000 in LNG Projects Underway." *American Gas Journal,* August 1966.

Hamilton, J. *A Life of Discovery: Michael Faraday, Giant of the Scientific Revolution*. New York: Random House, 2002.

Hammer, L. "Letter Hints of Gas Blast." *Cleveland Press,* October 20, 1949. Cleveland Press Collection, Special Collections, Michael Schwartz Library, Cleveland State University.

Hardin, W. L. *The Rise and Development of the Liquefaction of Gases*. New York: Macmillan, 1899.

Hatheway, A. "History and Chronology of Manufactured Gas Plants." Former Manufactured Gas Plants. 2012. http://www.hatheway.net/history.htm.

Haynes, P. E. "Liquefaction and the Fuel-Gas Industry." *Gas Age,* May 8, 1941.

Helman, C. "Shell Investing $300M to Fuel LNG-Powered Trucks." Forbes. June 13, 2012. http://www.forbes.com/sites/christopherhelman/2012/06/13/shell-investing-300m-to-fuel-lng-powered-trucks/.

Heritage Research Center, Ltd. "Manufactured Gas—The Genie's Legacy." 2013. http://www.heritageresearch.com/ourlibrary/histories/manufactured_gas.html.

———. "What Is Manufactured Gas?" 2012. http://www.heritageresearch.com/documents/More%20About%20Manufactured%20Gas.pdf.

Hidy, R. W., and M. E. Hidy. *Pioneering in Big Business 1882–1911*. New York: Harper, 1955.

"History of the East Ohio Gas Company." September 1953. Dominion East Ohio Gas Company Records, YHC MSS 0164, Ohio Historical Society, Youngstown Historical Center of Industry and Labor.

Holmes, R. *The Age of Wonder*. New York: Vintage, 2010.

Hope Natural Gas Company. Letter to J. French Robinson, president of East Ohio Gas Company, October 30, 1944. Folder 9, Dominion East Ohio Gas Company Records, YHC MSS 0164. Ohio Historical Society, Youngstown Historical Center of Industry and Labor.

Howard, W. V. "Experiment with Liquefied Natural Gas Storage." *Oil and Gas Journal,* May 9, 1940.

Hrastar, T. *The Gilded Age—1865–1900*. Lecture Notes. The Growth of Modern America Series. N.p., 2012.

Hubpages. "What Is Absolute Zero?" 2013. http://kirstenblog.hubpages.com/hub/What-is-Absolute-zero.

Huppi.com. "Timelines of the Great Depression." 2013. http://www.huppi.com/kangaroo/Timeline.htm.

Hurlich, A. "Low Temperature Metal." *Chemical Engineering,* November 25, 1963.

Innovateus. "What Is Ethane?" 2013. http://www.innovateus.net/science/what-ethane.

Inter-American Corporation. "Helium Processing History." 2012. http://www.helium-corp.com/processing/history.

International Gas Union. "World LNG Report 2010." 2010. http://www.igu.org/igu-publications/IGU%20World%20LNG%20Report%202010.pdf.

Iowa Department of Public Safety. "History of Fire and Fire Codes." 2013. http://www.dps.state.ia.us/fm/inspection/history/History_of_Fire_and_Fire_Codes.pdf.

Jackson, J. O. "Liquefied-Gas-Storage Containers." *Gas Age,* April 22, 1943.

———. *Method and Apparatus for Storing Gaseous Materials in the Liquid State*. U.S. Patent No. 2,328,647, filed August 6, 1941, issued September 7, 1943.

———. Pittsburgh Des Moines Steel Company. Letter to W. G. Hagan, East Ohio Gas Company, July 3, 1944. Dominion East Ohio Gas Company Records, Box 130, Folder 9, YHC MSS 0164. Ohio Historical Society, Youngstown Historical Center of Industry and Labor.

———. "Welded Liquefied Natural Gas Storage Tanks." *Welding Journal* 20.12 (December 1941).

_____. *Welded Steel Structure*. U.S. Patent No. 2,337,049, filed January 6, 1942, issued December 21, 1943.
Jackson, J. O., and H. C. Cooper. *Low Temperature Storage Tank*. U.S. Patent No. 2,329, 765, filed November 12, 1941, issued September 21, 1943.
Jefferson Lab. "The Element Helium." 2012. http://education.jlab.org/itselemental/ele002.html.
Justia U.S. Law. "183 F.2d 467: Moran, v. Pittsburgh-des Moines Steel Co. et al." 2013. http://law.justia.com/cases/federal/appellate-courts/F2/183/467/266790/.
Kelly, C. I. "Liquefied Natural Gas, Part I." *Petroleum Times*, January 31, 1958.
Kelso, J. R. *The Spirit of Progress: The Story of the East Ohio Gas Company and the People Who Made It*. A speech to the Newcomen Society of Cleveland, Ohio, November 3, 1988. Newcomen Publication 1317. New York: Newcomen Society of the United States, 1988.
Leagle. *Foley v. The Pittsburgh-Des Moines Co*. 2013. http://www.leagle.com/xmlResult.aspx?xmldoc=1949364 363Pa1_1364.xml&docbase=CSLWAR1-1950-1985.
Lederman, P. B., and B. W. Williams. "Economics of Gas Liquefaction." *Gas Age*, November 14, 1957.
Le Moyne College. "Joseph Black (1728–1799)." Excerpted by William Francis Magie, *A Source Book in Physics* (New York: McGraw-Hill, 1935). 2013. http://web.lemoyne.edu/~giunta/blackheat.html.
Leong, Y. H. "The Birth of a Code: ASME Boiler and Pressure Vessel Code." Pressure Systems Interest Group. 2010. http://www.psig.sg/Birth%20of%20a%20Code.html.
Library of Congress. "The Life of Thomas A. Edison." 2013. http://memory.loc.gov/ammem/edhtml/edbio.html.
Linde Group. "Cryogenic Air Separation–History and Technological Progress." 2013. http://www.linde-le.de/process_plants/air_separation_plants/documents/L_2_1_e_09_150dpi.pdf.
LPGA Times. "The First Fifty Years of LP-Gas: An Industry Chronology. Chapter 1: The Dream of LP-Gas Becomes Reality." January 1962, pp. 16–28.
_____. "The First Fifty Years of LP-Gas: An Industry Chronology. Chapter 3: The Years of Slow Growth." March 1962, pp. 21–23.
Marine Insight. "What Is a Floating Storage Regasification Unit (FSRU)?" 2013. http://www.marineinsight.com/marine/types-of-ships-marine/what-is-floating-storage-regasification-unit-fsru/.
Markowitz, H. "Portfolio Selection." *Journal of Finance* 7.1 (March 1952).
McKinley, H. A. "The Prospects for Liquefied Natural Gas in the European Energy Market." Symposium on Petroleum Economics and Evaluation, February 8–9, 1965, Dallas, Texas, Society of Petroleum Engineers. OnePetro. http://www.onepetro.org/mslib/servlet/onepetropreview?id=00001108.
Mounce, W. S. "Nine Percent Nickel—28 Years of Reliable Service in Liquefied Natural Gas Containment." 2013. http://www.nickelinstitute.org/en/TechnicalLiterature/Technical%20Series/NinePercentNickel_28Yearsof ReliableServiceinLNGContainment_10030_.aspx.
National Academies Press. "1. Chemical composition of Petroleum Hydrocarbon Sources." 2013. http://www.nap.edu/openbook.php?record_id=314&page=17.
National Aeronautics and Space Administration (NASA). *Liquid Hydrogen as a Propulsion Fuel, 1945–1959*. NASA SP-4404. 2013. http://history.nasa.gov/SP-4404/ch6-4.htm.
_____. *NASA Systems Engineering Handbook (2007)*. NASA/SP-2007-6105, Rev 1. Washington, D.C.: NASA, 2007.
_____. *Probabilistic Risk Assessment Procedures Guide for NASA Managers and Practitioners*. NASA/SP-2011-3421. 2nd ed. Washington, D.C.: NASA, December 2011.
National Board of Fire Underwriters. "Standard of the National Board of Fire Underwriters for the Storage and Handling of Liquefied Petroleum Gases at Utility Gas Plants." Pamphlet NBFU No. 59, July 1954.
National Fire Protection Association. "History: Birth of the NFPA." 1996. http://www.nfpa.org/itemDetail.asp?categoryID=500&itemID=18020&URL=About%20NFPA/Overview/History&cookie%5Ftest=1.
_____. *National Fire Codes for Flammable Liquids, Gases, Chemicals and Explosives*. Boston: National Fire Protection Association, 1943.
_____. "Standard for the Production Storage and Handling of Liquefied Natural Gas (LNG)." NFPA 59A. Quincy, Massachusetts: National Fire Protection Association, 2009.
National Institute of Standards and Technology. "Cryogenic Engineering." 2013. http://nvlpubs.nist.gov/nistpubs/sp958-lide/107–110.pdf.
_____. "Cryogenics Technologies Group: About Cryogenics." 2013. http://cryogenics.nist.gov/AboutCryogenics/about%20cryogenics.htm.
NaturalGas.org. "Background." 2012. http://naturalgas.org/overview/background.asp.
_____. "The History of Regulation." 2013. http://www.naturalgas.org/regulation/history.asp.
Neenah Wisconsin. "History of Building Codes." 2013. http://www.ci.neenah.wi.us/assets/files/inspections/BuildingCodeHistory.pdf.
Nelson, P. L. *Inferno on the East Side: The Incident Revisited, a Half Century Later*. Cleveland, Ohio: Western Reserve Fire Museum, 1997.
New York Times. "Liquid Air and Some of Its Uses." June 6, 1897.

Newell, R. "Shale Gas and the Outlook for U.S. Natural Gas Markets and Global Gas Resources." Organization for Economic Cooperation and Development. June 21, 2011, Paris, France. U.S. Energy Information Administration.
NNDB. "Evangelista Torricelli." 2013. http://www.nndb.com/people/605/000087344/.
———. "Jan Baptist van Helmont." 2013. http://www.nndb.com/people/852/000103543/.
———. "Karl von Linde." 2013. http://www.nndb.com/people/861/000268057/.
Noble, P. G. "A Short History of LNG Shipping 1959–2009." Texas Section—SNAME. February 10, 2009, http://higherlogicdownload.s3.amazonaws.com/SNAME/1dcdb863-8881-4263-af8d-530101f64412/UploadedFiles/c3352777fcaa4c4daa8f125c0a7c03e9.pdf.
North, O., and A. Marks. "Perlite." *Bureau of Mines/Minerals Yearbook Metals and Minerals (Except Fuels) 1952*. Vol. 1. 1955. http://images.library.wisc.edu/EcoNatRes/EFacs/0041/0001/XL/0798.gif.
Ohio Historical Society. "The Dominion East Ohio Gas Company: History of the Dominion East Ohio Gas Company." 2005. http://www.ohiohistory.org/resource/archlib/dominion/history.html.
Oil and Gas Journal. "Huge Growth Seen for Liquid Methane Both Here and Abroad." Vol. 57.11 (March 9, 1959).
OilVoice. "Hassi R'Mel." 2013. http://www.oilvoice.com/well/Hassi_RMel/3c9efe40b2bb.aspx.
Ormston, R. H. "Liquefaction: The Answer to Storage?" *Gas Age*, February 25, 1954.
Peebles, M. W. H. *Evolution of the Gas Industry*. New York: New York University Press, 1980.
Perlite.info. "Early History." http://www.perlite.info/hbk/0031443.html.
———. "What Is Perlite?" 2011. http://www.perlite.info/hbk/0034409.htm.
Perry, J. M. "Some Data on Railroads." 2013. http://cprr.org/Museum/Railroad_Statistics.pdf.
Petsinger, R. "LNG Serves Industry's Needs." *Oil and Gas Journal*, November 25, 1968.
Petty, P. B. "Metals for Service at Subzero Temperatures." *Chemical and Metallurgical Engineering*, June 1945.
Pittsburgh Corning. "A History of Innovation." 2013. http://pittsburghcorning.com/about-us/company-history.aspx.
ProPublica. "What Is Hydraulic Fracturing?" 2013. http://www.propublica.org/special/hydraulic-fracturing-national.
Purdue University. "Gases, Liquids, and Solids." 2013. http://www.chem.purdue.edu/gchelp/liquids/character.html.
Reed, S. "The History of Oil Pipeline Regulation." Association of Oil Pipelines. September 17, 2009. http://www.ferc.gov/help/pub-ref-rm/history-oil-pipeline-regulation.pdf.
Richardson, E. "History Lessons: Gas Holders." *Blogdowntown*. Southern California Public Radio. November 21, 2006. http://blogdowntown.com/2006/11/2417-history-lesson-gas-holders.
Robertson, D. *The Greatest Thing Since Sliced Bread*. New York: Harper, 2008.
Robinson, J. R. "The Storage of Natural Gas." *Gas Age*, February 10, 1944.
Rosen, W. *The Most Powerful Idea in the World*. New York: Random House, 2010.
Rosenberg, S. J., and D. H. Gagon. *Effect of Grain Size and Heat Treatment upon Impact-Toughness at Low Temperatures of Medium Carbon Forging Steel*. National Bureau of Standards, Research Paper RP1410, August 1941. http://nvlpubs.nist.gov/nistpubs/jres/27/jresv27n2p159_A1b.pdf.
Rostoker, D. "Specialty Cellular Glass Products and Their Applications." *Proceedings from the First Industrial Energy Technology Conference, Houston, TX, April 22–25, 1979*. http://repository.tamu.edu/bitstream/handle/1969.1/93794/ESL-IE-79-04-119.pdf?sequence=1.
Safety Emporium. "Flash Point Definition." 2013. http://www.ilpi.com/msds/ref/flashpoint.html.
Saybolt, G. M. *Obtaining Naphtha from Natural Gas*. U.S. Patent No. 989,927, filed September 1, 1906, issued April 18, 1911.
Science Daily. "Superheating." 2013. http://www.sciencedaily.com/articles/s/superheating.htm.
Sears, F. W., and M. W. Zemansky. *College Physics: Mechanics, Heat, and Sound*. Cambridge, MA: Addison-Wesley, 1952.
Seltzer, R. "Robinson Says Gas Supply to Improve by Late 1948." *Cleveland Press*, 1947 (n.d., n.p.). Cleveland Press Collection, Special Collections, Michael Schwartz Library, Cleveland State University.
Sham, R., T. Jindal, and B. Pabla. "Cryogenic Processes—A Review." *International Journal of Engineering Science and Technology (IJEST)* 3.1 (January 2011).
Siewert, T. A., M. P. Manahan, C. N. McCowan, J. M. Holt, F. J. Marsh, and E. A. Ruth. "The History and Importance of Impact Testing, May 1, 2002." 2002. http://www.nist.gov/manuscript-publication-search.cfm?pub_id=851287.
Silver, N. *The Signal and the Noise: Why So Many Predictions Fail but Some Don't*. New York: Penguin, 2012.
Silverman, A. "34 Dead, Scores Missing, 10,000 Driven Out in Blast." *Cleveland Plain Dealer*, October 21, 1944, p. 1.
Sliepcevich, C. M. "Liquefied Natural Gas—A New Source of Energy, Part I, Ship Transportation." *American Scientist* 53.2 (June 1965).
———. "Liquefied Natural Gas—A New Source of Energy, Part II, Peak Load Shaving and Other Uses." *American Scientist* 53.3 (September 1965).
Sloane, T. O. *Liquid Air and the Liquefaction of Gases*. 1899. Reprint, Bradley, IL: Lindsay, 1988.

Small, J. "He Stands Alone—He Flinches—His Family Three Charred Bodies." Unknown Cleveland newspaper (*The Cleveland News, The Cleveland Press,* or *The Plain Dealer*) and date (week or weeks after the fire).
Spangler, C. V. "A Safer Way to Stockpile Natural Gas." *Gas,* May 1950.
Stanford University. "Von Neumann and the Development of Game Theory." 2013. http://www-cs-faculty.stanford.edu/~eroberts/courses/soco/projects/1998-99/game-theory/neumann.html.
Steinwedell, W. E. "Liquefaction, Storage, and Regasification of Natural Gas for Peak Loads." *American Gas Journal* 158.1 (January 1943).
Stotz, L., and A. Jamison. *History of the Gas Industry.* New York: Stettiner, 1938.
Strazar, A. Cimperman. "Memories That Will Remain Forever." *Ameriska Dominivia (American Home)* Anniversary Edition, September 1987. Cleveland, Ohio.
Tabler, D. "The World's Largest Carbon Factory." Appalachian History. April 30, 2010. http://www.appalachianhistory.net/2010/04/worlds-largest-carbon-factory.html.
Taleb, N. N. *The Black Swan: The Impact of the Highly Improbable.* New York: Random House, 2010.
Teachers College, Columbia University. "Reform of NYC Public Schools, 1896." http://www.tc.edu/faculty/waite/teach/texts/txt01.htm.
Thomas A. Burke Papers. Western Reserve Historical Society, Cleveland, Ohio.
Thomson, T. *A System of Chemistry in Four Volumes.* Vol. 2. Edinburgh: Printed for Bell and Bradfute, and E. Balfour; London: G. and J. Robinson, 1802.
Thomson, W. (Lord Kelvin). *Mathematical and Physical Papers: Collected from Different Scientific Periodicals from May, 1841, to the Present Time.* Vol. 1. Cambridge University Press, 1882.
_____. "On an Absolute Thermometric Scale." *Philosophical Magazine,* October 1848, pp. 100–106. In *Mathematical and Physical Papers,* ed. Sir William Thomson, vol. 1. Cambridge University Press, 1882.
Torono, Y. "LNG Propulsion System Flight Demonstration Project." Japanese Exploration Agency (JAXA). 2013. http://theknowledgeworld.com/world-of-aerospace/JAXA-Japan-Aerospace-Agency.htm.
Tupolev. "Cryogenic Aircraft: Development of Cryogenic Fuel Aircraft." 2013. http://www.tupolev.ru/english/Show.asp?SectionID=82.
Tusiani, M. D., and G. Shearer. *LNG: A Nontechnical Guide.* Tulsa, OK: Pennwell Corporation, 2007.
Tussing, A. R., and C. C. Barlow. *The Natural Gas Industry: Evolution, Structure, and Economics.* Cambridge, MA: Ballinger, 1984.
Twomey, L. S. *Method of Liquefying and Storing Fuel Gases.* U.S. Patent No. 2,082,189, filed May 9, 1934, issued June 1, 1937.
United States Census Bureau. Census of Population and Housing. 1860 U.S. Census and 1900 U.S. Census.
_____. Census of Population and Housing. U.S. Census Data from the Fifth Census (1830) and the Sixth Census (1840).
United States Energy Information Administration. "Annual Energy Output 2011 with Projections to 2035." 2010. http://www.eia.gov/oiaf/aeo/gas.html.
_____. "Annual Energy Outlook 2013: Natural Gas from Executive Summary." 2013. http://www.eia.gov/forecasts/aeo/source_natural_gas_all.cfm.
_____. "History of Energy Consumption in the United States, 1635–1945." 2013. http://www.eia.gov/totalenergy/data/annual/index.cfm#appendices.
_____. "History of Energy Consumption in the United States, 1775–2009." 2011. http://www.eia.gov/todayinenergy/detail.cfm?id=10#.
_____. "Natural Gas Compressor Stations on the Interstate Pipeline Network: Developments Since 1996." Energy Information Administration, Office of Oil and Gas. November 2007. http://www.eia.gov/pub/oil_gas/natural_gas/analysis_publications/ngcompressor/ngcompressor.pdf.
_____. "Natural Gas, U.S. Dry Natural Gas Proved Reserves." 2013. http://www.eia.gov/dnav/ng/hist/rngr11nus_1a.htm.
_____. "Shale Gas Production." 2013. http://www.eia.gov/dnav/ng/ng_prod_shalegas_s1_a.htm.
_____. "Total Energy: Annual Energy Review: Table E1. Estimated Primary Energy Consumption in the United States, Selected Years, 1635–1945." September 2012. http://www.eia.gov/totalenergy/data/annual/showtext.cfm?t=ptb1601.
_____. "Total Energy: Annual Energy Review: Table 1.2: Primary Energy Production by Source, 1949–2010." 2012. http://www.eia.gov/totalenergy/data/annual/showtext.cfm?t=ptb0102.
_____. "Total Energy: Annual Energy Review: Table 8.4a. Consumption for Electricity Generation by Energy Source: Total (All Sectors), 1949–2011." 2012. http://www.eia.gov/totalenergy/data/annual/index.cfm#electricity.
_____. "U.S. LNG Markets and Uses: June 2004 Update." 2004. http://www.eia.gov/pub/oil_gas/natural_gas/feature_articles/2004/lng/lng2004.pdf.
_____. "U.S. Natural Gas Imports and Exports 2011." 2012. http://www.eia.gov/naturalgas/importsexports/annual/.

_____. "U.S. Natural Gas LNG Storage Net Withdrawals." 2013. http://www.eia.gov/dnav/ng/hist/na1350_nus_2a.htm.

_____. "U.S. per Capita Use of Petroleum." 1998. http://www.eia.gov/pressroom/archive/speeches/25thann/sld008.htm.

United States Environmental Protection Agency. "11.18 Mineral Wool Manufacturing—Final Section—July 1993." In *Technology Transfer Network—AP 42*. 5th ed. Vol. 1, ch. 11: "Mineral Products Industry." http://www.epa.gov/ttnchie1/ap42/ch11/final/c11s18.pdf.

United States History. "Unemployment Statistics During the Great Depression." 2013. http://www.u-s-history.com/pages/h1528.html.

United States Patent and Trademark Office. "U.S. Patent Activity Calendar Years 1790 to the Present." March 19, 2013. http://www.uspto.gov/web/offices/ac/ido/oeip/taf/h_counts.pdf.

United States Steel. *Low Temperature and Cryogenic Steels: Materials Manual*. 2nd revised printing. Pittsburgh: United States Steel Corporation, February 1967.

University of Arizona, Department of Chemistry and Biochemistry. "The Joule Expansion." 2013. http://www.chem.arizona.edu/~salzmanr/480a/480ants/jadjte/jadjte.html.

University of Cambridge. "The Ductile-Brittle Transition." 2012. http://www.doitpoms.ac.uk/tlplib/BD6/printall.php.

University of Iowa. "Intermediate Thermodynamics; Thermodynamic Properties." 2013. http://www.engineering.uiowa.edu/~me140/Lecture/Thermodynamic%20Properties.pdf.

University of Tennessee. "A Runaway Greenhouse Effect?" 2013. http://csep10.phys.utk.edu/astr161/lect/venus/greenhouse.html.

Van Wylen, G. J., R. E. Sonntag, and C. Borgnakke. *Fundamentals of Classical Thermodynamics*. 4th ed. New York: John Wiley and Sons, 1994.

Vaughan, H. E. "Liquefied Natural Gas Projects Today." *Hydrocarbon Processing* 44.3 (March 1965).

Von Drehle, D. *Triangle: The Fire That Changed America*. New York: Atlantic Monthly, 2003.

Waples, David A. *The Natural Gas Industry in Appalachia: A History from the First Discovery to the Maturity of the Industry*. Jefferson, NC: McFarland, 2005.

Warwick, G. "LNG Propulsion—A Cool Idea?" Aviation Week. March 19, 2012. http://www.aviationweek.com/Blogs.aspx?

West, H. H., and M. S. Mannan. "LNG Safety Practice and Regulations: From the 1944 East Ohio Tragedy to Today's Safety Record." AIChE meeting, Houston, Texas, AIChE Topical Conference on Natural Gas Utilization and LNG Gas Transportation, April 2001.

West, J. B. "Robert Boyle's Landmark Book of 1660 with the First Experiments on Rarefied Air." *Journal of Applied Physiology* 98: 31–39.

White, L. C. "History of Petroleum and Natural Gas Developments and Statistics of Production." In *West Virginia Legislative Handbook and Manual and Official Register*, ed. John T. Harris, 1917.

Wilson, R. W., and H. R. Newsom. "Helium: Its Extraction and Purification." *Journal of Petroleum Technology*, April 1968.

Wolfram Research. "Kamerlingh-Onnes, Heike (1853–1926)." 2013. http://scienceworld.wolfram.com/biography/Kamerlingh-Onnes.html

Woodenergy.ie. "List and Values of Wood Fuel Parameters—Part 3." 2013. http://www.woodenergy.ie/woodasafuel/listandvaluesofwoodfuelparameters-part3/.

Wouter, P. "FLEXLNG: Developing the World's First Floating LNG Production Vessels." FPSO 2009 Conference, Oslo, Norway. 2013. http://intsok.com/style/downloads/Flex-L-PDF-Flex-LNG.pdf.

Yergin, D. *The Prize: The Epic Quest for Oil, Money, and Power*. New York: Simon & Schuster, 1991.

Young, A. R. "Liquefaction and Storage of Natural Gas for Peak Shaving." CEP-59-17, American Gas Association (AGA) Operating Section Conference, 1959.

Zick, L. P., J. W. Crosett, and W. T. Lankford. "Nickel-Steel Tank Tests at Minus 320." *Mechanical Engineering*, July 1963.

Index

Numbers in *bold italics* indicate pages with photographs.

Abbott, E.J. 145
Abington, Massachusetts 181
absolute zero temperature 83, 84, 86, 103, 198
Accum, Frederick 87
Addams, Jane 38
adiabatic expansion 95, 98, *99*, 100
AEO *see* Annual Energy Output
Africa 236, 245; North 245
L'Air Liquide Company 107
Air Reduction Company 107
Akron, Ohio 42, 43, 45, 53, 57–59, 63, 66, 70, 73
Algeria 221, 222, 224, 229, 232, 234, 238
Amarillo, Texas 107, 122
American Gas Association (AGA) 12, 60, 68, 144, 145, 147, *163*, 187
American Gas Institute 68
American Gas Light Association 56
American Institute of Architects 181
American Insurance Association *131*
American Merchant Marine at War *205*
American Red Cross 38
American Society for Testing Materials (ASTM) 114, 167, 176, 194
American Society of Mechanical Engineers (ASME) 108–111, *113*, 118, 120, 121, 154, 158, 176, 179, 188, *193*–195, 213, 215, 224
American Water Works 181
Ameriska Dominivina (American Home) 10, 142
ammonia 33, *88*, 89, *91*, 101, 103, 122, 123, 125, 147, *163*, 197, 224
Amonotones, Guillaume 83, 86, 101
Anchorage, Alaska *231*
Andrews, Samuel 39
Andrews, Thomas *92*, *94*, 101
Annual Energy Output (AEO) *243*–245, 247
Apollo 29, 210

Appalachia 2, 29, 30, *35*, 43, 47, 49, 50, 52, 56, 58–*64*, *65*, *67*–73, 75, 107, 203, 206, 230, *233*
Arcadia Parish, Louisiana 72
Arctic Princess 236
Aristotle 78, 81
Armengaud, J. *100*
Armstrong, T.N. 191, 195, 199
Armstrong County, Pennsylvania 41
Arzew, Algeria 221, 229
Ashtabula, Ohio 201
Asia *244*
Atlanta, Georgia 71, 239
Australia 206, 234, 235, 245

Bacon, Francis 85, 101
Baku, Russia 29
Baltimore 33, 44, 55
Baltimore and Ohio Railroad *35*
Baltimore Gas Light Company 32
Baraga, Father 18
Barnes, George 144
Bates, R.L. 43
Battson, E.F. 203
Bayou, Louisiana *205*
Beaumont, Texas 71
Becker, Johann 32
Beckfield, J.C. 58
Belfast, Ireland *92*
Bell, A.G. 38
Benz, Karl 39
Bernoulli, Daniel 84
Bernstein, Peter 207
"Big Inch" pipeline 72
Bishop-Babcock Company 145
Bishop of Durham 31
Bissell, George 36
Black, Joseph 90
Black Swan 206–209
Bloomfield and Rochester Natural Gas Light Company 37
Blue Ridge Mountains 44
Board of Boiler Deputies of the Industrial Commission of Ohio 186

Boiler and Pressure Vessel Code 109–111, 118
boiler code 109, *193*, 215
Boston Gas Light Company 33
Bownocker, J.A. *64*
Boyer, L. Lee 201
Boyle, B.E. *20*
Boyle, Robert 4, 7, *79*–86, *91*–93, 101–103; Law 81, *82*, 84, 86, *91*–93, 101, 102, 108; *New Experiments Physico-Mechanicall, Touching the Spring of Airs, and Its Effects (1660)* 81, 85
BPVC *see Boiler and Pressure Vessel Code*
Bradford, Pennsylvania 41
Braxton County, west Virginia 61
Brewster, Benjamin 41
Bridgeport Station 75
Bridgeville, Pennsylvania 154
Brignano and McCullough: *The Spirit of Progress: The Story of the East Ohio Gas Company and the People Who Made It* 53, 71
brine 4, 30, *35*–37
British Gas Council 220
British Thermal Unit (BTU) 33, 34, 39, 51, 57, 60, 73, 104, *126*, 127, 141, 171, 172, 196, 204, 211, 216, 232; *see also* heating value
brittle fracture 105, *113*, 114, 127, 152, 154, 165, 175, 177, 190, 191, 194, 213
Brockton, Massachusetts 109
Brophy, G.R. 192, *193*, 195, 199
Brown, Francis C. 63
Brown's *Directory of American Gas Companies* 52
Brush Farm Station (Cleveland) 72
Buffalo, New York 40, 41, 58, 63, 75
Buffalo Gas Company, New York 63
Buffalo Natural Gas Fuel Company 44
Bunsen burner 50, 57

Index

Bunsen, Robert 51
Burke, Thomas 144
Burning Springs, West Virginia 54
Bussy, A.A.B *88*, 89, *96*
butane 28, 59–61, 112, 130, 142, 169, 184
Butler County, Pennsylvania 36, 41

Cabot, Godfrey Lowell *54*, 55, 63, 68, 76, 107, 111–*113*, 115, 139, 203
Cailletet, Louis-Paul *94*, 101
Calhoun County, West Virginia 55, 61, 63
CAMEL (Cie Algiericcene du Methane Liquid) 221
Canada *228*, 229, *243*
Canadaway Creek 30
Canton, Ohio 23, 42, 196
Canton Gas Light and Coke 62
Canvey Island, London 201, 204, 206, 213, 220, 221, 230
carbon 23, 26, 28
carbon black *54*, 55, 61, 63, 68, 73, 111
carbon dioxide 26–28, 80, *88*, 89, 93, *96*, 103, 111, 122, 123, 125, 129, 192, 194, 246, 247
carbon monoxide 26, 27, 32, 33, 34, *94*
carbon oil 36
carbureted water gas *see* manufactured gas
Carey, John 181
Carlstadt, New Jersey 224
Carnegie, Andrew 38
Carnegie-Illinois Steel Company 155, 156, 158, 159, 175
Carnot, Nicholas Leonard Sadi 86
Carter Oil Company 42, 46, 59
Case School of Applied Science (Case Institute of Technology, Case Western Reserve University) 2, 141, 144
Caspian Sea 29
Castenada, C. *Invisible Fuels: Manufactured and Natural Gas in America 1800-2000* 30
Central Asia 245
Charles, Jacques A.C. 83, 87
Charleston, West Virginia 30
Charpy, Georges 114
Charpy impact test 111, 114, 115, 117–121, 129, 152, 154–159, 161, 174–176, 189, 190, 192–194, 200, 212, 213
Cheniere Energy *244*
Chew, Roger 59
Chicago, Illinois 6, 10, 38, 71, 197, 200, 204, 213, 239; Stock Yards 203
Chicago Bridge and Iron (CB&I) 196, 201, *202*, 224, *225*, *226*
Chile 245

China 52, 235, 236, 245; provinces 29
Chippewa, Ohio 75
chlorine 87, 88, *92*, 93, 101, 103
Chula Vista, California *226*
Cimperman, Ann 14, 130, 146
Cincinnati, Ohio 72
Cincinnati Gas and Electric Company 190
City Council (Cleveland) 178
City Record (Cleveland) 178
Clarion County, Pennsylvania 41
Clark, John A. 115, *131*
Clark, Maurice 39
Clarksburg Light and Heat 46
Claude, Georges *100*, 102, 121, 122, *205*
Clayton, Reverend John 32
Cleaveland, Moses 66
Clendenin, West Virginia 68
Clermont 35
Cleveland, Ohio 1, 4, 6, 9, 10, 12, 33, 38, 39, 40, 43–45, 53, *54*, 62–*64*, 66, *67*, 70–72, *74*, 75, 77, 105, 110, 111, 115–123, *126*, 129, 130, *131*, 133, 138, 139, 141, 142, 144, 150, *160*, 174, 178, 185–187, 191, 196, 197, 199, 200, *202*, 203, 206, 213, 214, 222, 223, *228*, *233*, 238; Department of Public Safety 130
Cleveland City Gas Light and Coke Company 10, 43, 44
Cleveland Press 196
Cleveland Public Library Digital Gallery *11*, *12*
Cleveland State University, Cleveland Press Collection *12*, *16*, *19*, *20*, *160*
Clouet, Jean Francois 87
coal 3, 4, 23, 25, 26, 28, 31–*35*, 39, *48*, 49, 51, 52, 54–59, 62, 63–*67*, 69, 70, 71, 73, 76, 80, 102, 196, 204, 206, 216, 220, *227*, 232, 234, 245, 247
coal gas *see* manufactured gas
coal tar *see* manufactured gas
code 6, 23, 108–111, 118, 119, 121, 154, 155, 176, 178, 179, 181–183, 185–189, *193*, 195, *202*, 209, 211–215, 224
coke 10, 32, 33, 39
Cold War 209, 215
Columbus, Ohio 72, 212, 214
Commerce Act of 1887 218
Commerce Clause 218
Committee on Fuel Gases 187
Committee on Liquefied Natural Gas 187
Commonwealth Services Incorporated 186
compressor 45, 46, 61–63, *65*, 68, 70, 71, *99*, *100*, 101, 112, 123, 125, 130, *131*, 144, 145, 152

Conch International Methane Ltd. 221
condensation 87, 153; heat of 90, *91*, 93
Connecticut 66; Land Company 66
ConocoPhillips *237*, *244*
Consolidated Natural Gas Company 47
Constantine the Great 29
Constock International Methane Ltd. 201, 203, 204, 223
Constock Liquid Methane Corporation 204, 206, 220, 221
Continental Oil Company 203
Continuous Risk Management System 171
Cook Inlet, Alaska *231*
Cooper, Howell C. 76, 105, 107, 108, 110–121, *134*, 137–139, 154–156, 167, 171, 173, 174–177, 179, 191, 192, 195
Copernicus 78
cork 5, 60, 115, *126*, 127, 129, *134*, 137, 138, 149, 150, 151, 164, 166, 167, 176, 190, 195, 196, 198, 200, 213
Cornwell Station *see* John J. Cornwell Station
Corry, Pennsylvania 41
Corton, West Virginia 68, 71, 112
Cove Lick, West Virginia 61
Cove Point, Maryland (Chesapeake Bay) *231*, 232, 238, *244*
critical pressure *92*–94, 123
critical temperature 89, *92*–*96*, 98, 101–104, 122, 123, 125, 184
cryogen 5, 6, 106, 110, 119, 189, 194, 195, 198–*202*, 213, 215, 224, *226*, 239
Cuba, New York 29, 36, 63
Cuyahoga River (Ohio) 66
Cuyahoga Steam Furnace Company 66

Daiber, Conrad 147
Daimler, Gottlieb 39
Dallas, Texas 197
Daly, Martin 44, 45
Darling, Paddy 61
Darwinism 38
Davis compressor station 46
Davy, Sir Humphrey 31, 87
Dayton, Ohio 44, 72
death toll 19
de la Roche, Joseph 29, 36
de la Salle 29
de la Tour, Charles Cagniard 89, *92*, 101
de Mere, Chevalier 207, 208
Dennison, Ohio 43
Denver Colorado 71
Depression 18, *48*, 49, 50, *67*–70, 72, 128
design flaw 144

Detroit, Michigan 10, 66
Dewar flask 198
Dexter, Kansas 106
dike 172, 173, 177, 183–185, 187, 212, 224
Distrigas 230
Doddridge County, West Virginia 61
Doherty, Henry 56
Dominion Resources 16, 61, *132*, *136*, *143*, 229, *231*
Dover, Ohio 43
Drake, Edwin 37
Dresser Industries Limited 197
Driscoll, Texas 72
ductile-to-brittle transition temperature (DBTT) *113*–115, 154, 191, *193*, 199
Duke of Northumberland 31
Dunkirk, New York 63
Duquesne Hotel 56

East Coast 72, 108, 222, 230
East Liverpool, Ohio 52
East Ohio Gas Company 1, 3, 4, 5, 6, 7, 10, 12, 15, *20*, *21*, 22, 33, 41–47, 50, 53, 54, 57, 59, 61, 62, *65*, *67*–70, 72, 75–77, 105, 111, 116, 117, 123, *124*, 127, 129, 130, *131*, *132*, 133, *136*, 137, 138, 140, *143*, 146, *148*, 149, 153, 155, 157, 161, 171, 172, 174, 175, 183–187, 190–198, 200–203, 206, 208, 209, 211, 212, 214, 219, 222, 223, *225*, *227*, *228*, 230, 234, 235, 238
Edinburgh, Scotland 87, *92*
Edison, T.A. 38, 50
Edison Electric Light Company 50
Egerton, Professor 204
Elba Island, Georgia *231*, 232, 238, *244*
Elk County, Pennsylvania 41
Elk River 68, 112
Ellenboro, West Virginia 68
Emerson, E.O. 53
energy 2, 3, 4, 7, 23, 25, 27, 28, *35*, 38, 39, 42, *48*–52, 55, 60, 66, 69, 72, 73, 83–85, 90, 98, *100*, 101, 104, *113*, 114, *126*, 129, 133, 138, 139, 141, 171, 179, 190, 194, 196, 197, 199, *202*–204, 206, 211, 214, 216–219, 220, 222, *225*, *227*, 229–236, 238, 240, *241*, *243*–247; *see also* work
England 26, 31, 32, 80, 203
English Civil War 81
Enlightment 78
Erie, Pennsylvania 36, 41
Erie Canal *35*, 39
Erie Gas Company 73
ethane 28, 59, 60, 61, 77, 112, 122, *123*, 130, 169, 184, 194
ether *88*, 89, 93, 98
ethylene 89, 93, 98, 103, 122, 123, 125, 129, 147, 197, 224

Everett, Massachusetts 221, *226*, 230, 232
Excelsior Works 39
explosion 1, 4, 10, 14, 15, *16*, 18, 31, 38, 53, 71, 87, 109, 140, 145, 146, 151, *163*, 173, 178

Factory Mutual Insurance Companies 181
Faraday, Michael 7, 31, 51, 60, 87–89, *96*, 98, 102, 103
Feightner, John Roy 9, 10, *17*, 144–152, 169, 172
Felling colliery 31
Fermat, Pierre 207
Ferris, Timothy: *The Science of Liberty* 78
"fire damp" 31
Fitzgerald, H.H. 186
Flager, Henry 39, 40
Flaggy Meadows Gas Company 45
Flint, Kendall 144
floating, storage and regasification unit (FSRU) 239
Florence, Italy 31, 80, 81
Florida 72
Foamglas 200–*202*, 215
Ford, Henry 39
Forrest County, Pennsylvania 41
Fort Pitt Glass Works 53
Fort Worth, Texas 107, 122
fossil fuels 7, 28, 31, 245, 246
Fountaine Ardente 29
fracking *see* hydraulic fracturing
France *205*, 220, 221, 236, 245
Francis, James Bichon 181
Franklin, Benjamin 56, 179
Fredonia, New York 30, 32, 34, *35*, 42, 52, 57, 63
Freehold Oil and Gas Company 61
Freeman, John Ripley 181
French Academy *94*
French and Indian War 30
fuel 4, 6, 7, 23, 25–28, 31, 36, 40, 41, 44, 48–52, 56, 58–63, *65*, 75, 122, 129, 138, 142, 183, 185, 187, 197, 199, 206, 212, 223, 239, 240, 245–247
Fulton, Robert *35*

Gagnebin, A.P. 191, 195
Galileo 80, 81
Garner, J.B. 158, 185
Gas and Machinery Company 116, 117, 119, 130, 153–155
Gas Council (England) 203, 206
Gas Light Company of Baltimore 32, 55
gas meter 46
gas well 29, 31, 37, 52, *54*, 59, 61, 75, 76, 196, 203
gasholder (gasometer) 34, 73, *74*, 130, *163*, 172, 184
gasoline 23, 27, 59, 60, 61, 135, 142, 173, 183–187, 212, 213

Gay-Lussac, Joseph Louis 83, 84, 87, 101
Genoa, Italy 29
Geology.com 240
Gerber, Samuel 185
Germany 9, 14, *74*, 128, 129, 220
Gesner, Abraham 36
Gibson, H.S. 203, 204
Gilded Age 38
Gilmer County, West Virginia 61, 65
Goddard, Robert 199
Gram, Ankar 239
Granberg, Al *241*
Grantsville, West Virginia *54*
Granville, West Virginia 68
Grdina, Anton 1, *21*
Great Britain 6, 106, 109, 129, *205*, 206, 215, *217*, 220, 221, 223, 234, 235, 236; British Isles 206
Great Fire of London 179, 209
Great Lakes 66
Greece 29, 36, 80, 198
Greenwich Village, New York 3
Grenoble, France 29
Gross Domestic Product 128
Gross National Product (GNP) 69, 128
Gulf Coast *202*, 203, 213, 221, 223, *226*, 230

Hackensack, New Jersey 224
Hagan, William *134*, 137, 138, 149, 172, 173, 184, 186
Hamilton, Ontario 107
Hampton, Robert 43
Hardin, W.L.: *The Rise and Development of the Liquefaction of Gases* 95
Harrison, Benjamin 180
Hart, William Aaron 30, 32
Hassi R'Mel, Algeria 221
Hastings Station 44–46, 59, 60, 62, 71, 185
Haworth, Erasmus 106
Haymaker, Michael 53
Haymaker, Obediah 53
Haynes, P.E. 170
heating value 26, *49*, 51, 169; *see also* BTU
helium 4, 5, 28, 76, 102, 104, 106–108, 121, 122, 138, 194, 198, 200
Hense, Hans 144, 145
Hepburn Act of 1906 218
Hindenburg 23, 106, 140, 179
Holland 201
Holmes, R.: *The Age of Wonder* 32
Hooke, Robert 81
Hope Natural Gas Company 2, 4, 5, 7, 41–47, 50, 53, 59, 60–*65*, 68–72, 75, 76, 105, 112, 114–116, 121, 122, 129, 130, *131*, 139, 149, 171, 176, 185, 238
House of Commons 204
Houston, Texas 239

Index

Hughes, Jesse 30
Hugoton, Kansas 71
Hurlich, A. 154, 157
Huron Indians 29, 36
hydraulic fracturing *241*, *242*, 247
hydrocarbon 27, 28, 32, 59, 60, 61, 106, 112, 130, 149, 169, 171, 173, 183, 184, 194, 212, 245, 246
Hydrocarbon Research 194
hydrogen 23, 27, 28, 31–34, 61, *97*, 106, 140, 198–200, 240, 246, 247

ideal gas *82–86*, *92*, *94*, 95, *99*, 101, 103
illuminants 36, 38
immigrant 10, 38, 66, 141
Imperial College of Science, London 204
Indianapolis, Indiana 71
Industrial Revolution 3, 4, 26, 31, 32, *35*, 109
Ingall's Ship Yards 203
Institute of Petroleum, London 204
insulation 6, 10, 18, 76, *113*–115, 127, 135, 137, 147, 149, 151–153, 155, 161, 164, 166, 167, 170, 174–176, 190, 195–198, 200–*202*, *205*, 213–215, 221–223
International Gas Union *244*
International Nickel Company 191, 192, 195, 215
investigation 2, 6, 18, 85, 105, 121, *136*, 139, 153–157, 159, 161–167, 174, 176, 178
Iraq Petroleum Company 203
Italy *205*

Jackson, James O. 77, 111, 116–121, 133, 139, 149, 152, 154–156, 158, 164, 174, 191, 192, 195, 212
Japan 29, *205*, 220, *231*, 236, *244*
Japanese Aerospace Exploration Agency (JAXA) 240
Jefferson, Thomas 30
Jeffries-Norton Company 107
John J. Cornwell Station 68, 71, 72, 75, 112, 129, 238
Johnson, Tom 44
Joule, James 98, 102
Joule-Thomson effect 98–*100*, 102–104, 107, 112, 121, 123
Journal of Finance 208
Judge, W.J. 75
Jules Verne 221, 222

Kalm, Peter 36
Kanawha River 30, *54*; Little Kanawha 30
Kanawha Salines 36
Kansas 70
Kasic, Anthony 15, 130
Kekic, Peter 142
Kelly, Charles 204

Kenai, Alaska *227*, *244*
Kenai Liquefied Natural Gas Plant *231*
Kenai Peninsula, Alaska *231*
kerosene 3, 27, 36, 39, 40, 51, 60, 183
Kier, Samuel 36
King Charles I (England) 81
Klegecell 222

LaCrosse, Wisconsin *226*
Lake, Russell 145, 146
Lake Charles, Louisiana *202*, 204, *205*, 221, 230, *231*, 323
Lake Court neighborhood (Cleveland) 140
Lake Erie 10, 12, 130
Lakewood, Ohio *64*
Lamson and Sessions 14, 130
Lausche, Frank 1, *21*, 140, 144
Leimbach, Bernard 14
Liberty ship 205
Lightburn, West Virginia 61
Lima, Ohio 43
Linda Hall Library of Science, Engineering and Technology 202
Linde *see* von Linde
Linde Air Products Company 107
Linde Group *99*
Linden, New Jersey 72
liquefaction process 9, 76, *79*, 89, *92*, 121, 123, 146, 197
Liquefaction, Storage, and Regasification (L.S. and R.) 5, 12, *22*, 42, 130, *131*, 138, 140, 151, 152, 166, 171, 196, 197, 214, 219, 222
liquid petroleum gases (LPG) *49*, 60, 183–185
"Little Big Inch" pipeline 72
load factor 50, 73, 105, 222, 223, *225*, *227*
Locke Machinery company 146
London, England 32, 81, 213, 221
London and Westminster Gas Light and Coke Company 32
Longview, Texas 72
Los Angeles 10, 73
Louisiana 6, 70, 71, 72, 196, 213, 214, 223
Lowe, Professor L. 34
Lowell, Massachusetts 181
L.S. and R. *see* Liquefaction, Storage, and Regasification
Lukens Steel Company 114
Luoma, Herbert, 144
Lynn, Massachusetts 109

MacLaren, A.W. 158, 159
Madison Gas and Electric Company 56
Magdeburg, Lower Saxony 81
Magnolia Gas Company of Dallas 71
Mahoning Gas Fuel 44
Mahoning Valley Ohio 43, 53

Mannington, West Virginia 46
manufactured gas 3, 4, 32–36, 39, 44, 46, 48–52, 55–57, 62, 63, *67*, 68, 70, 73, 77, 80, 133, 206, *228*, 234
Manufacturers Gas Company 56
Manufacturers Light and Heat Company 61
Manufacturers Mutual Insurance Companies of New England 182
Marietta, Ohio 42
marine terminals 229, *243*
Marion County, West Virginia 45
Markowitz, Harry 208
Marts, West Virginia 61
Massachusetts 54, 109, 224, 226, 230
Massachusetts Institute of Technology 181
Massillon, Ohio 42
Matter, John 144, 145
Maumee, Ohio 72, 75
Mayor's Board of Inquiry (MBI) 114, 116, 141, 144, 153, 156, 159, 161, 165–170, 184, 185, 188, 189, 194
McKean County, Pennsylvania 41
McLaughlin, T.A. 43
McQuaid-Ehn 158, 159
McSweeney, H.W. 43
McWhorter County, West Virginia 46
Meadville, Pennsylvania 41
Mechanical Engineering 195
Mellon Institute 118, 158, 164
methane 4, 6, 28, 30–32, 34, *49*, 59, 60, 61, 77, 89, 93, *94*, 98, 104, 106, 107, 112, 114, 121–123, 125, 130, 149, 169, 170, 184, 185, 191, 194, 198, *202*–206, 214, 215, 220, 221, *243*, 246, 247
Methane Pioneer 6, *202*, 203, *205*, 206, 214, 215, *217*, 220, 221, 223, 229, 230, 234, 236
Methane Princess 221
Methane Progress 221, 222
Methanite 198
Mexico *228*, 229, *243*
Michigan *35*
Middle East 203, 204, 206, *217*, 221, 229, 234, 236, 245
Miller, A.J. 192, *193*, 195
Miller, R.W. 115
Minneapolis, Minnesota 71
Mississippi 6, 23, *35*; River 66, 203, 204, 213
Mohican Oil and Gas Company 62
Monge, Gaspard 87
Morocco 245
Moscow, Russia 197
Moundsville, West Virginia 42, 43
Mountain State Gas Company 42, 44, 45

Muirkirk, Scotland 32
Murdock, William 32, 33
Murrysville, Pennsylavania 53
Muskingum River, Ohio 36

naphtha 34, 60, 60, 89, 183
Naples, Italy 29
NASA 171, 199, 209, 210, 240
Nashville, Tennessee 72
National Board of Fire Underwriters (NBFU) 153, 180–182, 187; "Pamphlet 59" 187
National Board's Model Building Law 180
National Coal Board 204
National Commercial Gas Association 68
National Conference on Standard Electrical Rules 181, 182
National Electrical Code (NEC) 181, 182
National Electrical Contractors' Association 181
National Fire Code *see* NFPA National Fire Code
National Fire Protection Association (NFPA) 181–183, 185–188, *202*, 212, 215; NFPA 59A 187, 188, 212
National Fuel Gas Company 75
National Gas Trust 40, 41
National Institute of Standards and Technology (NIST) *see* U.S. National Institute of Standards and Technology (NIST)
National Transit Company 40–43, 46, 47, 53
Native Americans 29, *35*
Natural Gas Act 70, 72, 218, 219
natural gas liquids (NGL) *49*
Natural Gas Pipeline of America 71
Natural Gas Policy Act (NGPA) of 1978 219, 232
Natural Gas Wellhead Decontrol Act (NGWDA) of 1989 220
natural gasoline 59, 60, 61, 183
NBFU *see* National Board of Fire Underwriters
Neighborhood 9, 10, 14, 19
Nesis (near Naples) 29
Netherlands 236
New England 35, 68, 109, 181, 182, 230
New England Association of Gas Engineers 68
New Haven, Connecticut 181
New Jersey 23, 30, 41, 47
New Philadelphia, Ohio 43
New York 29, 30, 39, 40, 41, 63, 72; City 35, 36, 38, 40, 50, 128, 180, 199
New York Central Railroad 10, 15, 151, 166
New York Gas Light Company 33

New York Times 199
Newcomen, Thomas 25, 81
NFPA *see* National Fire Protection Association
NFPA National Fire Code 182
nickel-steel 5, 110, 115–119, 139, 154, 174, 176, 189, 192–194, 212, 213; 3 1/2 percent 105, 106, 116, 117, 119–121, *136*, 139, 154–156, 158, 159, 174–176, 189–192, 195, 199, 212, 213, 215; nine percent 121, 194, 195, 199, 200, *202*, 213, 215, 224
North Africa 221
North American Gas Light Company 36
North Cook Inlet, Alaska *231*
North Sea 223, 234
North Thames Gas Board 204
Northampton, England 56
Northmore, Thomas 87
Northwestern Ohio Gas Company 44
Norway 236
Norwood *see* St. Clair–Norwood
Novak, John 146

octane 247
O'Day, Daniel 4, 40, 43, 46, 53
Ohio 4, 10, *22*, 28, 30, *35*–37, 40, 41–43, 45, 53, 58, 62, *64*–*67*, 70, 72, 73, 75, 76, 109, 186, 196, *242*
Ohio Administrative Code 188
Ohio Department of Industrial Relations, Division of Boiler Inspection 185
Ohio Historical Society 43
Ohio Inspection Bureau 153
Ohio Public Utilities Commission 23, 196
Ohio River 30, 42–44
Ohio Unfired Pressure Vessel Code 185, 186
oil 3, 25–28, 31–43, 46–50, 52–*54*, 56, 58–63, 60, 66, 70–73, 86, 125, 130, 135, 142, 164, 172, 173, 183–185, 200, 203, 204, 206, 212, 213, 216–221, *227*–229, *231*–234, 238, 240, 245, 247
Oil City, Pennsylvania 37, 41, 42, 43, 56, 61, 63, 73
Oil City Derrick 37
Oil City Fuel Supply Company 41
Oil City Gas Company 73
Oil Creek, Pennsylvania 52
oil gas *see* manufactured gas
Oil Industries Club 203
Oklahoma 55, 70, 142
Olszewski, Karol *97*, 98, 102, 104, 107
Onnes, Heike Kamerlingh 102, 198
Ontario County, New York 29
OPEC 216, 219, *227*, 232
Operation Cryogenics *202*, 224

Oracle of Delphi 29
Oriskany Sands 68
Ormston, Robert 190
Otto, Nikolaus August 39, 46
Oxford, England 81

Paine, Thomas 30
Panhandle, Texas 71
Panhandle Eastern 75
Panhandle Eastern Pipeline Company 72
Parkersburg, West Virginia 30
Parmalee, Henry 181
Pascagoula, Mississippi 203
Pascal, Blaise 207, 208
patent 38, 59, 60, 76, 107, 108, 111, 112, 115, 120–123, 125, 130, 138, 139, 155, 181, 192, 201, 203, 215, 223
Payne, C.N. 42, 46
peak load 1, 4, 5, 50, 73, 76, 105, 141, 204, 218, 222, *227*, *233*, 234
peak shaving 23, 76, 107, 122, *126*, 127, 133, 178, 186, 187, 197, 222–*227*, *233*
Peale, Charles Wilson 32;
Peale, Rembrandt 32
Peebles, M.W.H.: *Evolution of the Gas Industry* 32, 70
Penca, John 14, 18, 130
Pennsylvania 3, *22*, 28, 30, 34, *35*, 39, 40, 41, 42, 43, 52–*54*, 56–59, 61, 63, *64*, 66, 72, 73, 130, 137, 152, 154, 157
Pennsylvania and Reading Railroad 40
Pennsylvania Gas Company 41
Pennsylvania Railroad 130, 152
Pennsylvania Rock Oil Company 36
Peoples Gas Light Company 33, 43, 44
Peoples Natural Gas Company 53, 61, 62
perlite 200–*202*, 213, 215, 223
Perrysville, Louisiana 72
Persian Gulf 223
Persians 29
petroleum *see* oil
Petsinger, Robert 239
Petty, Paul 194
Pew, J.N. 53, 76
Philadelphia, Pennsylvania 40
Philosophical Society of London 29
Pictet, Raoul Pierre *94*–*97*, 101, 121, 122
pilot plant 2, 5, 12, 68, 76, 105, 110–112, 114–117, 119, 121–123, 125–127, 129, 130, 139, 149, 150, 174, 175, 198, *205*, 214, *226*
Pine Grove, West Virginia 44, 45
Pipe Creek, Ohio 43
pipeline 4, 23, 37, 37, 40–43, 45, 46, 50, 53, *54*, 56, 59, 61–*64*, 68,

70–73, 76, 105, 122, 123, 171, 178, 188, 196, 206, 218–223, *226*–229, *233*, 234, 236, 238
Pipeline Safety Act of 1979 188
Pittsburgh, Pennsylvania 30, 33, *35*, 37, 53, *54*, 60–63, 71, 72, 121, 156–158, 185
Pittsburgh Corning Corporation 201
Pittsburgh-Des Moines Steel Company 77, 116, 117, 119, 130, 133, *134*, 137, 138, 147, 149, 150, 152, 153, 155, 156, 158, 159, 164, 167, 174, 176, 212
Pittsburgh Plate Glass 53
Pittsburgh Testing Laboratories 157, 158
Plant of the Proprietors of the Locks and Canals on the Merrimack River 181
Plutarch 2
Poland 129, 245
Pomeroy, Ohio 30
population 10, 26, 33, *35*, 38, 53, 66, *67*, 172, 180, 196, 236
Portugal 200
Pratt, J.W. 204
Pratt, Phillip 181
pressure 4, 5, 12, 14, 15, 26, 28, 31, 32, 34, 37, 38, 44, 45, 47, 50, 53, 55, 58, 60, 62, 63, 70, 71, 73–77, *79*–104, 109–112, 118, 121–123, 125, 129, 152, 155, 159, 166, 169, 170, 178, 184, 186, 194, 195, 215, 242, 246; *see also* critical pressure
Prince, William Wood 203, 206, 215, 234
Pritchard, O.R. 146
probabilistic risk assessment (PRA) 210
propane 28, *49*, 59, 60, 61, *91*, 93, 112, 122, 123, 169, 184, 194, 197, 224
ProPublica *241*
Public Utility Holding Act 47

Q-Flex 236
Q-Max 236
Qatar 234, 236
Qatargas 236
Quadricycle 39
Queens College, Belfast *92*

RAND Corporation 209
Regnault, Henri *91*, 93
regulation 6, 69, 70, 75, 109, 137, 178, 187–189, 216, 218–220, 220, *231*, 232, 238
Renaissance 4, 78
Republic Steel Corporation 116, 118, 119, 154, 156, 157, 159, 174, 175, 192
Reserve Gas Company 42
Richmond, Canada *226*
risk 31, 38, 39, 55, 68, 142, 159, 171, 172, 177, 180, 182, 186, 204, 206–211, 214, 215
Ritchie County, West Virginia 61
River Gas Company 42
Robertshaw, R.W. 58
Robertson, Don: *The Greatest Thing Since Sliced Bread* 20
Robinson, J. French 196
rock wool (stone wool, mineral wool) 18, 137, 150–153, 195, 198, 213
Rockefeller, John D. 2–4, 7, 39, 40, 41, 43, 53, 66, 218
Romans 29
Round Bottom, West Virginia 43, 44
Royal Dutch/Shell 221
Royal Institution 31, 87
Royal Society 81
rupture 1, 5, 12, 14, 15, 18, 130, *131*, 144, 146, 152, *163*, 165, 166, 168, 170, 171, 173, 177, 185
Russell, Jack P. 178
Russia 29, 240
Ruud, Edwin 58

Sabine, Louisiana *244*
Sabine Pass 230, *244*
Safety Committee 31
St. Augustine 29
St. Clair–Norwood 9, 10, 12, 14, 15, 18, *21*, 44, 146
St. Louis, Missouri 71
St. Vitus parish 10, 12, 15, 18
Salamanca, New York 41
Salt Lake City, Utah 156
Salvation Army 38
San Diego Gas and Electric Company (SD&GE) *226*
Saratoga, New York 34
Saw Mill Run (Pittsburgh) 35
Saybolt, George 59
S.B. Martin Company 146
Scandinavia 26
Scheide, H.C. 43
Schorlemer, Carl 60
Scientific Revolution 4, 31, 78, 81, 86
Sears, F.W.: *College Physics: Mechanics, Heat, and Sound* 95
Seneca Indians 36
Seneca Oil Company 36
shale gas 216, 229, 235, 240, *241*, *242*–245, 247
Sharon County, Pennsylvania 41, 63
Sharp, James 56
Shell Petroleum 204
Sherman Anti-Trust Law 41, 46
Shirley, Thomas 29
Siberia, Russia 245
Siewert, Thomas 157, 158
Silver, Nate 206
Siverlyville, Pennsylvania 41
Sliepcevich, C.M. 203
Slovene 1, 10, 14
Snelling, Walter O. 60, 112, 184
South Africa 245
South America 236, 245
South Penn Oil Company 42, 46
Southeast Asia 234
Southwest 45, 46, *49*, 50, *64*, *65*, 70, 72, 73, 75, 106, 145, 178, 197, 206, 222, 223, *233*
Spain 236
Stalbridge in Dorset, England 80
standard 51, 68, 108, 109, 111, *113*, 114, 1116, 119, 120, 127, 139, 154, 155, 157, 161, 167, 173, 176, 178–183, 185–189, *193*, 212–215, 236
Standard Oil 40–43, 47, 53, 61, 66, 130; Standard 40–47
Standard Oil of New Jersey 41, 42, 47, 61
Standard Oil Trust 41, 61
Stark Summit, Ohio 75
Stilwell, "Buffalo Joe" 37
storage tank 5, 12, *74*, 77, 105, 108, 110–114, 116, 120, 121, 125–127, 130, 133, 135, 139, 142, *163*, 164, 171, 172, 174, 179, 183, 186, 190, 191, *193*, 194, 196, 197, 199, 201, *202*, *205*, 206, 213, 224–*226*, 230
Stotz and Jamison: *History of the Gas Industry* 44, 52
Strong, Elizur 42, 43, 44, 46
Stuchell, R.M. 158
Sunderland, England 31
Supreme Court 63, 218, 219; Ohio 41, 46, 47; Pennsylvania 137, 157
swamp gas 30
Sweden *205*, 220

Taleb, Nassim Nicholas 206
technical consultants 23, 141, 144, 153–156, 159, 165, 167, 173, 175, 188, 189, 209
temperature 5–7, 9, 12, 14, 28, 32, 51, 58, 60, 68, 75–77, *79*, 80, *82*–96, 98, *99*–105, 107, 108, 110–123, 125, 127, *136*, 138, 139, 142, 147, 148, 150, 152–159, 161, *163*–195, 168–170, 173–176, 183–*202*, 212, 213, 215, 222, 246; *see also* critical temperature
Tennessee Gas 75
Tennessee Gas Transmission Company 72
Terry, L.B. 62
Terry, L.F. 56
Texas 5, 23, 28, 70, 196, 203, *233*; Revolution *35*
Texas Panhandle 72, 169
Thilorier, Charles *88*, 89, 98
Thomson, Thomas 87
Thomson, William (Lord Kelvin) 83, 86, 98, 102
Tidewater 40
Titanic 190, 191

Titusville, Pennsylvania 36, 37, 42, 59
Tobey, H.A. 58
Tokyo, Japan *244*
Tonkin, Captain John 42, 46
Torricelli, Evangelista 80, 81
Treasury Department 18
Triangle shirtwaist 3, 23
Trinidad and Tobago 220, 232, 23
Turkey 245
Tussing and Barlow: *The National Gas Industry: Evolution, Structure, Economics* 70, 71
Twomey, Lee 76, 107, 122, 123, 125, 130, 138
Tyler County, West Virginia 61

Uhrichsville, Ohio 43
Ukraine 245
Underwriters Electric Bureau 182
Underwriters Laboratories (UL) 182
Union Stock Yards and Transit company 203
United Kingdom (U.K.) *see* Great Britain
U.K. Gas Council 204
United Natural Gas 41
U.S. Bureau of Mines 60, 107, 121, 138, 141, 154, 156–159, 161, 165, 167, 187, 189, 190, 197, 201; Metallurgy of Steel Section 156; Salt Lake 157
U.S. Coast Guard 230
U.S. Department of Transportation 188
U.S. Economic Defense Board 150
U.S. Energy Information Administration (EIA) *225*, *227*, 229, 232, *241*, *243*–245, 247
U.S. Federal Energy Regulatory Commission (FERC) 219, 220, 230
U.S. Federal Power Commission (FPC) 19, 72, 218, 219, 220
U.S. Geological Survey 28, *241*
U.S. Maritime Administration (MARAD) 230
U.S. Maritime Commission *205*
U.S. National Institute of Standards and Technology (NIST) 157, 199

U.S. Office of Production Management 150
U.S. Steel 195
U.S. Supply Priorities and Allocation Board 150
U.S. War Production board 150
University of Chicago 208
University of Southern California, USC Libraries Special Collection *74*

Vanadium Corporation 154
Vancouver, Canada *226*
Vandaveer, F.E. 145
van Helmont, Jan Baptista 32, *79*, 80
Van Marum, Martin 90, *91*
vapor 10, 12, 14, 59, *79*, 90, *91*, 93, *95*–97, 104, 123, 125, 144–146, 166, 187, 188
vaporization *88*, 90, *91*, *226*; heat of 89, 90, *97*, 103, 123, 125, *126*
Venango County, Pennsylvania 41, 52, 55
Venezuela 220, 223
Venus 246
Virginia 30, 36
von Guericke, Otto 81
von Karman, Theodore 210
von Linde, Carl 98–102, 104, 106, 107, 121, 122, 198
von Neumann, John 209

Waples, D.A.: *The Natural Gas Industry in Appalachia: A History from the First Discovery to the Maturity of the Industry* 29, 37, 63
war 1, 3, 5, 6, 9, 12, 14, 18, 19, *22*, 30, 38, 47, *48*, 50, 52, 61, 62, *65*, 66, 70, 72, *74*–76, 81, 102, 106, 107, 114, 121, 128, 129, 133, *136*–139, 141, 142, 150, 155, 175, 176, 186, 187, 191, 192, 196, 197–*202*, *205*, 207, 209, 211, 212–216, 221, 222, *233*
Warner, R.C. 43
Warren County, Pennsylvania 41
Warren Light and Heat Company 41
Warsaw, New York 63
Washington, George 29, 30, *54*

Welland, Ontario 75
wellhead 70, 73, 75, 219, 229, 232
West Bloomfield, New York 37
West Bridgton, Maine 181
West Virginia 2, 4, *22*, 30, 42, 43, 45, 46, 53–55, 58, 61–*65*, 68–71, 73, 76, 105, 112, 129, 139, 169, 185, 222, 238
West Virginia Geological Survey 55
Western Reserve (Ohio) 66
Western Reserve Fire Museum, Inc. *131*
Wetzel County, West Virginia 43, 45
whale oil 33, 34, 36, 40, 50
Whewell, William *79*
White, I.C. 63
Whitney, Eli *35*
Wigan, England 32
William W. Goodman and Company 56
Williamsport, Pennsylvania 40
Wilson, Walker, and Company 53
Winzer (Winsor), Albrecht 32
Wirt County, West Virginia 61
Wisconsin Natural Gas 223, 224
Woman's Christian Temperance Union 38
wood 25, 26, 27, 31, 34, 35, 73, 102, 164, 190, 203, 205, 206, 215, 234, 245
work 25, 26, 86, *95*, *100*, 101, 121; *see also* energy
World LNG Report *244*
Wright, Franklin 144, 145, 146
Wroblewski, Zygmunt *97*, 102, 104, 107

Yergin, Daniel *The Prize* 27
Youngstown, Ohio 53, *54*
Youngstown Historical Center Dominion East Ohio Company Collection *16*, *132*, *136*, *143*
Yugoslavia 10

Zemansky, M.W.: *College Physics: Mechanics, Heat, and Sound* 95
Zick, L.P. 195
Zigman, Frank 15